THE NEW AGE IN PHYSICS

Colour photographs of auroral displays, taken by Dr. J. Paton.

THE NEW AGE IN
PHYSICS

Professor Sir Harrie Massey F. R. S.

Quain Professor of Physics in the University of London

HARPER & BROTHERS, PUBLISHERS, NEW YORK

CONTENTS

7276

Contents

Contents

Contents

PREFACE

The progress made in physical science during recent years has been so phenomenal and its impact on everyday life so great that it seemed worthwhile to attempt in this book the task of explaining in terms as non-technical as possible what it is all about. Although it is out of the question to avoid technicalities completely, a special effort has been made to use language free of scientific jargon. It is too much to hope that this effort has been completely successful and it is inevitable that some parts of the subject will present tougher reading than others.

The question of the choice of level at which to aim in the presentation was a difficult one. Most, if not all, can be understood by anyone who is prepared to take the trouble to read seriously, even if he has only a slight background knowledge of the subject. Mathematics, except of the most elementary character, is avoided completely and many illustrative diagrams have been included. It is hoped also that the wide range of subjects covered will make the book of value to the reader who has considerable acquaintance with physical science. Care has been taken to describe not only current ideas and interpretations, but the reasons why they have been introduced and the techniques that have provided information on which they are based.

The author was painfully aware, during the preparation of the book, of the dynamic character of the subject. Many additions and modifications had to be made in the proof stage but despite the further progress which will inevitably occur, much of the material discussed should stand the test of time.

My grateful thanks are due to my colleagues in the Physics Department at University College, London, Dr. R. L. F. Boyd and Dr. F. Heymann, and also to Dr. R. A. Buckingham for reading some of the chapters in the manuscript stage and for making valuable suggestions. A colleague in the College – from the classical side – Mr. J. H. Kells, also helped me by commenting on some of the chapters from the standpoint of the interested but non-scientific reader. Mr. M. Farley performed a similar service by reading much of the first draft of the book from the engineer's view-point.

I am indebted to Professor L. F. Bates, F.R.S., Dr. E. H. S. Burhop, Mr. S. A. H. Dakin, Dr. D. W. O. Heddle, Professor D. Glaser, Dr. E. Lofgren, Dr. R. S. Longhurst, Professor Dame Kathleen Lonsdale, F.R.S., Professor A. C. B. Lovell, F.R.S., Dr. J. Paton, Dr. R. Pease, Dr. D. H. Perkins, Mr. H. S. Tomlinson and Professor J. Z. Young, F.R.S., for supplying illustrations. Acknowledgment is gladly made also of the skilled assistance afforded me by Mr. C. A. R. Taylor in the supply and photographic reproduction of many of the plates and by Mr. D. E. Strachan in drawing the line diagrams. I am grateful for the permission granted me by the Royal Society, the Editors of the Physical Review, the Clarendon Press, the Pergamon Press, Messrs. Ferranti Ltd., the Atomic Energy Authority, the Lick Observatory, the Mount Palomar Observatory and the Observatory, Utrecht, to reproduce illustrations.

Finally, it was a pleasure to work with the publishers who at all times were most accommodating.

London

14th March 1960.

INTRODUCTION

Towards the end of the nineteenth century there was a general feeling of complacency among physical scientists. It seemed that the basic laws of Nature had all been discovered and that it was only necessary to continue the application of the principles of the mechanics of Galileo and Newton in order to understand all natural phenomena. The greatest degree of scepticism only went so far as to doubt whether all phenomena associated with living things could be included. As far as inanimate objects were concerned there was no suspicion that the innermost details of their structure and behaviour involved anything but the detailed interplay of already well-established principles. And yet a quarter of a century later the whole situation had been completely changed. Two drastic modifications of classical ideas, in relativity and wave mechanics, had been discovered and found essential for the understanding and description of the fine structure of matter. It was realised also that, just as Newton's mechanics was only an approximate description of the workings of Nature, which became unreliable for dealing with very small scale or very high velocity phenomena, we must regard the newly discovered modifications as approximations only. They extend greatly the range of effects which can be understood, interpreted and predicted, but there are limits, not yet clearly defined, beyond which they also will be inapplicable. At the present time no one any longer believes that all that is necessary is further application of established laws which Nature follows exactly.

The revolution in physical thought, due to the discovery of the principles of relativity and of quantum mechanics, is a very great one. Because of the unfamiliarity of these new principles in daily life, it is not possible to use just common sense to understand atomic and high speed phenomena. This does not mean, however, that one must discard entirely the pictorial, mechanistic approach, so popular in Victorian days. It is remarkable how far it is possible to develop means of extending this fruitful mode of thought to deal with situations which are nonsensical by ordinary standards. In saying this one cannot overemphasize the fact that these apparently nonsensical ideas are not the product of uncontrolled imagination but are forced upon us by the observed behaviour of Nature. The scientist always has the severe tests of experiment and observation with which to check any theoretical speculation or hypothesis. Progress in the subject depends on the interplay between new experimental discoveries and new theoretical ideas.

This brings out one further vital factor which has contributed so much to the dynamic character of physical science at the present time, the very rapid expansion in scope of practical techniques. The importance of precision of measurement and sensitiveness of detection by scientific instruments is obvious. Great advances have been made in these directions. It is possible to count individual atomic particles and to make visible the tracks they have pursued through gases and liquids. The physicist nowadays can study the properties of certain unusual kinds of matter, which are available to him in amounts so small that the chemist processing a millionth of a gram of a substance for analysis would seem, by comparison, to be dealing with matter in bulk. Even that particularly elusive particle the neutrino, which can pass uninterruptedly through millions of miles of lead, has been observed. Frequencies may be measured with extraordinary accuracy, to at least 1 part in ten million, so all determinations which can be made to depend on a frequency measurement may be carried out to the same accuracy. Time intervals as small as one thousand millionth of a second can be made significant, not only in measurement, but also in the design of control systems.

In all attempts to detect faint effects one of the chief difficulties is to discriminate between the sought-for effects and those due to background phenomena. Very powerful methods for doing this have been introduced in recent years, particularly in nuclear and high energy physics and in radioastronomy. Detection of the neutrino mentioned above was only made possible through the application of methods for deciding when a signal in the apparatus should be rejected, for the background signals occur very much more frequently than the wanted ones. In radio-astronomy very faint signals from extraterrestrial sources must often be disentangled from a background of local noise which may be a thousand times more intense.

In parallel with these advances there has been a great increase in man's power to influence his environment so as to carry out experiments of crucial importance. Thus, for a long time, the only sources of very energetic particles were natural ones – the rays from radioactive substances and cosmic rays. Now, through the steady development of artificial means of accelerating particles, we may produce beams of particles with controllable intensity, energy and nature which may have energies well up to those of the particles which form the major component of the cosmic rays. Enormous energy can be released in a controllable way in nuclear power reactors, and with high power rockets instruments may be transported far away from the earth's surface, through the ultimate confines of the earth into inter-planetary space, the neighbourhood of the moon and beyond.

We must not omit to mention the great importance of the high speed computer which brings within the range of practicability the solution of numerical problems far outside the scope of ordinary manual computing, and provides a means for very rapid calculation which is essential for such purposes as the tracking of artificial satellites and the control of high speed space-probing vehicles.

It is interesting to note the genesis of many of the powerful techniques of today from wartime developments. The development of the technique of radar, primarily a British achievement, not only provided sources of short radiowaves (microwaves) of unimagined intensity but also introduced methods of wide usefulness for studying and utilising these waves Applied to research in pure physics these techniques have made practicable means of accelerating particles to high speeds, have yielded information of outstanding importance about atomic and nuclear particles and made possible the great new science of radioastronomy.

The wartime achievement of means to utilise nuclear energy

was largely American, with some British assistance, particularly in the early stages. Although this effort was initially directed only to the manufacture of atomic bombs it led to the prospect of many widespread peaceful applications as in the generation of industrial power, etc. The importance for pure science is also very considerable, both in providing directly new tools for research and in solving difficult technical problems so that new procedures become generally available. Thus the high energy accelerators of the present day owe much to the technical progress achieved as part of the nuclear energy project during the war.

In the same vein we must regard the outstanding German work on high-power liquid fuel rockets. The infamous V2 has acquired a new dignity as the precursor of all ballistic rockets for space research.

Automatic high-speed computer development, though actually begun before the war, was greatly hastened by American effort during the war.

We shall not attempt in this book the wellnigh impossible task of describing the whole range of modern physics. Instead we shall choose a number of outstanding theoretical and experimental developments which illustrate the remarkable position which has been reached and the extraordinary rate of progress.

We shall begin with a brief historical account of the course of events during the first twenty-five years from the beginning of the century, the prelude to the discovery of the laws of quantum, or wave, mechanics which marked one of the greatest forward steps in the history of science. In the same Chapter an account of the atomic structure of matter, as far as it does not require any knowledge of quantum mechanics, will be given together with an indication of some of the methods used to determine the masses and other properties of atoms and of their constituent electrons. The stage is then set for a consideration, in the next Chapter, of wave mechanics and some of its extraordinary consequences. Opportunity will then be taken to fill in some of the chief gaps in the description of atomic structure which were perforce left in the account given in the preceding Chapter.

The third Chapter includes a variety of rather loosely connected subjects. It begins with an account of some practical applications of the diffraction of particles, as in the electron microscope, and then describes some other ways in which electrons are put to work, mainly through the influence which they exert on the electrical and magnetic properties of solid materials as in valves, transistors and ferromagnets. A brief description of the principles involved in high speed computation, depending heavily as they do on the behaviour of electrons in solids, is also regarded as appropriate for inclusion in this Chapter.

Somewhat less obviously an account is also given of certain phenomena observed near the absolute zero of temperature. At first sight one would not imagine that anything of interest would be observed at such very low temperatures. We can imagine everything then as immobilised and quiescent. However, this ignores the fact that even quite weak ordering forces may become effective when the random effect of temperature motion is sufficiently reduced. Fascinating possibilities arise in this way at temperatures a degree or less from absolute zero and the technique of attaining very low temperatures has advanced so far that some of these possibilities are already being realised. Even more interesting still are two unexpected and still very imperfectly understood phenomena – superconductivity and superfluidity – which are properties acquired by certain materials at very low temperature. They are so extraordinary that any account of modern physics which omitted any reference to them would be incomplete indeed and we have devoted some part of Chapter 3 to their consideration.

The next six chapters are concerned with the atomic nucleus, with the strange particles which are produced in very energetic collisions between nuclei and with the strangest one of all, the neutrino, which has been mentioned above. As a prelude we must begin with an account of the second major modification of Newtonian mechanics, which was introduced by Einstein in 1905, the theory of relativity. The basis of this theory and its consequences for very fast motion of large scale bodies are discussed in Chapter 4. When the bodies concerned are of atomic dimensions both quantum and relativistic modifications must be introduced together. Chapter 5 discusses what progress has been made to achieve this. It outlines some of the consequences which would be incredible but for the fact that they provide a satisfactory basis for the prediction in detail of many extraordinary phenomena, including the creation and annihilation of matter and the idea of anti-matter. It is in this direction that some of the most accurate measurements of the properties of electrons have been made which agree in detail with some of the more subtle predictions of relativistic quantum theory.

We turn in Chapter 6 to describe the tools employed in studying the atomic nucleus, the accelerators to produce high speed particles as missiles with which to achieve transmutations far beyond the imagination of the alchemist, the counters, the cloud chambers, the bubble chambers and the specially sensitive photographic emulsions which detect and identify the occurrence and products of the transmutations. Some of the results obtained with their use are also described.

Chapter 7 is mainly concerned with the large scale utilisation of nuclear energy through the use of uranium fission. It describes the present state of peaceful applications of fission for power development, propulsion, in medicine and in research. Opportunity is taken to describe the method of dating by radio-carbon which is of such value in archaeological research today.

We return in Chapter 8 to a rapidly developing branch of high energy particle physics which as yet has no practical application but which is of great scientific interest and importance. Through the study of cosmic rays and, more recently, the reactions of particles produced in the highest energy accelerators, we are now aware of the existence of many particles whose *rôle* in nature is far from clear. These strange particles are all unstable with lifetimes less than one millionth of a second. It may well be that, from the study of their properties, we shall arrive at a new and deeper insight into the basic laws of nature.

Chapter 9 is devoted to a related subject of great topical interest, largely but not wholly concerned with Nature's oddest particle, the neutrino, the most significant property of which is that it has practically no observable properties at all! And yet we know quite a lot about it today and have been led, through its study, to the realisation that right-handedness and left-handedness are not on the same footing in our universe.

After reaching the extreme in unorthodox behaviour among particles we turn abruptly in the remaining Chapters to the description of applications of physics to the study of phenomena on the very large scale, beginning in Chapter 10 with radio-astronomy, the new science which has already expanded our knowledge of the shape of our own galaxy and revealed in the depth of space such vast events as the collisions of galaxies. Finally in Chapters 11 and 12 we deal with the probing of space by instruments transported directly in rocket-propelled vehicles. Chapter 11 deals with the introductory phase, the study of the high atmosphere of the earth, followed in the next Chapter by a discussion on artificial satellites, lunar probes and more ambitious projects. This will conclude with an account of the largest scale scientific experiments ever carried out.

CHAPTER I

ATOMS AND ATOMIC STRUCTURE: HISTORICAL PRELUDE

> '*And the end men looked for cometh not,*
> *And a path is there which no man thought,*
> *So hath it fallen here*'
> EURIPIDES, 'THE BACCHAE'

Atoms and Elements

Although the possibility that matter is built up of individual units or atoms was realised by the Greek philosophers, no real evidence in support of it was forthcoming until the dawn of chemistry as a science at the end of the eighteenth century. The work of Lavoisier and others during this period began for the first time to establish a sound basis for the subject to develop. One of the most important steps taken was the discovery of the conservation of mass in chemical reactions such as the production of water from hydrogen and oxygen. No less important was the distinction between elements and compounds – the realisation that most substances are compounds formed by an intimate combination of two or more elementary substances such as hydrogen, oxygen, the metals and so on. Once these two vital concepts were appreciated the way was open to the systematic measurement of the mass relations in chemical reactions. The most effective work in this direction was carried out by Dalton who, in 1808, was able to distinguish, on the basis of his measurements, two important regularities of a general character.

The first is that the proportions by weight of the two elements in a chemical compound are always the same, no matter how it is produced. Thus in water the masses of oxygen and hydrogen are always in the ratio 8:1. This strongly suggests that each element is built up of a number of structural units, which are indivisible in any chemical reaction, and which we call *atoms*. Further, it suggests that the reaction occurs through the formation of compound structural units or *molecules* which contain one or more atoms of each kind in a definite ratio.

The second regular feature, the law of multiple proportions, states that, when two elements form more than one chemical compound with each other, the proportions by mass of the two in the different compounds may be represented in terms of simple fractions. Thus nitrogen and oxygen form a number of compounds. If x is the mass ratio of nitrogen to oxygen in nitric oxide, then in nitrous oxide it is $2x$, in nitrogen peroxide $\frac{1}{2}x$ and so on. This law also receives a very direct interpretation in terms of atomic theory. The several nitrogen-oxygen compounds differ in that the corresponding molecules contain nitrogen and oxygen atoms in different but small numbers. If N and O denote nitrogen and oxygen atoms respectively the molecule of nitric oxide has the structure NO and contains one atom of each kind while that of nitrous oxide is represented by N_2O and of nitrogen peroxide by NO_2.

From the weight, or more properly mass, relations in different chemical compounds, a scale of relative weights of atoms may be set up. In the initial preparation of this scale the weight of the oxygen atom was chosen to be 16.

A further important step was taken in 1811 by Avogadro who suggested that equal volumes of all gases at the same pressure and temperature contain the same number of molecules. This was based on the volume relations in chemical reactions between gases. For example, a few years earlier, Gay-Lussac found that two volumes of hydrogen gas always combine with one volume of oxygen to form two volumes of water vapour. Denoting a hydrogen atom by H and an oxygen atom by O as above, this reaction can be written as

$$2H_2 + O_2 \rightarrow 2H_2O,$$

which is a shorthand way of stating that two molecules of hydrogen (each containing two atoms) combine with one of oxygen (also containing two atoms) to form two molecules of water (each containing two hydrogen atoms and one oxygen atom). It is important to notice that, even for elementary substances, the molecules need not consist of single atoms. Avogadro's hypothesis provides a means of determining relative molecular weight so that, by comparison with the relative atomic weight scale, it is possible to determine the number of atoms per molecule for elementary substances.

The volume of oxygen which at standard temperature (0° C) and pressure (1 atmosphere) weighs 32 grams is known as the *gram molecular volume*. It follows from Avogadro's hypothesis that the mass of any other gas occupying the same volume is equal in grams to the molecular weight on the scale in which the atomic weight of oxygen is taken as 16. The number of molecules in a gram molecular volume is known as Avogadro's number N and is one of the important atomic constants (see pp. 27, 30).

Once the atomic nature of matter was discovered rapid progress was made in the laboratory study of chemical phenomena and the interpretation of the results obtained. It was soon realised that a further degree of order existed in the chemical behaviour of different elements. This culminated in 1869 in the periodic table of the elements proposed by Mendeléef.

In general terms the different elements ware assigned positions in a rectangular table as in Fig. 1.1. Elements in a particular column show very similar chemical properties and the atomic weight both increases in going down a column and to the right along a row. The pristine simplicity of the original table has been complicated to an extent for reasons which are now thoroughly understood but the periodic variation in chemical behaviour, as the atomic weight increases, is still highly significant.

If we pause for a moment to survey the situation which had been reached by about 1870 we must be impressed by the great progress which had been made. The seemingly infinite diversity of matter had been reduced to that of the properties of a quite limited number, about 90, of elements, the combinations between which provide the variety of materials we encounter. Even further relations had been discerned between the elements themselves so that the prospect opened of an even greater reduction to basic essentials. Already in 1815 Prout had pointed out that the weights of the atoms were, within the accuracy of

Fig. 1.1. *Periodic Table of the Elements.*

COLUMN

Period	1	2	3	4	5	6	7	8	0
1	Hydrogen H1								Helium He2
2	Lithium Li3	Beryllium Be4	Boron B5	Carbon C6	Nitrogen N7	Oxygen O8	Fluorine F9		Neon Ne10
3	Sodium Na11	Magnesium Mg12	Aluminium Al13	Silicon Si14	Phosphorus P15	Sulphur S16	Chlorine Cl17		Argon A18
4	Potassium K19 / Copper Cu29	Calcium Ca20 / Zinc Zn30	Scandium Sc21 / Gallium Ga31	Titanium Ti22 / Germanium Ge32	Vanadium V23 / Arsenic As33	Chromium Cr24 / Selenium Se34	Manganese Mn25 / Bromine Br35	Iron Fe26 / Cobalt Co27 / Nickel Ni28	Krypton Kr36
5	Rubidium Rb37 / Silver Ag47	Strontium Sr38 / Cadmium Cd48	Yttrium Y39 / Indium In49	Zirconium Zr40 / Tin Sn50	Niobium Nb41 / Antimony Sb51	Molybdenum Mo42 / Tellurium Te52	Technetium Te43 / Iodine I53	Ruthenium Ru44 / Rhodium Rh45 / Palladium Pd46	Xenon Xe54
6	Caesium Cs55 / Gold Au79	Barium Ba56 / Mercury Hg80	Rare Earths 57-71 / Thallium Tl81	Hafnium Hf72 / Lead Pb82	Tantalum Ta73 / Bismuth Bi83	Tungsten W74 / Polonium Po84	Rhenium Re75 / Astatine At85	Osmium Os76 / Iridium Ir77 / Platinum Pt78	Radon Rn86
7	Francium F-87	Radium Ra88	Actinides* 89-103						

* Includes thorium (Th90) and Uranium (U92) as well as other elements.
Elements 43, 85, 87 and 93-103 are not known in Nature but have been produced artificially. Note that after the third period the columns are divided into left hand and right hand halves. Whether an element is placed on the left or right hand side of a column is indicated by the position of its chemical symbol and mass number. The arrangement is such that elements in the left hand halves of one column show similarity of chemical and physical properties as do elements in the right hand halves. There is usually little resemblance between elements placed in different halves of the same colum.

observations available at the time, whole number multiples of that of hydrogen. He went on to suggest that all atoms may be built up out of hydrogen atoms. This was not very far from the truth but it fell into disrepute when more accurate measurements showed that the atomic weights are not exact whole number multiples of that of hydrogen. It is neither the first nor the last occasion in which an important relation seemed to exist on the basis of rather rough observation, was then discarded when more accurate data became available only to be revived again when the reasons for the departure from the simple rules, at first proposed, became clear.

Electrons

The periodic system of the elements pointed to common structural units in the atoms of different elements but there was no notion at the time what these units might be, Prout's hypothesis having been rejected. It was not long before the first evidence about the electron as a common constituent of all atoms became available but, before discussing this, we must draw attention to another investigation of paramount importance.

Electrolysis

When an electric current is passed through a solution in water of a salt such as silver sulphate, the salt is decomposed, silver is deposited at the cathode* and oxygen liberated at the anode.* This is the phenomenon known as electrolysis which is used in the electroplating industry and in many other industrial applications. In 1833 Faraday formulated two basic laws of electrolysis on the basis of measurements which he had made in the preceding years. The amount of material deposited on an electrode is proportional to the quantity of electricity which has passed through the solution, and to the atomic weight of the material. These relations suggest immediately that a particular quantity of electricity, a particular electric charge, is associated with each atom of the material. This electric charge must then

---

* The anode is the plate or electrode from which current enters the solution while the cathode is the electrode by which it leaves.

be regarded as an atom of electricity, a highly significant result for atomic structure.

If the atom of electric charge is a quantity e of electricity, then the amount of electricity required to deposit a molecular weight of material on an electrode will be given by*

$$F = Ne,$$

where N is Avogadro's number. This amount F is known as the Faraday and may be measured with high precision if suitable precautions are taken. It will be seen that it involves two very important atomic quantities, N and the smallest electric charge e. Moreover, from the Faraday, we can obtain directly the ratio of the fundamental electric charge e to the mass M of an atom, a quantity of much importance.

Cathode Rays in Electric Discharges

The next major step was the measurement by J. J. Thomson in 1897 of the ratio of the charge to mass for the negatively charged particles streaming towards the anode (see footnote p. 26) in an electric discharge. In preceding years there had been great activity devoted to the study of discharges and this in turn was made possible by the invention of methods for exhausting the gas from vessels much more completely than hitherto. If a potential difference of 1,000 volts or so is maintained between two metal plates in a gas and the pressure is gradually reduced the insulating properties of the gas suddenly break down at some pressure and an electric current flows between the plates. This is accompanied by a bright glow, characteristic of the gas and the pressure, and is known as an *electric discharge*. The negative plate or electrode is the cathode, the positive the anode. The principles employed in J. J. Thomson's experiment are so important that we shall pause to outline them here.

Fig. 1.2 illustrates the general arrangement used. Some of the negatively charged particles in the discharge, which move from the cathode towards the anode A, are allowed to pass through a small hole in this plate into the low pressure region behind.

---

* Actually for the atoms of some elements, said to be divalent, the charge per atom is $2e$, for others $3e$ etc., but in all cases it is either e or a small integral multiple of e.

After passage through a second hole B, which serves to outline the stream more definitely, they travel between two plates D between which a voltage difference is maintained so that the particles are subjected to an electric force tending to drive them sideways. In addition to the electric force, a counter force could be applied by means of a suitable magnetic field.

The force which a magnetic field applies to a moving charge is perpendicular to the direction both of the field and that of motion of the charge (see Fig. 1.3) so that the direction of the magnetic field must be perpendicular to the plane of the paper in Fig. 1.2. The forces due to the electric and magnetic fields

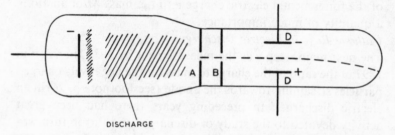

DISCHARGE

Fig. 1.2. Illustrating the principle of J. J. Thomson's experiment for measuring the charge to mass ratio of the cathode rays in an electric discharge.

respectively are given per unit charge by E and vH/c respectively where E and H are the electric and magnetic field strengths, v is the velocity of the particles and c is the velocity of light. If the two fields are adjusted so as to balance exactly, then the velocity v must be given by cE/H. Having obtained the velocity in this way – it is found to be greater than 10,000 miles per second – the ratio of charge to mass may be obtained by switching off the voltage between the plates D and measuring the deflection produced by the magnetic field alone. This may be seen as follows.

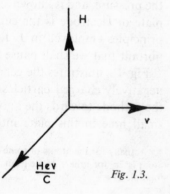

Fig. 1.3.

A charged particle moving in a plane perpendicular to the direction of a uniform magnetic field H will describe a circle in which the centrifugal force is balanced by the force due to the magnetic field. Thus, referring to Fig. 1.4 we see that, if v is the speed and m the mass of the particle, the centrifugal force is mv^2/r where r is the radius of the circular path. The opposing force due to the magnetic field is evH/c where e is the charge on the particle. For balance we then have

$$\frac{mv^2}{r} = \frac{evH}{c},$$

or

$$\frac{e}{m} = \frac{vc}{rH}.$$

As v is determined by the preceding balance experiment and r may be derived from the observed deflection, e/m can be obtained.

J. J. Thomson found that the ratio e/m for the particles which pass through the anode (cathode rays as they were called) is over 1,000 times greater than that for the lightest carriers of charge in electrolysis, suggesting that the mass of a cathode ray particle is less than one thousandth of that of the lightest atom, that of hydrogen. Further less direct evidence of the existence of such light particles in matter had been forthcoming from the theory of dispersion (the variation with frequency of the speed of light in condensed materials) and of the Zeeman effect (the effect of a magnetic field on the frequencies of the light emitted by different substances).

The particles discovered by J. J. Thomson are, of course, the now very familiar *electrons*, one of the basic constituents of atoms. We now know a great deal about their properties, some of which have proved of vital importance in modern industry and research (see Chapter 3).

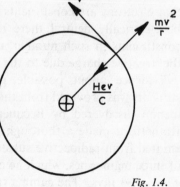

Fig. 1.4.

The next stage was the separate measurement of the electronic charge and mass. This was first done roughly by J. J. Thomson using a principle which has proved of great importance in other directions, (see the description of the Wilson cloud chamber in Chapter 6 p. 164). It depends on the fact that, if charged particles enter a gas containing supersaturated vapour, condensation of droplets occurs around each charge. By collecting the condensed vapour on a positively charged plate, the total mass condensed and the total charge carried can be measured. Also, from the rate at which the droplets fall, their individual masses can be determined. This gives the mean number of drops and hence the charge per drop. The method was modified and greatly refined in the experiments of Millikan in the period just before the first world war and provides a precise value of the fundamental electric charge e.

Having measured e, e/m and the Faraday F, Avogadro's number N as well as the respective masses m, M of the electron and of the hydrogen atom may all be obtained. The best values available at present are

$$m = 9.1085 \times 10^{-28} \text{ gms. } M = 1.6724 \times 10^{-24} \text{ gms.}$$
$$N = 6.0247 \times 10^{23}.$$

Atomic Structure

The Atomic Nucleus

It seemed clear from the researches of J. J. Thomson and others that electrons are constituents of all atoms. Since atoms must be electrically neutral there must also be positively charged constituents in such number as to balance, with their charge, the negative charge due to the atomic electrons.

Evidence about possible positively charged atomic constituents was provided from the study of radioactivity, a phenomenon discovered by Becquerel in 1897. A few years later Rutherford made a thorough study of the nature of the rays emitted from radioactive substances. He found that they were of three main types, which he christened *alpha* (α), *beta* (β) and *gamma* (γ) rays. The gamma rays are electromagnetic waves of very high frequency (see Chapter 2 p. 52) and are undeflected by electric or magnetic fields while the beta rays are negatively charged particles identified, from the measurement of their charge to mass ratio, as energetic electrons (see Chapter 9 p. 226). It was the alpha rays which presented new evidence. They were found to have a positive charge equal in magnitude to twice that of the electron and a charge to mass ratio one half of that expected for singly charged hydrogen atoms. Rutherford further showed that helium gas was produced by radioactive substances which emit alpha rays and he made the bold suggestion that these rays are charged helium atoms. According to this, radioactivity is a demonstration of the spontaneous breakup of one element into others.

It was natural to suppose that helium atoms are obtained from alpha particles by the addition of two electrons to balance the double positive charge. The contribution of the electrons to the mass of the atom would therefore be very small, almost all of this mass being associated with the positively charged constituents. Further very important evidence about the number of electrons in atoms came from the observation of the intensity of scattering of X-rays* by different materials. The scattering is entirely due to the atomic electrons because they are so much lighter than the positively charged constituents. It was found that, at least for the lighter atoms, the number of electrons is approximately one half the atomic weight.

By 1911 there was general agreement that atoms contain a small number of electrons so that most of the mass resides in the positive charge. The problem was to determine how the positive charge is distributed. Two extreme views were advocated by J. J. Thomson and by Rutherford. The former considered an atom as a sphere of positive charge in which the electrons were embedded. Rutherford, on the other hand, produced a model in which the positive charge was contained within a central massive nucleus. Around this the electrons revolved in orbits under the action of the electrical attraction of the nucleus in

---

* X-rays are short electromagnetic waves (wavelengths between 10^{-9} and 10^{-6} cms.) produced when a stream of fast electrons (cathode rays) impinge on a solid target (see pp. 38, 52).

much the same way as the planets revolve round the sun under the influence of its gravitational attraction.

Whereas with the J. J. Thomson 'plum-pudding' atom condensed matter would be very solid with only small gaps between the atoms, in Rutherford's picture it would be mainly empty with all the actual mass concentrated on the very minute atomic nuclei. Such a difference would be clearly apparent to fast particles such as the alpha particles from radioactive substances which, on the nuclear model, would be helium nuclei. An alpha particle impinging on a metal foil would have a very good chance of passing right through without encountering any appreciable deviating influence. Occasionally, however, one would pass quite close to an atomic nucleus and would then suffer a large deflection. On the other hand, with the plum-pudding model, all alpha particles would pass through charged matter and be deflected. Quantitative prediction of the effect expected on passing a stream of alpha particles through a thin foil could be made. Experiments carried out by Geiger and Marsden, at Rutherford's suggestion, on the fraction of alpha particles incident on a metal foil which suffered a deflection through a given angle, showed quite definitely that the nuclear model is correct. This was a great landmark in the study of atomic structure.

The Problem of The Stability of Atoms

Attractive as the nuclear atom model undoubtedly is, particularly because of its close similarity to the structure of the solar system, there is a very big difficulty which confronts it at an early stage. An electric charge moving with varying velocity radiates energy in the form of electromagnetic waves. This applies in particular to a charge describing a circle with uniform speed because, even though the magnitude of its velocity is constant, it is continually changing in direction*. Because of this continual loss of energy, an electron revolving round an atomic nucleus should spiral in gradually to be merged with the nucleus in a time much shorter

---

* Velocity is a directed or vector quantity whose magnitude is the speed. Two velocities are only equal if their directions as well as their speeds are the same.

than the known span of the earth's existence. This does not happen, but why not?

The problem is not the same for the solar system because there is a negligible rate of radiation of energy for a body revolving, as do the planets, under the force, not of electrical, but of gravitational, attraction.

Another aspect of the remarkable stability of atoms is also apparent when one considers that in a gas at ordinary pressure the average atom, moving at a speed of about 1,500 feet per second, makes about 10^{10} collisions per second with other atoms, from which they all emerge unscathed.

Bohr's Hypothesis about Electron Orbits in Atoms –
Introduction of the Quantum of Action

As it seemed clear that it was not possible to understand the stability of atoms in terms of the laws of classical physics, Bohr sought for some modifications of these laws which would provide a better description of the electron orbits in atoms. In doing this, he was greatly influenced by the work of Planck in 1901 and of Einstein in 1905, which had shown that radiation cannot be regarded, in all circumstances, as emitted or absorbed continuously. Instead, radiation of frequency ν (see Chapter 2 p. 46) can only be emitted or absorbed in discrete bundles, or quanta, of energy of magnitude $h\nu$ where h is a new fundamental magnitude which has proved to be of the greatest importance for atomic physics. It is known as the *quantum of action*.

This involves essentially the concept of a further indivisibility or atomicity in Nature but now of a different physical quantity, which could, in certain circumstances, be regarded as an angular momentum. Without pausing to explain here in any detail what is meant by angular momentum, we can say quite quickly how it is defined for a particle of mass m revol-

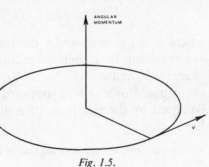

Fig. 1.5.

33

ving in a circle of radius r with speed v. The magnitude of the linear momentum is mv and that of the angular momentum is mvr. Actually angular momentum is a vector or directed quantity, and in this special case it is directed along the perpendicular to the plane of motion in the sense indicated (Fig. 1.5).

In Bohr's initial hypothesis he assumed that the magnitude of

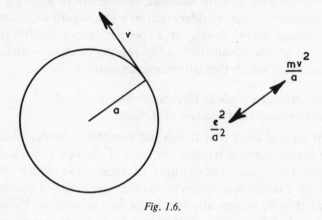

Fig. 1.6.

the angular momentum for an electron revolving in a circular orbit round the nucleus must be a whole number multiple of a fundamental quantity $h/2\pi$ where h is the quantum of action. If this is so it follows that an electron can revolve round a central positive charge only in one of a number of orbits selected by this condition. A simple calculation gives the formula for the radii of these orbits.

Thus, referring to Fig. 1.6, we have, from Bohr's assumption,

$$mva = nh/2\pi, \tag{A}$$

where m is the mass and v the speed of an electron of charge $-e$ revolving in a circle of radius a about a central positive charge $+e$, and $n = 1, 2, \ldots$ To maintain the circulation the centrifugal force mv^2/a outward on the electron must be balanced by the electrical attraction inwards e^2/a^2.* Thus we have

* Compare with the gravitational case of an artificial satellite (Chapter 12, p. 298).

$$\frac{mv^2}{a} = \frac{e^2}{a^2},$$

or

$$mv^2a = e^2. \qquad\qquad \text{(B)}$$

Dividing this equation by (A) we find

$$v = ne^2h/2\pi$$

so that, on substitution in (B),

$$a = n^2\, h^2/4\pi^2\, me^2.$$

This shows that the allowed orbits form a series in which the radii increase in the ratio $1:4:9:16$ etc. The closest orbit is at a distance $h^2/4\pi^2me^2$ from the central positive charge. If one puts in the observed values for the different quantities, this works out to be 0.53×10^{-8} cm. and is referred to as the radius of the first Bohr orbit of hydrogen.

The total energy of an electron revolving in a central orbit remains constant for a particular orbit but varies from orbit to orbit. A simple calculation shows that, for an orbit defined by the number n, the total energy is less than that which the electron would have, if it were at rest at an infinite distance from the centre, by an amount

$$E(n) = \frac{2\pi^2me^4}{n^2h^2}.$$

This shows that as n, and hence the radius, decreases the total energy becomes less and is lowest for the innermost orbit with $n = 1$.

Having selected the set of allowed orbits, Bohr postulated further that, in the normal hydrogen atom, the electron is circulating in the orbit for which $n = 1$ and that it cannot then lose energy by radiation. Any reduction of its energy would require it to move in an orbit of smaller radius and no such orbit is allowed, according to Bohr's first postulate. When left alone, the atom in this state would be absolutely stable.

Next, if an electron is circulating in one of the allowed orbits with n greater than 1, it was postulated that no gradual loss of energy by radiation occurs but that at some instant a jump, or transition, could be made to one of the inner allowed orbits. As the energy is less in one of these latter orbits, the surplus energy is then supposed to be emitted as radiation of frequency v given by the Planck-Einstein relation

$$hv = E_i - E_f,$$

where E_i is the total energy in the initial orbit and E_f in the final, inner, orbit to which the transition is made. Thus if n_i and n_f are the corresponding values of the number n defining each orbit, the frequency radiated is given by

$$v = \frac{2\pi^2 me^4}{h^3} \left(\frac{1}{n_f{}^2} - \frac{1}{n_i{}^2} \right). \tag{C}$$

The great initial success of Bohr's hypothesis rested on this formula. It gave the frequencies of the radiation which could be emitted from hydrogen atoms when excited. In other words, it described the line spectrum of hydrogen, and this in a remarkably successful way when compared with the already rich variety of experimental data on the radiation emitted from atoms. It was known quite early in the last century that the light emitted from an atomic source was not continuous in colour or frequency but concentrated in a number of very narrow regions of frequency. These appear on a photograph taken with a spectrograph as sharp lines. The existence of regularities in the series of such emission lines from a particular element was first observed by Ritz for the spectrum of the alkali metals (see Plate 1.1) and a little later Balmer distinguished his famous series of lines in hydrogen (see Plate 1.2). Bohr showed that, if we take n_i as 2 in the formula (C), then the frequencies of the observed lines of the Balmer series are given with very high accuracy by taking $n_f =$ 3, 4, ... etc. The Balmer lines thus arise from transitions to the allowed orbit with $n = 2$, from outer orbits (see Fig. 1.7).

As we shall see in more detail in the next Chapter, Bohr's hypothesis applied to circular orbits, and even its extension to elliptic orbits and to more complex atoms, proved to be only a

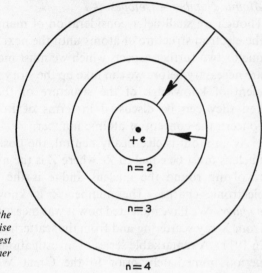

Fig. 1.7. Illustrating the transitions which give rise to the two lines of lowest frequency in the Balmer series of hydrogen.

very incomplete description of the true state of affairs. For many years a tantalising fragment, it nevertheless marked the beginning of a revolution in atomic physics. Until then the highly unconventional quantum of action, which had forced its attention upon those concerned with the study of emission and absorption of radiation, had not invaded the hitherto sacred domain of the seemingly solid edifice of classical mechanics, which had been laboriously erected on the foundations laid by Galileo and Newton. We shall see in the next Chapter how this intrusion developed and threatened to engulf all physics in confusion until the whole situation cleared miraculously with the discovery of quantum mechanics in 1926. This established firmly and clearly the rules which had to be followed in describing, interpreting and predicting the motion of electrons within atoms. It presented a revolution of such magnitude in physical thought that we must devote a separate Chapter, the next, to it. Meanwhile, in this historical account, we need only say that all phenomena involving the electrons within atoms, as distinct from the nuclei, are now interpretable, at least in principle, through use of quantum mechanics, as we shall have occasion to note in the next two Chapters in several contexts.

Atomic Number – Isotopes

Though we shall defer consideration of many major aspects of the electron structure of atoms until the next Chapter, there are one or two further aspects which we must mention here. These are necessary before we can take up the story about the development of knowledge of the structure of the atomic nucleus, and they can be discussed in terms of Bohr's orbits. They concern the concept of atomic number.

As an atom is electrically neutral, the positive charge on the nucleus must be equal to Ze where Z is the number of electrons revolving round the nucleus and e is the magnitude of the electronic charge. The number Z is known as the *atomic number*. We have indicated how it was measured approximately, from X-ray scattering and from the scattering of alpha-particles, in 1911. A remarkable series of investigations were made in the period immediately prior to the Great War of 1914-18 by Moseley who was destined to lose his life in the Gallipoli campaign. He measured the wavelengths of the lines which appeared in the X-ray spectrum emitted by various elements on bombardment by fast electrons. It soon appeared that the lines could be arranged in series in a similar sort of way to the Balmer and other series in the optical spectrum of hydrogen. This suggested that the X-ray emission arises from transitions between inner electron orbits in the field of the charge Ze of the nucleus. Bohr's formula (C) may then be used provided the frequency emitted is multiplied by Z^2. It follows that Z may be determined in this way and Moseley's observations gave the most extensive information up to that time about this most important quantity.

Meanwhile a flood of new light was being shed on the long-standing problem of the departures of the atomic weights of the elements from whole numbers which had caused Prout's hypothesis of 1815 (p. 24) to fall into disrepute. This all began with the study of the successive processes by which natural radioactive elements transformed into others until a stable product element resulted. It then appeared that the atoms of an element need not all have the same mass or weight. This remarkable result was found by J. J. Thomson to apply to many other elements. In 1913 he applied the method which led him to the identification of the electron in cathode rays, to determine the charge to mass ratio of the positively charged particles which constituted the anode rays (in Fig. 1.8 the anode rays pass towards the cathode as indicated). In order to improve the

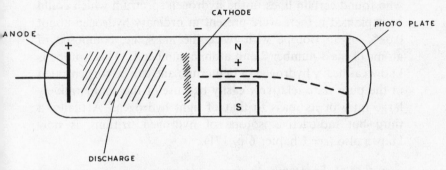

Fig. 1.8. Illustrating the method used by J. J. Thomson to determine the ratio of charge to mass for anode rays. N and S denote the north and south poles of a magnet between which an electric voltage difference is also maintained. The deflected anode rays are recorded on a photographic plate.

distinction between the traces produced on the recording screen by positively charged atoms with nearly equal masses, he used a different arrangement of electric and magnetic fields. These were now both parallel to each other and perpendicular to the direction of the anode rays. He found, for example, that with neon gas in the discharge tube, two kinds of positive rays were produced, one with atomic weight, or *mass number*, 22 and the other of mass number 20. It appeared that there are two kinds of neon atoms which in bulk are chemically indistinguishable but which have different masses. These are known as *isotopes* of each other.

Thomson's work was followed by a much more extensive investigation carried out by Aston. He improved the accuracy of the method of mass analysis to a great extent and his equipment is the first example of a mass spectrograph, an apparatus for precise comparison of nuclear masses. Many other types of precision mass spectrograph are now available.

It soon became apparent that most elements are composed of two or more isotopes and that the major part of the deviation of the atomic weights from whole numbers is due to this. There remains, however, an extremely important residue which will be discussed in Chapter 6 p. 143 and Chapter 7 p. 174.

One of the most important of all isotopes is that of hydrogen. This was discovered by Urey, Murphy and Brickwedde in 1932 who found certain lines in the hydrogen spectrum which could be explained if there were present in ordinary hydrogen about 0.02% of an isotope with twice the mass, i.e. composed of atoms of mass number 2 and atomic number 1. This isotope is known as heavy hydrogen or deuterium and can be concentrated in the pure state relatively easily because of the comparatively large ratio of its mass to that of light hydrogen. Actually, a third but radioactive isotope of hydrogen, tritium, is now known also (see Chapter 6 p. 171).

Structure of the Atomic Nucleus

We may now turn to consider how the problem of the structure of the atomic nucleus was being faced.

In all atoms but hydrogen the atomic number is less than the mass number. Thus for nitrogen the mass number is 14, the atomic number 7, while, for a heavy atom such as uranium, the main naturally occurring isotope has mass number 238 and atomic number 92. What do these nuclei consist of?

We may now feel free, through the discovery of isotopes, to return virtually to Prout's hypothesis by choosing the nucleus of the hydrogen atom, the proton, as one of the constituents of nuclei. The proton has a single unit of positive charge and a mass of 1 atomic unit. A nitrogen nucleus, having an atomic number 7, must have 7 units of positive electric charge. To supply these we can include 7 protons but we are still 7 units short in mass – each proton supplies one mass unit but the mass number is 14. One way of dealing with this is to suppose that there are also electrons within the nucleus. We then try to build up the nitrogen nucleus with 14 protons, giving the correct mass, and adding 7 electrons, which are far too light to affect the mass appreciably but neutralise 7 proton charges to give the required atomic number of 7.

Other nuclei could be considered in the same way and indeed

until 1932 there was no other known way of doing it. No other building stones but electrons and protons were available. By that time several serious objections had been raised against the assumption of electrons as nuclear constituents, even though in natural radioactive decay electrons may be emitted as beta rays (see Chapter 9). It was the discovery of the neutron by Chadwick in 1932 which provided the key to nuclear composition.

Events leading up to the Discovery of the Neutron

We have already pointed out how Rutherford perceived that natural radioactivity is due to the spontaneous transmutation of one element into another in the course of which certain atomic fragments are released in the form of energetic radiation. During the first world war Rutherford made a decisive step forward by producing the first artificial transmutation. He achieved this by using the alpha particles from radium to bombard nitrogen gas, and establishing beyond doubt that fast protons were produced. These could only have come from collisions between the alpha particles and nitrogen nuclei, so that we have here a transformation of helium and nitrogen into hydrogen and some other nucleus (actually an isotope of oxygen).

This marked the beginning of an extensive research programme devoted to the investigation of the effect of bombardment of different substances by alpha particles. In 1932 Chadwick turned his attention towards the mysterious results which had been obtained by earlier investigators, including particularly Joliot, when they bombarded the metal beryllium by alpha particles. Chadwick was able to establish quite definitely that among the products of the reaction were particles with masses very close to that of the proton but with no electric charge. These particles he called *neutrons* and it was soon recognized that they were the missing constituents of nuclei.

Electrons, Protons and Neutrons in Atoms

The picture of atomic structure which is now regarded universally as correct considers that the atomic nucleus is made up of Z protons and $A—Z$ neutrons, Z being the atomic number and A the mass number. The nuclear charge will be Ze so that there revolve, in allowed orbits round the nucleus, exactly Z electrons. The distribution of these electrons we shall discuss in the next Chapter and it will suffice to say here that the chemical behaviour of an element is determined by the number of electrons contained in its atoms and hence by its atomic number. Substances containing atoms of the same atomic number behave in the same way chemically no matter how the atoms may differ in mass number, i.e. in the number of neutrons.

An atomic nucleus contains no electrons. This may seem peculiar when it is remembered that beta rays are fast electrons, but more will be said of this in Chapter 9.

The nucleus of a hydrogen atom consists of a proton. Addition of a neutron gives a nucleus of deuterium, often referred to as a *deuteron*. The third isotope, tritium, has a nucleus composed of a proton with two neutrons. To give some idea of size we have already shown that the first Bohr orbit in hydrogen has a radius of 0.53×10^{-8} cms. The proton has a radius about 10,000 times smaller. For the heaviest naturally occurring atom, uranium, the innermost electron orbit has a radius of about 6×10^{-11} cms. as compared with the radius of the nucleus, about 8×10^{-13} cms.

Even at this early stage we must draw attention to an obvious question. The electrons are held in orbits round the nucleus due to the attraction of the equal and opposite electric charges. Neutrons have no charge. How then do they join so firmly with protons to produce the very compact and stable atomic nuclei which persist quite unaffected throughout the most intense chemical reactions? We still do not know the full answer to this highly topical question but much more will be said about it in Chapter 6.

Having brought the historical account up to this stage, which is somewhere about that reached by 1935, we may take up the story of the atomic nucleus in separate later Chapters to describe the present situation. Also we have made no attempt to do more than call attention in this chapter to the major development of quantum mechanics, still less of relativity. These, with their consequences and applications, we shall describe in the next few Chapters.

CHAPTER 2

ATOM MECHANICS AND THE UNCERTAINTY PRINCIPLE

> *... which rightly gazed upon*
> *Show nothing but confusion, eyed awry*
> *Distinguish form, ...*
> WILLIAM SHAKESPEARE, 'KING RICHARD THE
> SECOND'

Particles and Waves

In order to appreciate the remarkable sequence of events which led to the discovery of quantum or wave mechanics, it is necessary to be clear about certain of the characteristics attributed to particles and to waves.

Particles

We think of a particle as a small bundle of matter possessing a *mass* which determines its reaction to applied force. Two principal mechanical quantities are associated with the motion of a particle. These are the *momentum* and *energy*, both of which remain constant if it is free from interaction with an outside agent. This is also true of the mass. If v is the speed of a particle of mass m, it possesses an amount of energy due to its motion, known as kinetic energy, which is given by $\frac{1}{2}mv^2$. The momentum is of magnitude mv but, like velocity, it is a directed, or vector, quantity, its direction being that of the particle's motion. When acted on by a force the momentum changes at a rate equal to the magnitude of the force and increases in the direction of the force.

Consider now a collision between two particles as, for example, two billiard balls. As a result of the collision the kinetic energy and the momentum of each ball will be changed but the total energy and the total momentum will remain un-

---

* It is convenient to express the kinetic energy of an atomic particle in terms of *electron volts*. This is the energy acquired by an electron in falling through one volt potential difference. It is 1.6×10^{-12} times the kinetic energy of a body of mass 1 gram moving at a velocity of one cm. per second.

The New Age in Physics

altered. This is an example of the conservation of energy and of momentum. Fig. 2.1 illustrates a typical case in which one particle A strikes another B at rest. Before the collision, particle A is moving with a speed u in the direction shown. After-

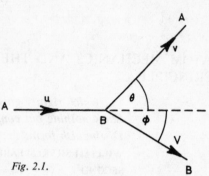

Fig. 2.1.

wards its speed will have changed to v in the different direction indicated. Furthermore, the particle B will now be moving with a speed V in a third direction as shown. To completely specify the collision we need to know v and V as well as the angles Θ and Φ which fix the directions of motion of A and B respectively after the collision. We may obtain 3 relations between these 4 quantities from the requirements of the conservation of energy and of momentum. The latter gives us two, as we shall see, because momentum is a vector quantity. Because of their importance in the history of the development of wave mechanics we shall write these equations down.

If the collision produces no change in the internal structure of the particles no energy will be used up thereby. The total kinetic energy before collision must therefore equal the total after. Only particle A is moving at first, with energy $\frac{1}{2}mu^2$, m being the mass of A. After the collision this will have changed to $\frac{1}{2}mv^2$ but, in addition, particle B now has kinetic energy $\frac{1}{2}MV^2$, M being the mass of B. The conservation of energy therefore gives us

$$\tfrac{1}{2}mu^2 = \tfrac{1}{2}mv^2 + \tfrac{1}{2}MV^2. \tag{a}$$

To deal with the conservation of momentum we must consider the momenta due to motion in two different directions. Both of these momenta must remain constant. Considering first the initial direction of motion of particle A, the initial momentum, due only to A, is mu. After the collision A is moving in a direction making an angle Θ with the initial direction. Hence only a component $v \cos \Theta$ of this motion is along the initial direction and contributes to the momentum in this direction. The momentum of A after the impact, in the direction of the initial motion of A, is therefore $mv \cos \Theta$. Similarly that of B is $MV \cos \Phi$. We must therefore have

$$mu = mv \cos \Theta + MV \cos \Phi. \tag{b}$$

It remains to consider the momentum due to motion perpendicular to the initial direction of motion of A. Initially there is no momentum in this direction. Finally, however, there is a component $mv \sin \Theta$ due to the motion of A in the sense indicated by the arrow in Fig. 2.1 and one $MV \sin \Phi$ due to B which is in the opposite sense so must subtract from that of A. We therefore have

$$0 = mv \sin \Theta - MV \sin \Phi. \tag{c}$$

Thus we have the three equations which are sufficient to determine any three of the quantities v, V, Θ, Φ in terms of the fourth and the initial velocity of particle A.

We think of particles then as bundles of energy travelling through space, retaining their compactness as they move. When two particles collide there is a redistribution of energy and momentum between them, subject to the overriding requirement that the total energy and momentum are unchanged. We have considered in detail only the simplest type of collision, from which the particles emerge quite unchanged – an elastic collision. There are many other possibilities but it would take us too far from the main line of argument if we stopped to discuss them here (see for example nuclear collisions discussed in Chapter 6 p. 169).

A stream of moving particles provides a means for transporting energy from one place to another. The nature of the particles and their speeds can be determined in principle by studying the effects they produce when colliding with other particles.

Wave Motion

There is an alternative way in which energy may be transmitted and that is through wave motion. A typical example, familiar to all, is provided by ocean rollers or by the ripples on a pond. In these cases there is no general transport of material in the direction of the wave. Other most important examples are sound waves, and electromagnetic waves which include visible light, as well as ultraviolet, infrared and X-rays, and radio waves. We must spend a little time recalling the characteristic features of this kind of motion.

A wave motion is a flow of disturbance which may consist of a surface deformation as in a ripple or ocean wave, or of compression or dilatation in a solid, liquid or gas as in a sound wave, or of the electromagnetic condition in space or a material medium as in an electromagnetic wave. All wave motions can be built up by superposing a number of specially simple types of waves known as simple harmonic waves in which the disturbance varies rhythmically both with position and with time. Thus Fig. 2.2(a) illustrates the typical shape of the disturbance at any instant. The distance between successive crests or troughs is the *wavelength* and at any instant the disturbance is

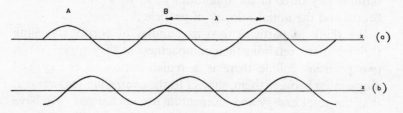

Fig. 2.2 (a). Illustrating the variation at some instant of the disturbance with distance x in the direction of propagation of a simple harmonic wave of wavelength λ. (b). The variation of the disturbance with distance at an instant one quarter of a period later than for (a).

the same at any two points which are a whole number of wavelengths apart. Similarly Fig. 2.3(a) shows how the disturbance at any one place varies with time. The time between successive maxima or minima is the *period* and a particular disturbance repeats itself at intervals equal to the period. It is usual to refer often to the *frequency* of the wave which is the reciprocal of the period and gives the number of complete cycles of disturbance which occur per second. In a simple harmonic wave both the wavelength and frequency are constant at all places and times.

The velocity of propagation of the wave is easily obtained

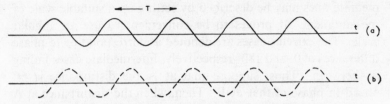

Fig. 2.3(a). Illustrating the variation of the disturbance with time t at some definite position along the direction of propagation of a simple harmonic wave of period T. (b). The dotted curve represents the variation of the disturbance with time t at the same position when the simple harmonic wave is of same period, wavelength and amplitude but is 90° behind in phase.

once these two quantities are known. In a time equal to one period the disturbance pattern will again be exactly of the same form as in Fig. 2.2(a) but the crest at A will have moved up to replace that at B and so on. Fig. 2.2(b) shows the disturbance one quarter period later when the crest initially at A has moved one quarter of the way to B. It will be seen that, in a period, the disturbance moves through one wavelength, i.e. it has a velocity equal to the wavelength divided by the period or, what is the same thing, to the product of wavelength and frequency.

Thus, if we denote the wavelength by λ and the frequency by ν the velocity v of the wave is given by

$$v = \nu\lambda.$$

A simple harmonic wave is not completely specified if we give its frequency and wavelength. The magnitude of the maximum disturbance at any point is also required. This is known as the *amplitude*. Finally there is the important quantity known as the *phase*. This determines the times at which the disturbance at any particular place reaches a maximum. Thus the two simple harmonic disturbances shown in Fig. 2.3 have the same frequency, wavelength and amplitude but differ in phase.

We may use the idea of phase more precisely by noting that, at each point along the wave track, an exactly similar oscillating disturbance is occurring. The disturbances at two points are said to be in the same phase if they are equal and of the same sign at all times, in opposite phase if they are equal and opposite at all times. These represent two extreme possibilities and intermediate ones may be described by setting up a suitable scale of measurement. It proves to be convenient to use an angular scale. The extreme cases are denoted as corresponding to phase differences of 0° and 180° respectively, intermediate cases falling in between. Thus, suppose that at A the disturbance is $\Theta°$ ahead in phase of that at B. Then, when the disturbance at A is a maximum in the positive sense, at B it will be a fraction cos Θ of the maximum. In Figs. 2.3(a) and 2.3(b) the two disturbances illustrated differ in phase by 90° so that when one is a maximum in either sense the other is zero.

The velocity of propagation of the wave which we have introduced is really a measure of the rate at which a given phase travels and is often referred to as the *phase velocity*. For a simple harmonic wave it is also the rate at which energy travels but this is no longer true for a wave motion made up of a number of simple harmonic waves of different frequency and phase velocity. Even if the frequencies are quite close to each other so that the phase velocities do not differ greatly, the velocity at which the energy travels in the composite wave may be very different from these phase velocities. It is known as the *group velocity*. If signals are being transmitted by the wave motion, as with radio waves, the velocity of transmission will be the group velocity if this is different from the phase velocity.

So far we have been dealing essentially with waves moving along a line as, for example, waves of extension and contraction along a taut straight wire. We must in practice deal with wave disturbances in three dimensions. In that case, at any time, points at which the disturbance is the same trace out a surface known as a *wavefront*. A plane wave is one in which the wavefronts are separate parallel planes perpendicular to the direction of propagation of the wave. In a simple harmonic plane wave the wavelength is the smallest distance between two wave fronts at which, at any time, the disturbance is the same in phase. All the arguments which we have introduced for the simple linear case remain valid.

An outgoing spherical wave is one in which the wavefronts are concentric spheres and the direction of propagation at any point is along the outward radius. The two-dimensional analogue is a circular wave on a surface, such as the ripples which spread over a pond from a central disturbance like that produced by dropping a stone into a pond (see Plate 2.1). Once again there is no difficulty, for a simple harmonic spherical or circular wave, in defining wavelength, period etc. and applying the same arguments as for other simple harmonic waves.

Distinction between Streams of Particles and Waves

If a flow of energy is taking place this can be due to a stream of particles or to a wave motion. How can one distinguish between these possibilities in any practical case? This has been a question faced many times in the past with reference to the nature of sound, of light and of X-rays, for example. There is, of course, the essential distinction of atomicity for particles and continuity for wave motion. If devices are available for detecting individual particles then this should provide adequate means for discrimination. This is possible for charged particles such as electrons, protons, atomic nuclei, etc. provided they are sufficiently energetic. One of the earliest ways of counting alpha particles was to observe the bright flashes they produced on a screen of suitable fluorescent material. The modern form of this technique, the scintillation counter, is described in Chapter 6 p. 160. Even if the particles are uncharged and so difficult to detect as such, they can be detected by allowing them to interact with matter. In the course of this interaction collisions will take place with the charged constituents of atoms, giving rise to charged secondary particles. These may be observed and the directions and magnitudes of their velocities determined. Using the laws of conservation of energy and momentum as on p. 44, information about the primary particles can then be obtained. This procedure was used in the discovery of the neutron (Chapter 1 p. 41 and Chapter 6 p. 170).

So much for the positive identification of particles but what about waves? Fortunately there exists a special feature of wave motion which offers the opportunity of unambiguous identification. This is the phenomenon of *interference*. If the directions of propagation of two simple harmonic waves of equal amplitude intersect at some point the net disturbance there will be the sum of those due to the separate waves, allowing for sign. This may be greater or less than the separate ones, depending on the phase relations between the waves. If at the point of intersection the two are always exactly in phase the net disturbance will always be twice that of either but if they are always exactly opposite in phase the two disturbances will always cancel giving no net disturbance at all! Thus two wave systems combined will in general give a disturbance distribution in which the amplitudes vary from point to point in some regular fashion, provided the phase relations of the two systems are not fluctuating. Plate 2.2 illustrates interference between the two sets of ripples set up on a mercury surface by the oscillation of the two prongs of a tuning fork. Regions of small disturbance can be clearly seen.

Consider now a plane wave impinging on an obstacle. Secondary waves will be scattered off the obstacle and will interfere with the primary waves to produce a more or less regular pattern of disturbance amplitude maxima and minima. This is known as a *diffraction pattern*. Because of diffraction the shadow cast by an obstacle is never completely sharp. This is illustrated in Plate 2.3 for the shadows cast by a circular disc and by a fine wire. The diffraction by an obstacle is only clearly apparent when the dimensions of the obstacle are comparable with the wavelength. If the wavelength is very small compared with the size of the obstacle the fluctuations due to diffraction are confined to a small region close to the edge of the geometrical shadow. Thus, for diffraction of waves of wavelength λ by a disc of radius a, the blurring of the shadow edge is confined effectively within an angle λ/a radians. Because of this, diffraction is not normally apparent with light waves, which have wavelengths between 4×10^{-5} and 7×10^{-5} cms. With sound waves, which may be of much greater wavelength, the lack of sharpness in sound shadows cast by obstacles of ordinary dimensions is more familiar.

The observation of interference and diffraction is therefore to be regarded as a definite test of the wave nature of the radiation concerned. Let us now see what results were yielded by these methods of discrimination between the particle and wave nature of different radiations.

The Nature of Light

Electromagnetic Waves

There was no doubt in the minds of all physicists at the beginning of the present century that light was a wave motion. The colour of the light is determined by the wavelength, the intensity by the square of the amplitude of the disturbance concerned. Maxwell in 1865 had produced his electromagnetic theory according to which these disturbances were identified as rhythmical fluctuations of electric and magnetic fields, the velocity of propagation in free space – the all-important velocity of light – being 186,000 miles per second. Not only did these considerations apply to visible light but to radiations both of longer and of shorter wave lengths. Part of the range of the electromagnetic spectrum is illustrated in Fig. 2.4, extending from gamma-rays at the high frequency end to long radio waves at the low frequency end.

Diffraction and interference phenomena had been observed extensively (see Plate 2.3) with light and indeed used as a basis for highly precise measurement of wavelength and of lengths generally. For shorter radiation the observation of characteristic wave effects is more difficult and some time elapsed after the discovery of X-rays by Röntgen in 1895 before von Laue first demonstrated in 1912 that they could be diffracted by passage through crystals. The distances between the atoms in a crystal are comparable with the wavelengths (10^{-8} cm) of X-rays so that an extensive diffraction pattern results. Plate 2.4 illustrates typical patterns obtained in this way. Observations of this kind may be used conversely to derive information about the distribution of atoms within the diffracting crystal. This has proved to be a tool of the greatest importance for investigating the solid and also the liquid state of matter, including biological materials (see p. 67).

Equally well there was general acceptance of the particle nature of the electron and yet, within a quarter of a century, a fantastic situation had developed in which all was back in the

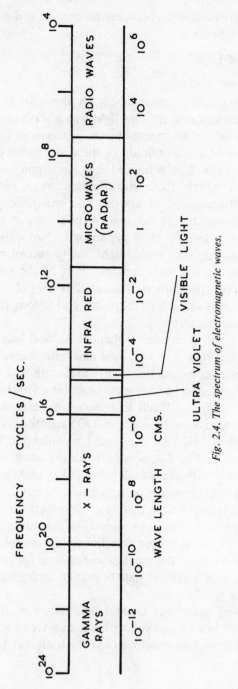

Fig. 2.4. The spectrum of electromagnetic waves.

melting-pot and an apparently completely contradictory position had been reached.

Waves and/or Particles?

The seeds of this conflict were already sown as early as 1901 by Planck. Theoretical developments had made it possible by that time to predict what would be the distribution in frequency of the electromagnetic radiation emitted by a hot body at a particular temperature. These predictions, which followed quite definitely from the current ideas about the nature of radiation, were quite unsatisfactory. According to them much too much energy would be radiated at very high frequencies. Planck showed that, if one makes the then very heretical assumption that radiation of energy in the form of electromagnetic waves does not take place continuously but in bundles or quanta of a certain magnitude, the difficulty is avoided and very good agreement is obtained with the observed variation of intensity with frequency. According to Planck, for a frequency v the energy bundle or quantum is of magnitude hv where h is a certain constant, the quantum of action, already referred to in Chapter 1 p. 33. It is as if, after a quantum has been radiated, no further radiation can occur until an amount hv of energy has accumulated.

The introduction of a discontinuous aspect into what was regarded as a characteristically continuous phenomenon was already a warning that in some way or other electromagnetic waves have a particle aspect but, in 1901, the whole idea was so foreign that the possibilities could only be dimly foreseen.

Four years later Einstein showed that the observations made by Lenard on the photoelectric effect, the emission of electrons by a surface when it is bombarded by electromagnetic waves of sufficiently high frequency, which were very puzzling for classical theory, could also be understood if energy could only be absorbed, from electromagnetic waves of frequency v, in quanta of amount hv.

We have discussed in Chapter 1 p. 34 how a few years later, in 1911, Bohr introduced Planck's constant h into a highly non-classical but promising description of the hydrogen atom and its spectrum. After considerable initial success this theory became confused, but all was worse confounded by the remarkable experiments of Compton in 1924.

Compton studied the scattering of X-rays by electrons in materials exposed to the rays. He found that, in many cases, the

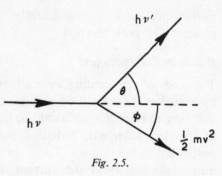

Fig. 2.5.

scattering took place just as if the X-rays were not waves but streams of particles, each possessing energy $h\nu$ and momentum $h\nu/c$, c being the velocity of light. The scattering process could be described just as if it were a collision between one of these X-ray 'particles' and an electron at rest. That is to say, the equations of conservation of energy and momentum applied exactly as in the collision between two particles which we discussed on p. 44. This is illustrated in Fig. 2.5. The reduction in energy of the scattered X-ray 'particle' is reflected in a reduction of frequency to ν' so that, with the geometry of Fig. 2.5, we have

$h\nu = h\nu' + \tfrac{1}{2}mv^2$, (conservation of energy),

$$\frac{h\nu}{c} = \frac{h\nu'}{c} \cos \Theta + mv \cos \Phi,$$ (conservation of momentum along the initial direction),

$$0 = \frac{h\nu'}{c} \sin \Theta - mv \sin \Phi,$$ (conservation of momentum along the direction perpendicular to the initial direction).

m is the mass of the electron and v the velocity it acquires. In Compton's experiments v, Θ, Φ and ν' could all be measured and shown to be related as in these three equations.

What could this mean? Taken alone it would imply that X-rays are not waves but streams of particles of energy $h\nu$ and momentum $h\nu/c$. On the other hand, the long-standing and quite definite evidence of the wave character, so manifest in the diffraction of X-rays by crystals, seemed to be equally decisive in establishing that the rays are electromagnetic waves of short wavelength. How could both be right?

Taken together with the failure to pierce behind the veil which hid the inner significance of the postulates introduced by Bohr in his quantum description of atomic structure, the apparently flat contradiction of equally decisive experiments concerning the nature of X-rays produced an atmosphere of unreality about atomic physics which, by 1925, was all-pervading.

Electrons as Waves!

A great clarification and simplification, but with far reaching consequences and implications, was near at hand. The cure, as it were, was homeopathic in character. Resolution of the difficulty came with the realisation that, not only was there a dual aspect of X-rays, but also of electrons. Just as the familiar wave nature of the former under certain conditions seemed to give way to particle behaviour, electrons were found to behave under certain conditions as waves. Wave-particle dualism in fact is universal though one or other aspect may be more apparent in any particular circumstances.

Already in 1924 L. de Broglie had suggested that electrons might be associated with waves. He predicted the correct wavelength and showed how this concept might be related to the selection of allowed orbits for electrons in hydrogen atoms. Little attention was paid to this work at the time, but in 1926 Schrödinger took up the matter and, in four classic papers, developed the foundations of wave, or quantum, mechanics.

Only a little later the diffraction of electrons in scattering from a nickel crystal was demonstrated by Davison and Germer. As in so many similar instances an element of luck attended their work. It was not begun in order to search for diffraction effects but to study the production of secondary electrons from the metal surface. At an early stage an accident occurred and the crystal, while hot, was exposed to the air. This so changed the surface of the crystal that, when the experiment was resumed, the intensity of the scattered electrons was found to vary rhythmically with the direction of scattering in just the way expected for waves of the wavelength associated with electrons in de Broglie's theory.

The energy E and momentum p of the X-ray particles are related to the fundamental wave properties of frequency v and wavelength λ by the simple rules

$$E = hv, \ p = h/\lambda,$$

remembering that the velocity c is given by the product $v\lambda$. If we apply the same relations in the converse fashion to electrons of energy $\frac{1}{2}mv^2$ and momentum mv we would obtain, for electron waves:

frequency $v = E/h$, wavelength $\lambda = h/p = h/mv$.

The experiment of Davison and Germer confirmed this choice of wavelength. They used electrons of such an energy that the wavelength $\lambda = 1.7 \times 10^{-8}$ cms. In 1927 G. P. Thomson studied the diffraction of electrons of rather higher energy, corresponding to a wavelength of 5×10^{-10} cms., by thin metal foils. Plate 2.4(c) illustrates the diffraction rings he obtained with a gold foil which may be compared with corresponding results for X-rays shown on the same Plate. Electron diffraction is now a well-known technique (see Plate 2.4(d)), made use of for the study of surface structure of solids (see Chapter 3, p. 68).

Interpretation of Wave-Particle Dualism

The Probability Interpretation

It was clear by 1927 that the Dr. Jekyll and Mr. Hyde behaviour of X-rays and of electrons must be accepted. Schrödinger had paved the way for the application of a new and powerful means of predicting the behaviour of atoms and electrons, free from the arbitrariness and uncertainty of Bohr's early theory, and of apparently unlimited scope. If the wavelengths associated with the motions of the various particles were all small compared with the dimensions of the particles and their range of interaction, then the new mechanics reduced to the classical mechanics of Newton. Otherwise, it gave quite different results which were found to agree, without exception, with what was observed.

The need for using the new mechanics, rather than the classical approximation to it, is seen when we note that the wavelength of an electron with say 20 e.volts energy is about 2.7×10^{-8}cms., of the same order of size as the diameter of the innermost electron orbit in a hydrogen atom in Bohr's theory.

Despite this widespread success there remained difficult questions of interpretation. Much attention to these difficulties was paid by many mathematical physicists, including particularly Dirac, Born, Jordan and Heisenberg who, in different ways, had, before Schrödinger, attempted to generalize Bohr's ideas to constitute a new form of mechanics appropriate for atomic phenomena. It was suggested that the key to the whole matter lay in a rejection of the complete determinism of classical mechanics.

According to this mechanics, if we are given the position and velocity of a particle at some initial time t_o, and the force which acts upon it at any point in space, then we can predict precisely where it will be and what velocity it will have at some subsequent time t. This, according to the new view, is no longer possible. Instead, it is only possible to assign a definite probability that, at any time t, the particle will be at a particular location and have a particular velocity. The wave aspect determines this probability but the particle aspect determines the nature of any interaction the particle may have with another particle if, for example, it happens to be at the same location at the same time.

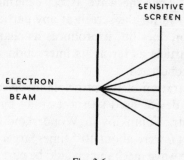

Fig. 2.6.

To put this in more definite terms, consider the following hypothetical experiment illustrated diagrammatically in Fig. 2.6.

57

A stream of electrons of a definite energy, and hence also definite wavelength, passes through a very fine hole and then impinges on a screen. We suppose that the hole is so small as to be comparable in diameter with the wavelength of the electrons (this is quite impossible to achieve in practice but will be assumed in order to make the vital point clear). The screen is supposed to be coated with a fluorescent material on which the impact of a single electron produces a bright flash. Because of diffraction the appearance on the screen when the electron beam is intense will consist of a series of bright diffraction rings similar to those in Plate 2.4. But what happens when the intensity of the beam is reduced so that electrons only pass through the hole at intervals say of a few seconds? Will the ring pattern persist, becoming fainter and fainter as the electron beam gets weaker, but always preserving its character? According to the probability inter-pretation the answer is definitely No! When the electrons pass through at widely separated intervals their impacts on the screen will be seen as single flashes, not as faint rings of light. It is not possible to predict where each such flash will occur on the screen but, if the positions of a great number of flashes are plotted, they will be found to trace out again the diffraction rings. In other words an electron has the greatest probability of hitting the screen where the intensity of the corresponding wave is greatest – where the diffraction pattern is brightest. It may, however, actually hit at any other point, except one where the wave intensity is zero. Thus the wave aspect determines the chance that an electron will hit the screen at any particular point but, where the electron does hit, it produces its characteristic flash, behaving as a particle as far as its interaction with the matter in the screen is concerned.

A further illustration of the principle involved may be made by adopting the device used so successfully by G. Gamow in his stories of 'Mr. Tompkins in Wonderland'! Suppose that Planck's constant h were about 10^{35} times larger than it actually is. If this were so wave mechanics would be part of our everyday lives – the wavelength associated with a man of 10 stone weight running for a train would be about 2 feet. Imagine now the plight, in such a world, of a man who has to take refuge from a man-eating tiger, in a hut with an opening through which the tiger can enter. As the wavelength of the tiger will be of the same order of size as the opening the probability that the tiger will hit any part of the hut wall in its leap at the man will take the form of a diffraction pattern, just as for the electrons passing through the fine hole in the experiment just discussed. The best the man can do to avoid the tiger will be to place himself at a diffraction minimum. If he still has the bad luck that the particular tiger leaps in his direction he will have no chance of escape as he will encounter the whole tiger, not the animal smeared over the diffraction pattern!

We now are assured that all particles have an associated wave aspect and the probability interpretation applies. It is not important in everyday life because the wavelengths associated with the motion of ordinary objects are so very small that diffraction effects are negligible and the probability that the paths prescribed by Newton's mechanics will not be followed can be completely ignored. On the other hand the wave aspects of many particles which are heavier than electrons, including particularly neutrons (see Chapter 3 p. 68) and helium atoms, have been demonstrated and found to agree exactly with the predictions of Schrödinger's wave mechanics.

The Uncertainty Principle

According to classical mechanics there is no limitation in the accuracy attainable in the measurement of any physical quantities associated with a system of particles and radiation. This is no longer true in the new wave mechanics because of the inherent lack of determinism. Heisenberg in 1927 first expressed these limitations in terms of an uncertainty principle.

This is best illustrated in the first instance in terms of the two quantities position, as measured in terms of displacement, and momentum. It is not possible, no matter how perfect the instruments used may be, to determine the position and the momentum of a particle simultaneously to any desired precision. If Δx is the uncertainty in the determination of position and Δp of momentum, then the product $\Delta x \Delta p$, assuming perfect instruments, will always be close to $h/2\pi$ where h is Planck's constant. Thus, if we wish to know the momentum of a particle precisely, we must sacrifice all knowledge of its position and vice versa.

A striking illustration of this is afforded by the case of a particle in a bowl (Fig. 2.7). According to the uncertainty principle it can never be at rest at the bottom of the bowl for, if so, its position and momentum would both be known exactly. The particle must always move about so that the product

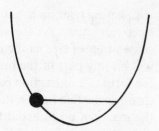

MEAN LEVEL OF PARTICLE DUE TO ZERO-POINT ENERGY.

Fig. 2.7. Illustrating the effect of zeropoint energy for a particle in a bowl. The situation illustrated would arise if Planck's constant were about 10^{35} times longer than it actually is.

of the mean uncertainty in position and in momentum is of order h. The energy associated with this motion is known as the *zero-point energy*. Think of the difficulty of laying out the red balls in a snooker triangle in a world in which Planck's constant was 10^{35} times larger than in our own. The zeropoint motion of the balls would be most irritating!

There are many other complementary pairs of quantities between which uncertainty relations apply. Thus we have, for the uncertainties ΔE, Δt of energy and time respectively, that

$$\Delta E\, \Delta t \simeq h/2\pi,$$

a relation of great importance in the interpretation of atomic and nuclear phenomena (see Chapter 8 p. 205).

The relations apply also between electric and magnetic quantities. Just as it is impossible for a particle to be at rest at the bottom of a bowl, it is equally so for electric and magnetic field strengths to be simultaneously zero at all points of space at a given time. An electromagnetic field can never be completely absent but can at best fluctuate about a zero mean value. This has far-reaching consequences, some of which are described in Chapter 5 p. 131.

Wave Mechanics and the Structure of Atoms

The Hydrogen Atom

The new mechanics met with overwhelming success when applied to atomic structure. We can see that there is likely to be a close association of the concept of electron waves with the postulates of Bohr's theory by recalling a result pointed out by de Broglie in his original suggestion that a wavelength h/mv should be associated with an electron of mass m moving with speed v. As described in Chapter 1 p. 34 the quite arbitrary condition introduced by Bohr for selecting the allowed circular orbit of electrons in hydrogen atoms took the form

$$mva = nh/2\pi$$

where a is the radius of an allowed orbit, v the speed of the electron in the orbit and n a whole number. This can be written

$$2\pi a/\lambda = n,$$

where λ is the electron wavelength, a relation which requires that the circumference of an allowed circular orbit include a whole number of electron wavelengths. This is the kind of condition we might expect to hold if the state is a stationary one.

Detailed application of wave mechanics shows that, for a system like the hydrogen atom, and indeed for any dynamical system, there are a number of allowed energy values. In a given range of energy only isolated values may be assumed, in which case the system is said to possess discrete energy levels within the range. Otherwise a whole range of energy may be allowed in which case the system is said to possess a continuous set of energy levels in the range of energy concerned.

Corresponding to each energy level there are one or more characteristic distributions of probability. For the motion of a single particle, as for an electron in a hydrogen atom, this characteristic distribution gives the probability that the particle, when it possesses a particular allowed energy, will be found in any particular small region of space.

For the hydrogen atom the allowed energy values come out to be exactly as given by Bohr's simple theory while the corresponding probability distributions are blurred versions of his allowed circular and elliptic orbits. Plate 2.5 illustrates the probability distributions for the lowest and next lowest allowed energy states of the electron. For the lowest, only one distribution is possible and this corresponds to Bohr's innermost circular orbit. Two distributions occur for the next state, corresponding respectively to the circular and elliptic orbit in Bohr's theory, which have the same energy, and so on. Actually the nth energy level of hydrogen is associated with n^2 independent probability distributions, or what is perhaps more correct, there are n^2 states having the same energy $E_n = -2\pi^2 me^4/n^2h^2$. In other atoms, containing more than one electron, the energy level system is essentially similar to that of hydrogen but, because of interaction between the electrons, some of the n^2 states associated with the hydrogen atom energy E_n, differ to some extent in energy. This is illustrated diagrammatically in Fig. 2.8.

Electron Spin

It was realized even before the introduction of wave mechanics

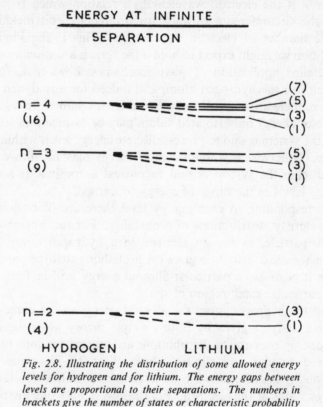

Fig. 2.8. Illustrating the distribution of some allowed energy levels for hydrogen and for lithium. The energy gaps between levels are proportional to their separations. The numbers in brackets give the number of states or characteristic probability distributions associated with each energy level.

that the detailed features of the spectra of atoms could not be understood unless an electron possesses an energy of motion additional to that due to its orbital motion. This could be ascribed most naturally to the possession, by an electron of an axial spin. Instead of regarding it as a point mass it should be considered rather as a small spinning sphere. As an electron carries an electric charge the spinning motion must lead to a circulation of charge and thus to electric current flow. These currents will in turn produce a magnetic field so that electrons behave as small magnets (see Chapter 3 p. 89 and Chapter 5 p. 135).

To fit with the observed spectra it is necessary to suppose that the angular momentum of the electron spin is fixed by wave mechanical limitations to a single magnitude $\sqrt{\frac{3}{4}}\, h/2\pi$, while the component of angular momentum in a chosen direction can be either $+\frac{1}{2}\, h/2\pi$ or $-\frac{1}{2}\, h/2\pi$. This means that the number of energy states of an electron must be doubled – associated with each state of orbital motion there will be two spin states corresponding to the two allowed components of spin angular momentum. In most atoms the interaction between spin and orbital motion is so weak that the energy differences due to difference in spin component are relatively small. They can be observed and measured, however, by the precise techniques of frequency measurement now available (see Chapter 5 p. 134).

An electron revolving round the proton in a hydrogen atom in general possesses angular momentum due to its orbital motion. The component of this angular momentum about any chosen direction is restricted by quantum mechanics to values $mh/2\pi$ where m is a positive or negative integer, or zero. This does not include the two possibilities due to the spin which are $\pm\frac{1}{2}\, h/2\pi$. The fact that, for the orbital motion, the allowed values of m are whole numbers whereas for the electron spin they are half-integral is of fundamental importance.

Although it is useful for conceptual purposes to think of the additional interaction as due to axial spin of a very small spherical electron its source is even more basic. Further discussion of its relationship to relativity theory will be given in Chapter 5 p. 126.

Other particles also possess intrinsic spin. Protons and neutrons, just as electrons, have allowed spin components $\pm \frac{1}{2} h/2\pi$. It is usual to refer to all these as particles with spin $\frac{1}{2}$ or *fermions*. Light quanta, or photons, have allowed spin $\pm h/2\pi$ and are known as *bosons* (a term used to characterise all particles with integral spins, including those with no spin, see Chapter 8 p. 209). Fermions and bosons are fundamentally distinct types of particle.

The Exclusion Principle of Pauli

In 1924 Pauli enunciated a general principle which has proved to be not only true universally but also of the greatest importance. As first expressed it states that, in a system containing more than one electron, no two of the electrons can occupy the same quantum state. Used in connection with the known distribution of allowed energy states for hydrogen-like atoms it provides the key to the electron structure of atoms and the periodic table. Before discussing this further we must note that the principle can be extended to apply not only to electrons but to all particles with half integral spins, i.e. to all fermions. It does not apply to bosons, and this is one of the big distinctions between the two sets of particles. More will be said about this in Chapter 3 p. 101 and Chapter 8 p. 209.

Electron Structure of Atoms

We have already described the allowed energies and corresponding probability distributions for the hydrogen atom. The atom with atomic number 2 is that of helium. Both of the electrons in this atom can occupy the lowest level in the field of the nucleus, despite the Pauli principle, provided they have opposite spins. Because the charge on the helium nucleus is twice that of a proton, the innermost orbit has half the diameter of that in hydrogen. It follows that the helium atom is more compact than that of hydrogen. Fig. 2.9 illustrates the relative dimensions.

The next atom, that of lithium, contains three electrons. Two of these are accommodated in the innermost allowed orbit which is even smaller than that of helium, but the Pauli

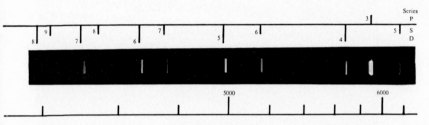

WAVELENGTH IN Å (200 Å divisions)

Plate 1.1   Lines in the visible region of the emission spectrum of the alkali metal sodium. These lines may be arranged in three regular series denoted as the P (for principal), S (for sharp) and D (for diffuse) series. Lines of each series are indicated on the overlay.

Plate 1.2   Hydrogen spectra showing lines of the Balmer series.

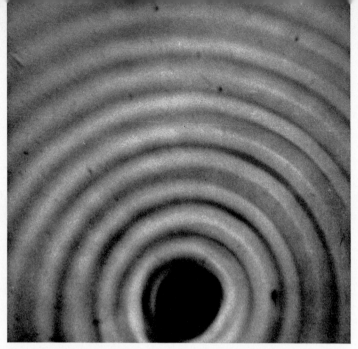

Plate 2.1   Ripples on a mercury surface as an illustration of outgoing circular surface waves.

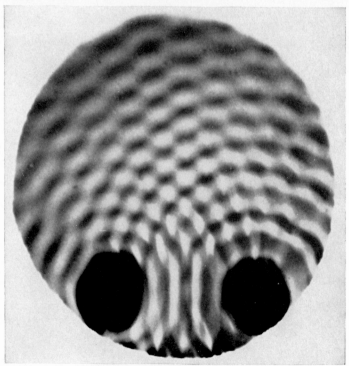

Plate 2.2   Illustrating interference between the ripples produced on a mercury surface by the two prongs of an oscillating tuning fork. The dark regions of small disturbance due to interference can be clearly seen.

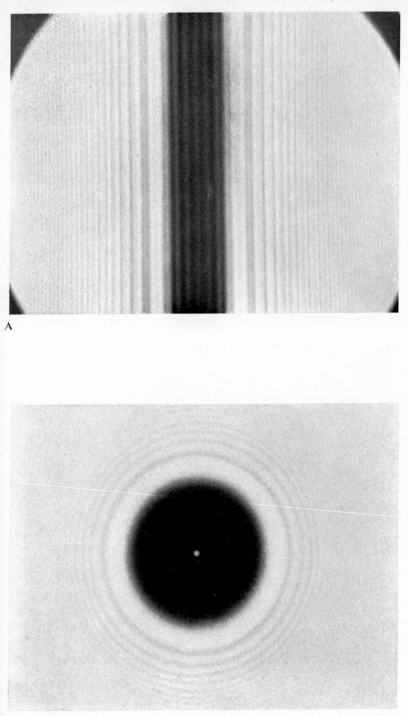

A

B

R. S. Longhurst

*Plate. 2.3   Photograph of a light shadow cast by (a) a fine wire and (b) a circular disc,
showing the fine structure due to diffraction.*

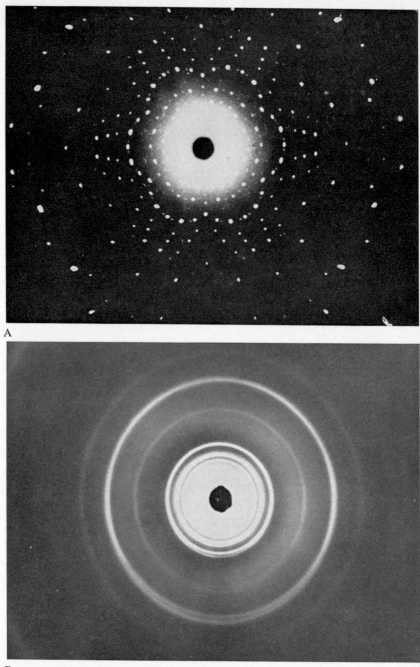

A

B

Plate 2.4 Patterns illustrating diffraction of X-rays and of electrons by crystals. K. Lonsdale
(a) X-rays diffracted by a crystal of beryl.
(b) X-rays diffracted by gold wire.
(c) One of the first electron diffraction photographs—obtained by G. P. Thomson from the passage of 40,000 volt electrons through a gold foil.
(d) Recent electron diffraction pattern obtained from zinc oxide. R. Bernard

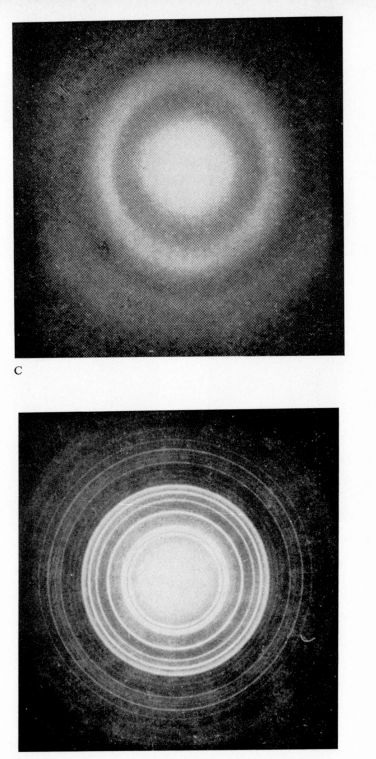

C

D

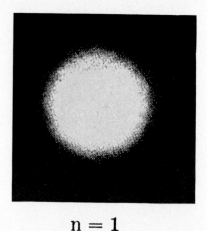

n = 1

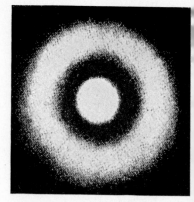

n = 2 (a)

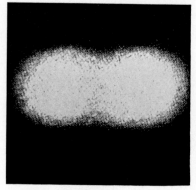

n = 2 (b)

n = 2 (c)

Plate 2.5 Probability distributions for electrons in the lowest stationary states of the hydrogen atom according to wave mechanics. The probability of finding the electron at any point is proportional to the brightness of the photograph there. The state with n = 1 is the ground state. There are 3 states (a), (b) and (c) with n = 2 with different characteristic probability distributions as shown. In all cases the proton is at the centre of the pattern. The magnification is about 100,000,000 times for n = 2 and twice that for n = 1.

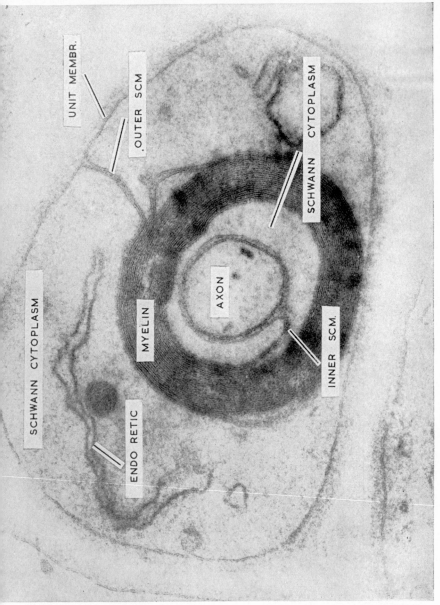

UNIT MEMBR.

.OUTER SCM

SCHWANN CYTOPLASM

SCHWANN CYTOPLASM

MYELIN

AXON

INNER SCM.

ENDO RETIC

J. Z. Young

Plate 3.1   Photograph, taken with an electron microscope, of a section of a young nerve fibre of a mouse, the magnification being 130,000 times. The section shows the axon surrounded by a Schwann cell which is wrapped many times around the axon to form myelin. The myelin repeating structure is formed by the closely packed spirally wound surface-connecting membrane (SCM). Schwann cytoplasm contains other paired membrane structures (endoplasmic reticulum—endo. retic.) and is bounded by a membrane (unit membr.) nearly 7.5×10^{-7} cm. wide, appearing as a pair of dense lines nearly 2×10^{-7} cm. wide separated by a light intervening layer.

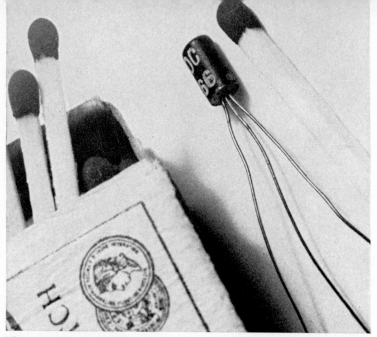

Plate 3.2   Photograph illustrating the size of a junction transistor element by comparison with a match-head.

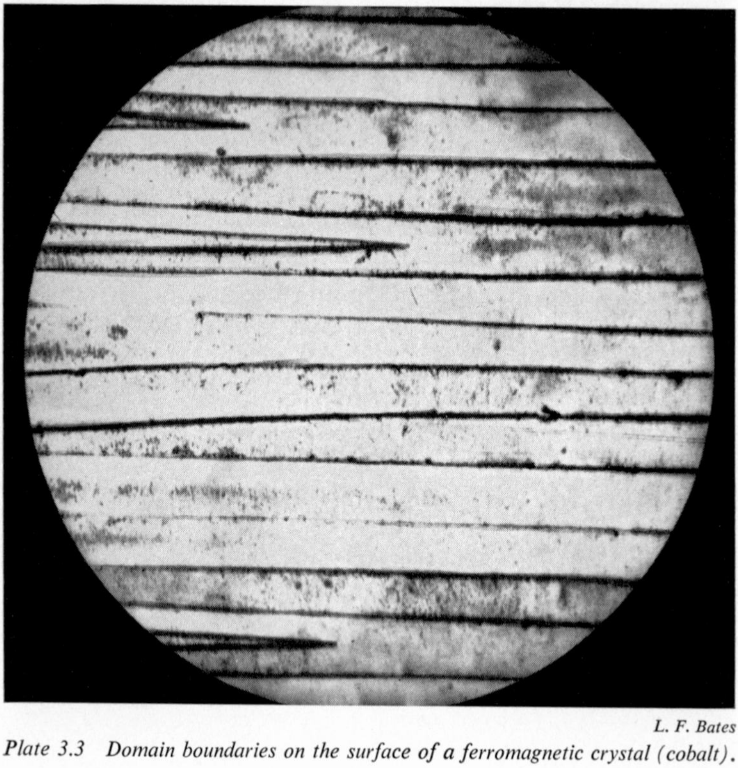

L. F. Bates

Plate 3.3   Domain boundaries on the surface of a ferromagnetic crystal (cobalt).

Plate 3.4 *Rapid access magnetic core store of a Mercury computer.*

Plate 3.5 *View of the drum store of a Mercury computer.*

J. Chadwick, P. M. S Blackett and G. P. S. Occhialini

Plate 5.1   Early cloud chamber photograph of the tracks of an electron-positron pair created
from gamma radiation. The tracks are curved in opposite sense by the magnetic field in which
the chamber was operated. This shows that they are due to particles with opposite electric
charges.

*Plate 6.1 General view of the frequency-modulated cyclotron at CERN, Geneva which
accelerates protons to an energy of 600 MeV.*

Plate 6.3   Aerial view of CERN, Geneva, March 1959. The ring building for the 25 GeV proton synchrotron is clearly visible on the right.

Plate 6.2   View of the bevatron at Berkeley, California.

Plate 6.4 Interior view of the ring tunnel of the 25 GeV proton synchrotron under construction at CERN, Geneva. The beam will circulate through a system of magnets fitted on the platforms visible in the centre of the photograph.

Plate 6.5 General view of the linear accelerator at CERN, Geneva for initial acceleration of protons to 50 MeV before injection into the proton synchrotron accelerator. Some drift tubes (see Fig. 6.6) are clearly visible in the opened cavity.

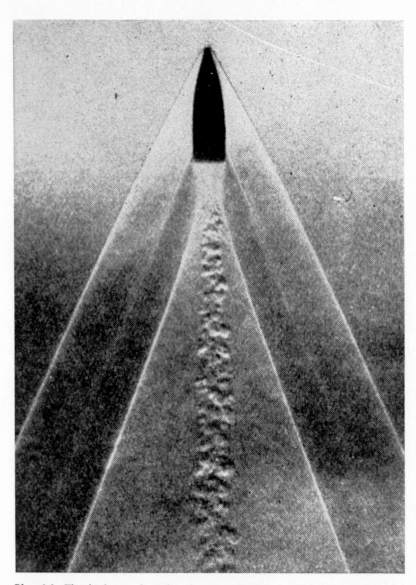

Plate 6.6 The shock wave formed at the nose of a bullet travelling at supersonic speed through air.

Plate 6.7 *An automatic high pressure cloud chamber, capable of operating at a pressure of 100 atmospheres.*

Plate 7.1 *Calder Hall, the world's first full-sized power station.*

Plate 6.9 Cloud chamber photograph showing the tracks of a proton and hydrogen 3 nucleus produced in a collision between a deuteron in an accelerated beam and a deuteron in a target. The longer track is that of the proton.

Plate 6.8 Wilson cloud chamber photograph of tracks of alpha particles in nitrogen. At the point A an alpha particle has collided with a nitrogen nucleus to produce a proton (p) and an O^{17} nucleus whose tracks are visible.

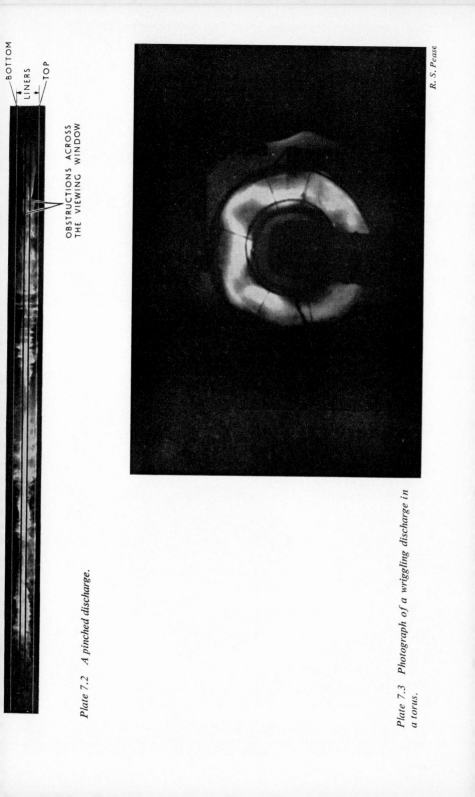

Plate 7.2 A pinched discharge.

BOTTOM

LINERS

TOP

OBSTRUCTIONS ACROSS
THE VIEWING WINDOW

*Plate 7.3   Photograph of a wriggling discharge in
a torus.*

R. S. Pease

Plate 7.4   *A photograph of Zeta.*

Plate 7.5   *The solar corona.*   *Lick Observatory*

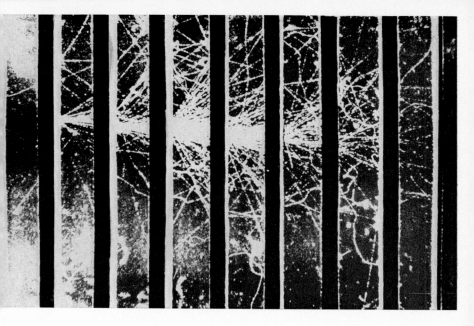

of heavy nuclei passing through nuclear emulsions exposed to primary cosmic rays. Note how the tracks get progressively thicker and more diffuse as the complexity of the nucleus increases.

D. F. Perkins

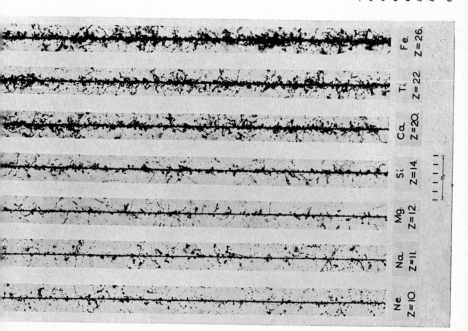

Plate 8.2 Showing the development of a soft cosmic ray shower as observed with a cloud chamber fitted with a number of parallel lead plates.

C· Y. Chao

Ne. Z=10   Na. Z=11   Mg. Z=12   Si. Z=14   Ca. Z=20   Ti. Z=22   Fe. Z=26.

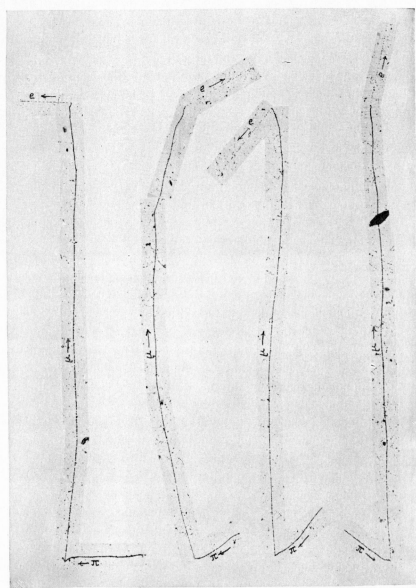

Plate 8.3   Micrographs showing the successive transformation of a π^{+}-meson into a μ^{+}-meson and thence into a positive electron.

Plate 8.4 *A typical medium altitude station for the observation of cosmic radiation at mountain altitudes. The site is at Mt. Marmolada in the Dolomites and was operated by the University of Padua and University College, London.*

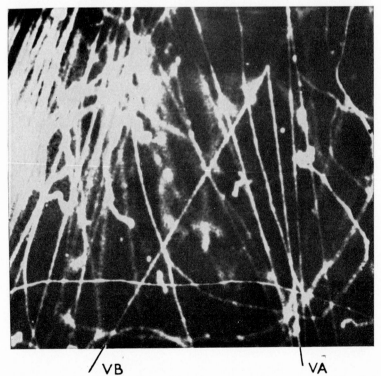

Plate 8.5 *Cloud chamber photograph taken at the station shown in Plate 8.4 illustrating the production of V-tracks due to breakup of a Λ° hyperon into a proton (VA) and a negative pi-meson (VB).*

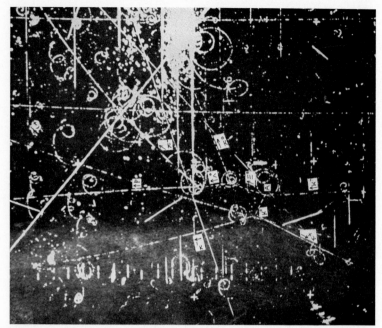

L. W. Alvarez et al.

Plate 8.6   Liquid hydrogen bubble chamber photograph showing an event involving production of a $\Xi°$ hyperon.   A K^- meson collides with a proton at A to produce a $K°$ meson and the $\Xi°$ hyperon.   The $K°$ meson eventually decays into a π^- and a π^+ meson whose tracks are visible.   The $\Xi°$ hyperon decays to a $\Lambda°$ hyperon and a $\pi°$ meson.   Eventually the $\Lambda°$ meson decays to a proton and a π^- meson whose tracks are visible.   None of the four neutral particles produces tracks but, from considerations of energy and momentum conservation, their paths can be deduced approximately as indicated by the dotted lines.

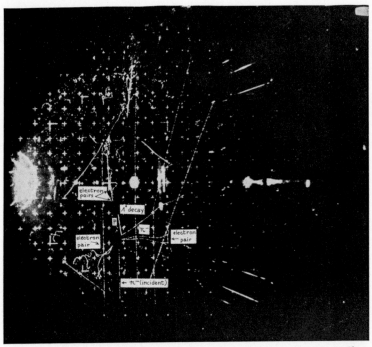

Plate 8.7   Bubble chamber photograph taken in liquid xenon which illustrates the associated production of a Λ° hyperon and a K° meson by impact of a π^- meson with a proton in a xenon nucleus at A.

The Λ° hyperon decays to produce the characteristic V-tracks (see plate 8.5). The K° meson decays to produce two π° mesons. These do not produce any tracks directly but through the successive decay processes

$$\pi^\circ \to 2\gamma$$
$$\gamma \to e^+ + e^-$$

four electron pais are formed. These produce the tracks seen in the photograph as indicated. (The white crosses on the background are reference marks to assist in analysis of the tracks)

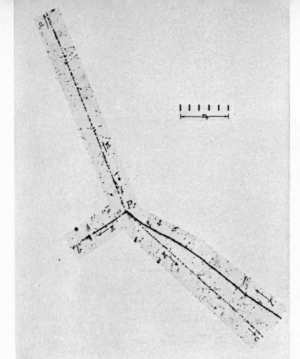

Plate 8.8 Micrograph of the decay in a photographic emulsion of a K-meson into three pi-mesons. The meson τ reaches the end of its range at the point P and transforms. The tracks a, b, c are produced by the three pi-mesons which result from the transformation.

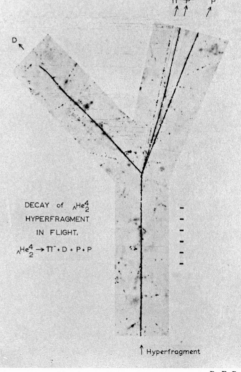

DECAY of $_\Lambda He^4_2$
HYPERFRAGMENT
IN FLIGHT.

$_\Lambda He^4_2 \rightarrow \pi^- + D + P + P$

↑ Hyperfragment

Plate 8.9 Micrograph of the decay of a hyperhelium nucleus (ΛHe^4) produced in a high energy reaction. The hypernucleus decays into a deuteron, two protons and a negative pi-meson (π^-).

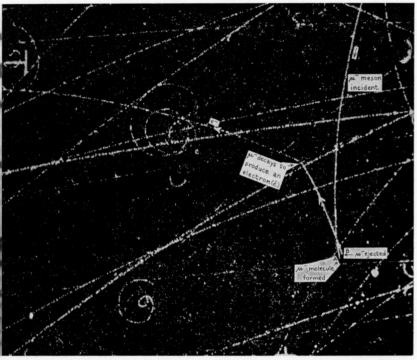

L. W. Alvarez et al

Plate 8.10 Bubble chamber photograph taken in liquid hydrogen containing the normal percent-age (0.014%) of deuterium. This illustrates induced reaction between a proton and a deuteron due to mu-meson capture. The incoming mu-meson (μ^-) comes to rest in the chamber and is captured to form a molecule μ HD in which an electron is replaced by the meson. After a short time, during which the molecule drifts from A to B, the proton and deuteron in the molecule react to produce an He³ nucleus and a neutron. Some of the energy released in the reaction is given to the mu-meson so that it again produces a track in the chamber. At a certain stage the meson decays into an electron whose track is visible.

Plate 9.1   Photograph of a right-handed screw and its image in a mirror. The image, seen on the right, appears as a left-handed screw.

Plate 9.2   The Crab nebula, the remains of a supernova which exploded in 1094.

Plate 10.1   The 32 element interferometer used by Christiansen.

Plate 10.2   The 250 feet diameter aerial at Jodrell Bank.

Plate 10.4   The external spiral galaxy M 51.   *Mount Palomar observatory*

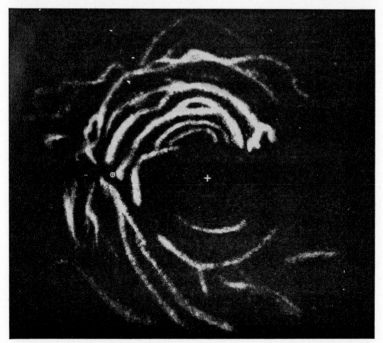

The Observatory, Utrecht

Plate 10.5   Illustrating the distribution of hydrogen in the equatorial plane of our galaxy as deduced from observations of the 21 cm. hydrogen line. + denotes the galactic centre, ○ the position of the sun. The concentration of hydrogen is proportional to the brightness at each point of the diagram.

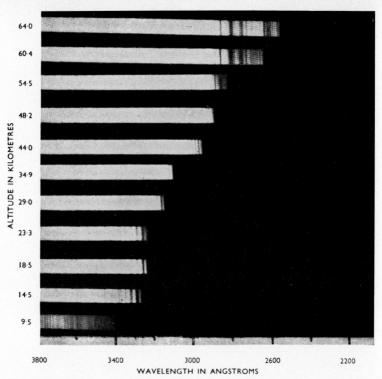

Plate 11.1   Spectra taken at different heights in the atmosphere during the flight of an Aerobee rocket on 14 June 1949. The extension of the wavelength range received to shorter wavelengths as the height increases is obvious.   Naval Res. Lab. (USA)

Plate 11.2   Photograph of a noctilucent cloud.   J. Paton

Plate 12.1   Photograph taken from a vertical sounding rocket showing the presence of a cyclonic disturbance in the atmosphere.   This photograph has been pieced together from a number of smaller pictures taken at different aspects as the rocket yawed, pitched and rolled.

Plate 12.2   A pictorial representation of the great radiation belts surrounding the earth. T*
smoothly curving white lines are lines of force of the earth's magnetic field, while the whi*
shaded areas indicate the inner and outer radiation belts. Typical orbits of trapped charg*
particles are shown within the outer belt.

In this representation the belts are shown in section. For a three-dimensional picture s*
Plate 12.3.

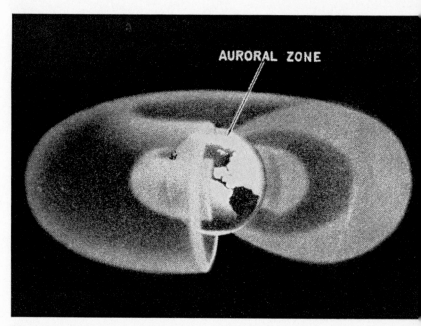

Plate 12.3   Representation of the radiation belts showing how they extend in a ring arour*
the earth.

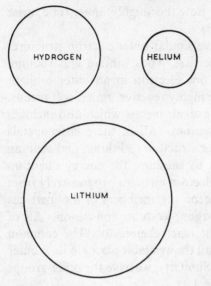

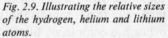

Fig. 2.9. Illustrating the relative sizes of the hydrogen, helium and lithium atoms.

principle prevents the third electron from also occupying this orbit. It must circulate in the first excited orbit. Furthermore, in this orbit, it feels a net positive charge of little more than one unit because the two inner electrons largely screen off two of the three units of positive charge on the lithium nucleus. The radius of the orbit is therefore nearly the same as that for the first excited orbit of hydrogen, about twice the Bohr radius $h^2/4\pi^2me^2$ (see p. 35). It follows that the lithium atom is considerably larger than that of hydrogen (see Fig. 2.9 for relative scale).

As one goes further no changes as sudden as that between helium and lithium occur until eight more electrons are added. This is because there are four states in hydrogen for which the energy quantum number n is 2. Two electrons, with opposite spin, can be accommodated in each so that no electron is forced out, by the Pauli principle, to occupy a state for which n is 3 until the total number of electrons in the preceding atom is twice $(2 + 4)$ or 12. This is the atom of neon, a gas which resembles helium in many ways. The next atom, that of sodium, must contain one electron in an orbit with $n = 3$ so that it is much larger than the neon atom in the same way as lithium is compared with helium. And so we may go on, although in detail certain complications, now thoroughly understood, arise with the more complex atoms.

Elements whose atoms have similar outer electron structures have generally similar properties. Thus lithium and sodium, each of whose atoms have one electron in an outer orbit of relatively large diameter, are highly reactive, rather soft metals. They belong to the group of alkali metals which also includes potassium, rubidium and caesium. All of these latter metals have atoms with similar outer structure to lithium and sodium. In proceeding from lithium to caesium, the energy quantum number of the single outer electron changes progressively from 2 to 6. Again, helium and neon are members of the inert gas group which also includes argon, krypton and xenon. All of these are gases which do not react chemically. The common feature of their atoms is that all the available places in their outer orbits are completely filled. Similarly, we have the other groups of the periodic table (see Fig. 1.1).

The fact that the chemical properties of the elements are determined by the outer electron structure of their atoms was realised before wave mechanics was discovered, but the nature of the forces which lead to combination of atoms to form chemical compounds was not understood until 1927 when Heitler and London produced their classic paper on the application of wave mechanics to the problem. There is now a flourishing subject of theoretical chemistry, based on the use of the new mechanics.

CHAPTER 3

MAINLY ABOUT ELECTRONS

> '*All hail, astonishing Fact!*
> *All hail, Invention new –*'
> GILBERT AND SULLIVAN, 'UTOPIA LIMITED'

Applications of the Diffraction of Particles

Determination of Crystal Structure

The separations of the atoms in a crystal are of the order 10^{-8} to 10^{-7} cms. This is comparable with the wavelengths of X-rays so that the diffraction of X-rays by crystals is readily demonstrated (see Chapter 2 Plate 2.4). As pointed out earlier, the nature of the diffraction pattern obtained with X-rays can be used to obtain information about the arrangements of the atoms. This has become a technique of the greatest importance and has developed so that the structures of very complex molecules which occur in living organisms can be unravelled.

Other possibilities for study of crystals by diffraction are afforded by the wave nature of matter. Electrons of energy 150 e.volts, and neutrons with energy 1840 times smaller, also have wavelengths of 10^{-8} cm. associated with their motion. We have already referred to the experiments which have demonstrated electron diffraction. Similar experiments may be carried out with neutrons, powerful sources of which are provided by nuclear reactors or piles as described in Chapter 7 p. 180. The neutrons which issue from such a pile have a distribution of energies around the desired value. To select neutrons of a particular wavelength, and hence particular energy, the following procedure may be adopted.

A fine stream of neutrons is allowed to fall at an angle Θ on the face of a crystal. The reflected beam, as shown in Fig. 3.1, will then contain only neutrons with wavelengths λ given by

$$n\lambda = 2d \sin \Theta,$$

where d is the effective separation between atoms in the crystal and n is a whole number. This relation was first established by

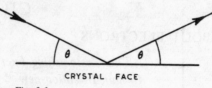

CRYSTAL FACE

Fig. 3.1.

W. H. and W. L. Bragg in their pioneering investigations on the diffraction of X-rays by crystals. It results from the interference of the waves scattered by the different atoms of the crystal. In this way a particular wavelength is selected as, in practice, only one of the wavelengths which satisfy the Bragg relation will be present in appreciable quantity in the incident stream.

Electron diffraction is specially useful for studying the surface structure of materials. This is because electrons do not penetrate as deeply as X-rays of the same wavelength so the diffraction pattern produced is therefore determined mainly by the arrangement of the surface atoms.

Neutron diffraction provides a particularly valuable additional tool for two main purposes. Hydrogen atoms are difficult to locate in a crystal by X-ray diffraction. This is because they have only very weak scattering power for X-rays. On the other hand, protons are very effective in scattering neutrons so that they substantially influence the neutron diffraction pattern. As hydrogen atoms are very common and important constituents of many crystals, the availability of neutrons is of considerable value.

There is, however, another special advantage of using neutrons and that is in the study of the makeup of those materials, of vast industrial application, known as ferromagnetic substances (see p. 85). These include, for example, iron, cobalt and nickel and are distinguished by their outstanding magnetic properties. They may be strongly magnetized and can retain the magnetism more or less permanently. X-rays are not responsive to magnetic forces and, while electrons are responsive, they do not penetrate into the body of a material. Neutrons, on the other hand, satisfy both requirements. Their great penetrating power is not surprising but it is quite remarkable at first sight that they should be affected by a magnetic field. Neutrons, in fact, do behave as small magnets, (see Chapter 6 p. 148), much weaker than electron magnets but strong enough to be affected by the strong magnetic forces which exist within ferromagnetic materials. Much use is now being made of neutrons to explore the interior of these materials, so that a more thorough understanding of the features which endow them with their special properties can be obtained. A brief account of the magnetic properties of matter and its origin in terms of electron spin and orbital motion is given on pp. 84 to 91.

The Electron Microscope

In Chapter 2 p. 50 we pointed out that the shadow cast by an object is not completely sharp because of diffraction. Thus, if the object is a disc of radius a illuminated by radiation of wavelength λ, the edge of the shadow cast by the disc will be indefinite within an angle λ/a radians. Remembering that 1 radian $\simeq 59°$ it follows that the disc will not be clearly distinguished as such if its radius is much less than the wavelength of the radiation in which it is viewed. In other words, the details of objects with dimensions much smaller than the wavelength cannot be distinguished or resolved. In practice the smallest resolvable dimension can be set at about $\lambda/3$. This limits the magnification which can be achieved with an optical microscope. For white light λ is about 6×10^{-5} cm. so that objects with dimensions less than 2×10^{-5} cm. cannot be resolved. As the naked eye can distinguish objects about 0.01 cm. in diameter the magnification attainable cannot usefully exceed about 500. It is possible to extend this somewhat by using ultraviolet light and photographing the image but this cannot be carried very far because it soon becomes impossible to construct suitable lenses and mirrors.

A great increase in resolving power, and hence in magnification, may be obtained by using electron waves. It is possible to construct lenses for electrons with energies as high as 100,000 e.volts by using suitable arrangements of electric and magnetic fields. These electrons have a wavelength as small as 0.2×10^{-8} cm. so that an electron microscope can, in principle, resolve objects with dimensions comparable with those of individual atoms. In practice limitations are introduced by inherent imperfections in electron lenses, but even so the increase in resolving power is so great that useful magnifications as high as 50,000 or more are attainable.

The electron microscope is now a standard instrument in medical and biological research as well as for many other purposes. As electrons have low penetrating power, specimens must be examined in the form of thin films. Biological specimens can therefore not be studied alive but, nevertheless, the high magnification is of the greatest value. Plate 3.1 illustrates a typical photograph taken with an electron microscope.

Electrical Properties of Materials

Electrical Conductors, Semi-conductors and Insulators

Substances such as the metals, particularly copper and silver, permit electricity to flow freely through them and are known as electrical conductors. The effectiveness of a substance in this respect is measured by its *specific conductivity*. Thus, suppose that a potential difference of 1 volt is applied between the ends of a block of material of fixed length and fixed cross sectional area. The magnitude of the electric current which flows is then proportional to the specific conductivity of the material. The spread of values of this quantity for different materials is very great indeed. For good conductors the current which will flow, when the length is 100 cms. and the cross sectional area is 1 sq.cm., ranges from 10 to 100 amperes. A good insulator, that is to say a material which is a very effective barrier to the flow of electricity, will have a conductivity as little as 10^{-26} of that for a good conductor.

It is hardly necessary to draw attention to the great importance of good conductors as well as good insulators in electrical industry. There is, however, a class of substances known as semi-conductors for which manifold applications are now being found. These have conductivities in between those of good conductors and good insulators. Thus, under the conditions outlined above, blocks of semi-conductors would transmit currents between 0.01 and 10^{-13} amperes, depending in the material.

There is also a basic distinction between good conductors and semi-conductors in that, with the former, the conductivity decreases as the temperature rises whereas for a semi-conductor it increases quite rapidly with the temperature.

It is clearly important to understand what differences in electronic structure make a substance a good conductor, a good insulator or a semi-conductor. Since the development of quantum mechanics, great advances have been made in this direction and we shall proceed to give some idea of what is involved.

Electrons in Solids

Conductors and Insulators

The earliest theory of the way conduction occurs dates back to long before wave mechanics. It was assumed that in conductors the electrons which are least strongly bound in the isolated atoms are actually free to move within the crystal. When a voltage difference is applied as in Fig. 3.2, the free electrons move

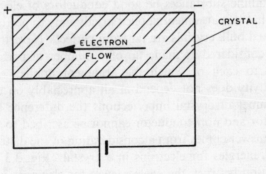

Fig. 3.2.

towards the high voltage end, so constituting a current. At first sight it would seem that the electrons would be continually accelerated so that the current would steadily increase. However, allowance must be made for the fact that the electrons lose energy in collision with the atoms of the crystal. A balance is set up when the rate of gain of energy from the voltage difference, or E.M.F., is equal to the rate of loss by collision. The application of the E.M.F. thus produces a steady current. This current will be proportional to the number of free electrons per unit volume and inversely proportional to the number of collisions per second made by electrons in passing through the material.

This simple picture can be used, with appropriate modifications introduced by wave mechanics, to describe a number of the properties of conductors. It does not tell us why some substances are conductors and others are not. If one looks at the situation in a little more detail this seems even more obscure. According to the simple theory, one can well believe that an element such as an alkali metal* (see Fig. 2.9), in which one electron is quite loosely bound in a large orbit, will be a conductor – it should be relatively easy to free these outer electrons. However, in a crystalline solid, such as a metal or salt, the atoms are arranged in a regular fashion characteristic of the crystal symmetry. Because of this symmetry, and the interaction between the atoms, it is no longer correct to think of electrons as attached to individual atoms. They must be regarded as free to wander throughout the whole crystal. Why then should not all crystalline substances be good conductors of electricity? It is true that this argument applies strictly only to perfect crystals and actual bulk crystals are far from perfect. Nevertheless they can be considered as made up of a number of perfect micro-crystals to each of which the argument applies. Since the conductivity does not depend at all appreciably on the nature and number of crystal imperfections the difference between a conductor and non-conductor cannot be ascribed to them.

The answer comes from a consideration of the distribution of allowed energies for electrons in a crystal. Fig. 3.3 illustrates the relation between the energy levels for electrons in the constituent atoms and for the electrons in the crystal. It will be seen that the atomic levels become broadened into bands in the crystal. The width in energy of the corresponding band increases as the binding energy of the atomic level decreases, the

* The alkali metals are lithium, sodium, potassium, rubidium and caesium (see Fig. 1.1).

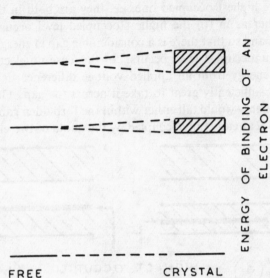

ENERGY AT INFINITE SEPARATION

ENERGY OF BINDING OF AN ELECTRON

FREE
ATOM

CRYSTAL

Fig. 3.3. *Illustrating the distribution of allowed energy levels for electrons in a crystal as compared with those for an electron in a single free atom.*

deepest atomic levels being only slightly broadened in the crystal.

It seems then that the allowed energy levels for electrons in a crystal consist of a series of bands with forbidden gaps in between. The Pauli exclusion principle (Chapter 2 p. 64) may now be invoked to examine how the electrons will be distributed among the levels. If there are N atoms in the crystal and n electrons per isolated atom the total number of crystal electrons will be nN. We can think of these being distributed among the levels, one at a time, in such a way that each occupies the lowest available energy level. This will be the distribution when there is no disturbance due to temperature.

According to the Pauli principle only two electrons, with opposite spin, can occupy a single energy level. The crystal electrons will therefore occupy the lowest $\frac{1}{2}nN$ energy levels. This may lead to either the situation indicated in Fig. 3.4 (a) or (b). In (a) the lowest unoccupied energy level lies immediately above the highest occupied one, i.e. they are both in the same band, whereas in (b) the highest occupied level occurs at the top of a band so that there is a considerable gap in energy before the first unoccupied level occurs. In this case no electron can pick up energy from an applied voltage difference unless this energy is sufficiently great to take it across the gap. Otherwise its final energy would fall either within the forbidden gap or take it to a level already fully occupied by the quota of two electrons.

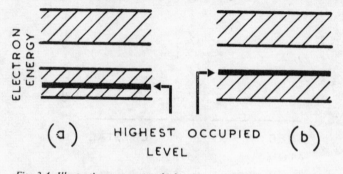

Fig. 3.4. *Illustrating two cases which arise in a solid*
(a) the highest occupied electron energy level occurs below the highest level of an allowed energy band
(b) the highest occupied energy level occurs at the top of an allowed energy band.
Allowed energy bands are shaded.

A substance in which the electron energy distribution is as indicated in Fig. 3.4(b) would therefore be a non-conductor unless such a great voltage, the breakdown voltage, were applied that electrons could acquire sufficient energy to enter the lowest unoccupied band.

The situation is quite different for a substance to which Fig. 3.4(a) applies. Here an electron near the top of the distribution can take up even very small amounts of energy because there are unoccupied levels immediately above. In this case the substance will be a conductor.

This very sketchy outline may be amplified in very considerable detail and it is found to provide an adequate basis for the interpretation of the electrical properties of materials. So far, however, the picture furnishes only two possibilities – the material is either a conductor or an insulator. Where do semi-conductors come in?

Semi-conductors

In a gas at a temperature $T°$ above absolute zero* the constituent atoms possess a mean energy of random motion equal to kT, where k is a universal constant (see p. 92). The fraction of electrons which possess an energy in a small range about E is approximately proportional to $e^{-E/kT}$ where the number e, the base of natural logarithms, is approximately 2.71. The Pauli principle prevents electrons in a crystal from acquiring energy due to random motion unless this energy is sufficient for the electron to occupy a level in the otherwise unoccupied band, separated from the occupied band immediately below by an energy gap V. It remains true, however, that the fraction of electrons in the occupied band which will acquire enough energy at temperature T is approximately proportional to $e^{-V/kT}$. These electrons can respond to an applied voltage as they occupy levels in a nearly empty band. A substance which is a perfect insulator at absolute zero of temperature therefore becomes partly a conductor at higher temperatures. Moreover the conductivity will increase with temperature (see Fig. 3.5 which shows how $e^{-V/kT}$ varies with T). This is the characteristic behaviour of a semi-conductor but it is not the only way in which semi-conducting properties can arise. To distinguish those semi-conductors which owe their electrical behaviour to temperature excitation they are known as *intrinsic* semi-conductors.

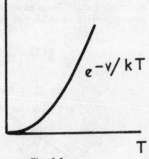

Fig. 3.5.

The other types of semi-conductors, which are the most important in practice, owe their properties to the presence of impurities. An *n-type* impurity semi-conductor is one which

* The absolute zero of temperature is $-273°$ centigrade. A temperature T on the absolute scale, usually referred to as $T°$ absolute or $T°K$, is the temperature above absolute zero and is therefore equal to the usual centigrade temperature less $273°$.

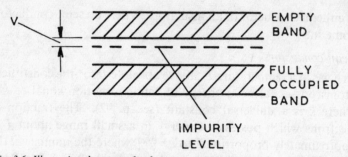

Fig. 3.6. Illustrating the energy levels in an n-type semiconductor. Electrons in the impurity atoms occupy the energy level indicated by the dotted line. These electrons tend to be raised by temperature motion into one of the lower levels of the unoccupied crystal energy band which lies not far above the impurity level.

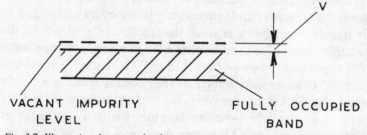

Fig. 3.7. Illustrating the energy levels in a p-type impurity semiconductor. Impurity atoms have vacant levels for electrons, which lie not far above a fully occupied band of crystal levels. These atoms tend to capture electrons into their vacant levels from the crystal band, thereby leaving gaps in this band.

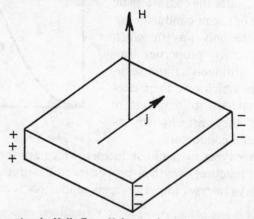

Fig. 3.8. Illustrating the Hall effect. H denotes the magnetic field and j the directed current. If the current is carried by electrons, the left-hand face of the block charges up to a higher voltage than the right hand.

contains a number of impurity atoms which tend to lose electrons to the surrounding crystal. The situation is then as in Fig. 3.6 from which it will be seen that these electrons must enter the otherwise empty band of energy levels and so will be responsive to an applied voltage. It is not so immediately obvious that, in this case, the number of electrons supplied to the otherwise empty crystal band will increase with the temperature. Actually, if V is the energy required to transfer electrons from an impurity atom to the empty crystal band, the probability of the transfer is proportional to $e^{-\frac{1}{2}V/kT}$, provided the proportion of impurity present in the crystal is small. Thus the conductivity will increase rapidly with temperature (as in Fig. 3.5).

A *p-type* semi-conductor is one in which the impurity atoms tend to capture electrons from the crystal. These electrons will be extracted from the uppermost levels of the fully occupied band so that it will no longer be completely full (see Fig. 3.7). This being so the substance will cease to be an insulator. Once again the number of vacancies left in the uppermost occupied band at temperature T will be proportional to $e^{-\frac{1}{2}V/kT}$ where V is now the energy required to transfer an electron from the uppermost level of the occupied band to an impurity atom.

The energy required to effect the electron transfer from the impurity to the crystal for an *n*-type, or to the impurity from the crystal for a *p*-type, semi-conductor can be quite small, of the order 0.1 e.volts or less. This is much smaller than the energy gap between the highest level of the occupied band and the lowest level of the band immediately above, in most non-conducting crystals. Thus, for germanium and silicon, about which we shall have more to say below, the gaps are 0.4 and 0.77 e.volts respectively. It is for this reason that impurity semi-conductors are much more important at ordinary temperatures, for which kT is about 0.03 e.volts.

Conduction by Positive Holes

It is possible to determine the sign of the electric charge which carries the current in any particular material, by making use of a phenomenon known as the Hall effect. This occurs when a current is passed through a block of material which is bathed in

77

a magnetic field in a direction different to that of the current flow. For simplicity we consider the current flow and the magnetic field to be perpendicular as in Fig. 3.8. Under these circumstances a voltage difference develops between the sides of the block, which are parallel to the directions of current flow and magnetic field. If the current is carried by positive charges the right hand face in Fig. 3.8 is at the higher voltage while the reverse is the case if the carriers are negative charges.

If the electron theory of conduction is correct it would seem that the carriers should always be negatively charged in any metallic conductor. Observation has shown that this is true for most metals but there are exceptions which include cadmium and zinc. How can it be that the current carriers are positively charged for these metals?

The resolution of this paradox comes from the concept of positive holes. Consider the case of a conductor in which the uppermost occupied band is nearly full. The energy levels near the top of the band, which are unoccupied, are quite strongly affected by the presence of the ions of the crystal lattice. It may be shown that, because of this effect, an electron occupying one of these levels would react to an applied electric field in a very different way from a perfectly free electron – in fact it would move under the action of the field in the opposite sense to a free electron. This means that it behaves as if its mass had become negative, so its response to an applied force is reversed in sense compared with a normal electron. Another way of seeing that this is not unreasonable is to recall that if the band were completely full no net current would flow. Electrons in levels near the bottom of a band are nearly free and they move in the normal way when the field is applied. To cancel this so as to give no net current for the band as a whole, electrons in levels near the top of the band must move in the opposite sense, as if they had negative mass.

A nearly full band can be regarded as a full band from which has been subtracted electrons from some of the topmost levels. The full band gives rise to no conduction. Any conductivity must therefore be due to the subtraction. Each of the absent electrons possesses negative charge and apparently negative mass, as we have explained. The absence of a charge $-e$ and a mass $-m$ is equivalent to the presence of a charge $+e$ and mass $+m$ (c.f. Chapter 5 p. 128). This means that the situation is the same as if the current were carried by these fictitious positive particles. Hence the possibility of the Hall effect being of unexpected sign.

The name *positive hole* has been given to the apparently positively charged carriers. As far as conduction phenomena are concerned, we may treat them just as if there were real positively charged particles. It is important to realise, however, that their effective mass m^* is not in general equal to the mass of a free electron, but is determined by the nature of the forces experienced by electrons in the crystal.

It follows that, whenever conduction is due to the presence of a relatively small number of unoccupied bands in an otherwise filled energy band, it can be regarded as due to the flow of positive holes. In particular, for a *p*-type semi-conductor, we can regard the conductivity as due to the presence of a number of positive holes which increases with the temperature. In some cases, as we shall see, a semi-conductor may include both mobile electrons and positive holes. If an electron encounters a hole which presents a vacant energy level it may make a transition to this level, in which case both the hole and electron will disappear as mobile carriers of electricity within the solid. This is known as electron-hole recombination.

Rectifiers, Amplifiers and Oscillators

A very great deal of industry today depends on the availability of devices which act as rectifiers, amplifiers or oscillators. A rectifier is a device through which current may be passed readily in one direction but with great difficulty in the opposite direction. An amplifier converts a varying voltage or current to one in which the variations are of greater amplitude. Finally, an oscillator generates an alternating current.

Electronic Valves

In recent years one of the most important means of performing all three of these functions has been by using thermionic valves. These depend on the fact that certain substances, when heated

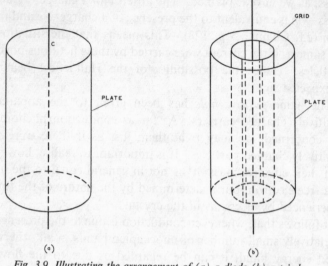

Fig. 3.9. *Illustrating the arrangement of (a) a diode (b) a triode valve.*

to a sufficiently high temperature, emit electrons. This is possible if the least energy required to be given to an electron in order to take it out of the material is not too large compared with the mean energy the electrons would possess at ordinary temperatures, due to random motion.

Given this phenomenon, a simple rectifier may be made in the form of a diode valve. Fig. 3.9(a) illustrates the principle. C is a wire of some material which emits electrons when heated. It lies along the axis of a cylindrical sheet of metal usually called the plate, the whole being in an evacuated vessel. When the wire is heated to emitting temperature the space between the wire and plate is filled with a cloud of free electrons. If a voltage is applied between wire and plate in the sense to pull electrons from wire to plate, a strong current will flow, the loss of electrons to the plate being replenished by the emission of further electrons from the wire. On the other hand, a reverse voltage will produce no current as the plate cannot supply electrons to cross the gap to the wire.

In order to obtain an amplifier it is only necessary to convert the diode we have been discussing to a triode, by inserting between wire and plate a coaxial grid of wires as in Fig. 3.9(b). Suppose that this grid is maintained at a voltage V_g with respect to the central wire, while the outer plate is at a voltage V_p. When the wire is emitting electrons, the current which reaches the outer plate will be very sensitive to changes in V_g. Thus, if V_g is only slightly negative, so as to repel electrons, very few will be able to pass through to the outer plate. Suppose that V_p and V_g are adjusted to steady values so that there is a steady current flow to the plate. If now a small alternating voltage is applied to the grid it will produce comparatively large fluctuations of current to the plate. These may be converted to voltage fluctuations between the ends of a high resistance through which the plate current fluctuations flow.

A triode may also be used to generate current oscillations by introducing suitable connections between grid and plate. These must be such that the voltage fluctuations produced in the plate circuit by fluctuations of grid voltage are fed back on to the grid to produce further amplified fluctuations and so on, until the system bursts into spontaneous oscillation.

It must be realised of course that the above account is extremely sketchy but must serve to indicate what is involved. Much more complicated electronic valves, incorporating more than one grid or plate, have been developed with great success. The art of connecting valves in electrical circuits together with resistors, inductors and capacitors is a very highly developed one. It opens the way to the automatic control of industrial processes and automatic methods of computation, etc. Electrons are truly the genii of modern industry.

Transistors

Although electronic valves have played a vital role in the development of electronic methods of control, they are now being superseded for many purposes by transistors which have a number of advantages.

Transistors are built up of semi-conductors which have controlled impurity content so that they are either of n- or of p-type, with conductivity, at ordinary temperature, within desired limits. That such substances can be manufactured is a great technical triumph and we shall begin by giving some idea of what is involved.

In principle, for the artificial preparation of semi-conductors, it is best to start with a pure non-conducting element which falls near the middle of the periodic table (see Fig. 1.1). Atoms of elements which appear on the right hand side of the table, if introduced into the pure element, will tend to lose electrons to the crystal while atoms of elements appearing on the left hand side of the table will tend to capture electrons from the crystal. In the former case introduction of the foreign atoms will produce a semi-conductor of *n*-type, in the latter of *p*-type.

Two elements which fulfil the initial requirement are germanium and silicon and both are used as bases for semi-conductor production. Addition of, say, arsenic will give an *n*-type semi-conductor while boron will give a *p*-type.

The big problem is to obtain the germanium in a pure enough state to begin with. The proportion of impurities of elements in neighbouring columns of the periodic table must be reduced to one part in 10^{10}, far beyond what is expected of chemically pure substances. Even so it is worth noting that the number of impurity atoms is still as high as 10^{12} per c.c.

To attain the high purity, a procedure known as zone melting is employed. Suppose that a germanium rod is to be purified. It is placed in a carbon boat within an atmosphere of some gas which does not react chemically. The boat can be pulled slowly through a heating coil. The procedure starts with one end of the rod within the coil so that a local melting takes place. As the rod passes slowly through the coil the melted zone gradually passes along from one end to the other, and in so doing carries the impurities along with it. The result is a rod which has been highly purified up to a short distance from the end which passed finally through the coil.

p-n Junction as Rectifier

It is possible, in several ways, to prepare a germanium crystal, one part of which is an *n*-type and the other a *p*-type semi-conductor, with an interface between them. One way of doing this is to melt germanium to which an *n*-producing impurity has been added. A seed of solid germanium is then added to the melt and slowly withdrawn to grow a crystal which will be of *n*-type. At a suitable stage an excess of a *p*-producing impurity is added to the melt and thereafter the crystal will be of *p*-type.

A germanium crystal with an interface between regions of *n*- and *p*-type will behave as a rectifier. Thus, if a voltage is applied to draw electrons from the *n*-type part, and hence holes from the *p*-type part, across the interface, a strong current can flow. This is because the loss of electrons from the *n*-type part or holes from the *p*-part can be made up by further supply from the impurities respectively present. On the other hand, if the voltage is reversed the thermal supply of electrons and of holes is inadequate to maintain anything beyond a very small current. In this way the *p-n* junction behaves in very similar fashion to the diode valve.

Junction Transistor as Amplifier

To obtain amplifying properties it is necessary to add the grid to a diode, the essential feature being the fact that the supply of current carriers, the net current of electrons emitted from the hot wire, is very sensitive to the voltage difference between grid

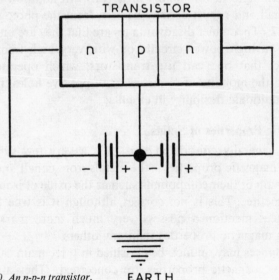

Fig. 3.10. An n-p-n transistor.

and wire – a small change in this voltage makes a big difference in the current to the plate. Similar behaviour may be secured by means of a semi-conductor with two *p-n* junctions, either of *n-p-n* type or of *p-n-p* type (see Fig. 3.10).

A steady voltage is now applied across the left hand *n-p* junction in Fig. 3.10 in the sense for easy current flow and across the right hand junction in the reverse sense (that of difficult current flow). Any change in the voltage difference across the left hand junction will produce a big change in the supply of electrons to the central region where, because of the electric field, they pass to the right hand junction, and hence cause a big change in the current flowing across this junction. Thus the left hand *n*-type region, often referred to as the emitter, is analogous to the hot wire, the *p*-type region to the region round the grid and the right hand *n*-type region to the plate, in a triode.

Similar behaviour occurs with the *p-n-p* type, positive holes replacing electrons.

These double-junction semi-conductors are examples of *junction transistors*. They have many important advantages over thermionic valves, in that they do not require any heating current, and operate at very low power with quite small applied steady voltages (a few tenths of a volt). In addition they are very small and robust as may be seen from the photograph in Plate 3.2. Their chief disadvantages are that they are unsuitable for use in high power circuits or with very high frequencies. The fact that one can use transistors, which operate either through the mobility of electrons or of positive holes, provides some additional flexibility in circuits.

Magnetic Properties of Solids

It is generally considered that only a very few substances exhibit magnetic properties – the metals iron, cobalt and nickel and certain of their compounds such as the oxide of iron known as magnetite. This is not correct, although it is true that the substances mentioned possess very much more marked and striking magnetic properties than any others.

Substances may, in fact, be classified in three main categories as far as magnetic properties are concerned. They are either *diamagnetic*, *paramagnetic* or *ferromagnetic*. The features which characterise these three categories depend on the behaviour of the material when placed in a magnetic field.

Diamagnetic and Paramagnetic Substances

A diamagnetic substance becomes very weakly magnetized and in a sense opposite to that of the magnetizing field. It follows that such a substance tends to move to the region where the field is weakest, and that the field within it is slightly smaller than the magnetizing field. A perfect diamagnetic substance (see p. 96) is one in which the internal magnetic field remains zero no matter how strong a field it be placed in. Apart from the superconductors discussed on p. 96, all diamagnetic materials are very far from perfect in this sense. The best they can do is to reduce the field within them by one millionth part as compared with the external field. At a given temperature the magnetization produced is proportional to the magnetizing field but the constant of proportionality, known as the *susceptibility*, is nearly independent of the temperature.

A paramagnetic substance in a magnetic field acquires magnetization in the same direction as the field, so the field within it is slightly greater than the magnetizing field. Such substances tend therefore to move into the region where the magnetic field is strongest. The susceptibility, although sometimes considerably greater than for diamagnetic materials, is still quite small. Except at very low temperatures (see p. 94), it varies inversely as the absolute temperature.

Ferromagnetism

In a ferromagnetic substance very strong magnetization may be present even in the absence of an external magnetizing field. The actual magnetization depends on the past history of the specimen so that the concept of susceptibility is somewhat confused. If a non-magnetized piece of ferromagnetic material is magnetized by placing it in a magnetic field which increases gradually from a small value, the magnetization at first increases linearly with the field but as the field increases the variation becomes more complicated. Fig. 3.11 illustrates the general behaviour. Initially the specimen is unmagnetized, in the condition corresponding to the point O in the diagram. As the field is gradually increased the magnetization changes in the way indicated by the curve OS. Increase of field beyond the value H_s leads to very little further increase in magnetization and the specimen is said to be magnetized to saturation. If now the field is gradually decreased again the magnetization does not follow the same cycle but returns as indicated by the curve SRC. Thus, when the field is reduced to zero the magnetization OR still remains. This is known as the remanent magnetization or *remanence*. To reduce this to zero it is necessary to increase the field in the reverse direction until it attains the value given by OC in Fig. 3.11. This field is known as the *coercive force*.

From the industrial point of view, the most important properties of a ferromagnetic material are the saturation magnetization, remanence, coercive force and initial susceptibility. Thus, for use in permanent magnets, materials with high

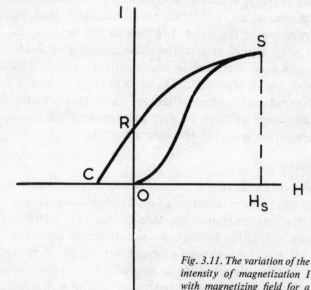

Fig. 3.11. The variation of the intensity of magnetization I with magnetizing field for a ferromagnetic substance. OR is the remanence and OC the coercive force.

coercive force and remanence are required. On the other hand, for electromagnets, high saturation magnetization and initial susceptibility are the desirable characteristics.

Ferromagnetic materials with an immense range of properties are now available. For permanent magnets an alloy of 50% iron with 24% cobalt, 14% nickel and 8% aluminium, known as alnico V, possesses the highest remanence and a high, but by no means the highest, coercive force. Another alloy containing 77% platinum and 23% cobalt has a coercive force 5 times greater still though this is achieved at the expense of a reduction in the remanence by nearly one-third, as well as greatly increased cost. As an indication of the magnitudes involved, the coercive force of platinum-cobalt is about 10,000 times greater than the strength of the earth's magnetic field at London, while the field within the alloy when in a state of remanent magnetization is nearly twice as great as the coercive force.

Turning to materials of high initial susceptibility, an alloy known as supermalloy has an initial susceptibility nearly 10^{12} times greater than that of a typical paramagnetic substance at ordinary temperature. It contains 15.7% iron, 79% nickel, 5% molybdenum and 0.3% manganese. The saturation magnetization is, however, not even as high as the remanence of alnico V. For pure iron it is much larger being such that, when magnetized to saturation, the field within the material is about 85,000 times the earth's field at London. The initial susceptibility depends very much on the purity of the iron. Thus in going from 99.91% purity to 99.95% it increases by a factor of 30 or more.

A remarkable material known as permendur, an alloy containing 49.7% iron, 50% cobalt and 0.3% manganese, has the highest saturation magnetization (about 15% greater than for iron) associated with an appreciable coercive force (about 8 times the earth's field at London).

For some industrial purposes it is desirable to use ferromagnetic materials which are very poor conductors of electricity. Materials satisfying these conditions are known as *ferrites*. They are usually derived from the oxide of iron known as magnetite, which has the structure $Fe_3 O_4$, by replacing one of the

87

iron atoms by manganese, zinc, nickel, etc. They have specific conductivities between 10^{-7} and 10^{-11} times that of iron.

The dependence of the magnetic behaviour of ferromagnetic materials on temperature is very characteristic and important. If the temperature of a magnetized specimen is raised there is very little change in magnetization until a critical temperature, known as the Curie temperature, is reached. Above this the magnetization disappears, together with other typically ferro-magnetic properties – the material behaves like a paramagnetic substance. For iron, cobalt and nickel the Curie temperatures are respectively 870°, 1127° and 358° centigrade. Below 16° centigrade the metal gadolinium becomes ferromagnetic while another metal, dysprosium, becomes so below −168° centigrade.

Relation of Magnetic Properties to Electronic Structure of Materials

The extraordinarily wide diversity of magnetic properties can be largely understood in terms of the electronic structure of the materials concerned.

Diamagnetism arises simply because, in the atoms of the material, the motion of the electrons is affected by the external magnetic field. New currents are thereby set up in the atoms in such a sense that the magnetic fields which they produce oppose the external field. This is an example of a well known law of electromagnetism, known as Lenz's law, which states that the currents induced by the application of a magnetic field always flow in such a sense as to tend to cancel the effect of the field on the material.

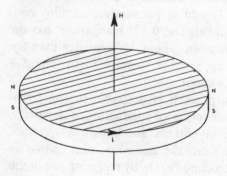

Fig. 3.12. Illustrating the equivalent magnetic shell to a circular current. The shell is a very thin disc bounded by the current circuit with the polarity and magnetic field as indicated.

Paramagnetism, on the other hand, is due to the fact that an atom may behave like a small magnet, for two reasons. An electric current flowing in a circle has a magnetic field associated with it as if it were a magnetized disc, the circumference of which is the current circuit (see Fig. 3.12). The electrons revolving in orbits within atoms represent small circulating currents and hence should contribute to the magnetization of an atom. A simple analysis shows that the contribution to the magnetic moment* is equal to $e/2mc$ times the angular momentum (see p. 33) of the electron concerned, e being the charge and m the mass of an electron and c the velocity of light. Electrons in states for which there is no angular momentum will not contribute anything, but electrons in other states will do so. In many cases the net effect may still be zero due to cancellation of equal and opposite contributions from different electrons. If the cancellation is not complete the atoms will behave like small magnets due to what is known as orbital magnetic moment of the electrons.

There is, however, another important contribution to the magnetic moment from the electron spin which is e/mc, not $e/2mc$, times the spin angular momentum (see however, Chapter 5 p. 135). It follows that an atom will also behave like a small magnet if there is a net spin magnetic moment.

If a small magnet is freely suspended in a magnetic field, it will tend to set itself, as does a compass needle, so as to point along the direction of the field at any time. This will also be the tendency for the atomic magnets in a material but they will be prevented from doing this at all completely by the disturbance due to random temperature motion. The average total magnetization due to the partial orientation of the atomic magnets will therefore decrease as the temperature rises just as it does for paramagnetic substances in general. At very low tempera-

---

* The magnetic moment of a small magnet is a directed quantity, the direction being along the magnet and the magnitude μ such that the force exerted on a similar magnet in the same line at a distance r is $6\mu^2/r^4$. The force is an attraction if the moments are in the same sense, a repulsion if in opposite sense. If the two magnets have unequal moments, μ_1, μ_2 the force becomes $6\mu_1\mu_2/r^4$.

The intensity of magnetization within a material is the net magnetic moment per unit volume of the material.

tures the alignment of the atomic magnets along the direction of the external field will be nearly complete so the susceptibility increases to a limiting saturation value as the temperature falls (see p. 94).

To interpret ferromagnetism we must seek for a much greater tendency to alignment than in a paramagnetic material. Long before quantum theory, Weiss suggested that a ferromagnetic material may in some respects be regarded as a paramagnetic one in which there exists a strong internal magnetizing field in addition to the external one. This would mean that a ferromagnetic crystal is in a state of spontaneous magnetization in which, as it were, the alignment of the atomic magnets produces a force on any one which keeps it aligned. The immediate objection which can be raised to this is the fact that a bar of iron, for example, is not always magnetized. However, this difficulty is overcome by recognizing that a bar of iron is not a perfect crystal but is made up of great numbers of domains with dimensions of order 10^{-5} cms., large compared with the sizes of atoms but small compared with ordinary lengths. These domains are each in a permanent state of magnetization but, in an unmagnetized bulk of material, there are as many domains magnetized one way as the other. Magnetization of the bulk material occurs through partial reorientation or distortion of domains so that cancellation of their magnetism is no longer complete.

The existence of domains has been thoroughly established and the way in which the magnetization of a bulk of ferromagnetic material varies with the external field has been interpreted in detail in terms of domain behaviour. This in turn has assisted the search for materials with special magnetic properties. Plate 3.3 illustrates the domain structure on the surface of a ferromagnetic crystal. This has been revealed by placing a drop of liquid, containing finely powdered magnetite, on the surface of the crystal. The fine particles of the magnetite, which are themselves ferromagnetic, collect where the magnetic field is strongest. This will occur at the boundaries between domains. Examination through a microscope then reveals the pattern shown in Plate 3.3.

There remains the important question of the origin of the spontaneous magnetization of the domains. This was a mystery until 1927 when it was first suggested by Heisenberg that, in the lowest energy state of a perfect ferromagnetic crystal, the net spins of the electrons in the different atoms or ions of the crystal lattice are all parallel, so that there is a large resultant magnetization. Although the details of this picture have since been modified somewhat, it still seems to be essentially correct. In most crystals the lowest electronic state is one in which the net electron spin is zero. We owe the extremely important existence of ferromagnetism to the detailed properties of a few types of atom which cause them to crystallize in such a way that the net electron spins on the different atoms remain parallel!

Mystery near Absolute Zero

Ferromagnetism provides a remarkable example of a phenomenon, the existence of which depends on details, too fine to be predictable, of the behaviour of complicated atoms. Nevertheless we do understand how it arises and, because magnets are well-known everyday objects, we tend to forget its more remarkable features. There are two other phenomena, which only become apparent at temperatures within a few degrees of absolute zero, which are more impressively mysterious and which are not yet understood. One of these certainly involves the behaviour of electrons and is known as *superconductivity*, while the other is a property called *superfluidity* which is exhibited by one substance only, liquid helium. Just as the magnetized domains of a ferromagnetic material owe their properties to the peculiar characteristics of the lowest electronic state, it seems likely that superconductivity and superfluidity also are due in some way to the nature of the ground state of the substance as a whole – both may in fact represent an influence of quantum mechanics on bulk flow of matter.

The discovery of these two fascinating phenomena at very low temperatures is somewhat surprising if it is recalled that, as absolute zero of temperature is approached, the random energy of motion of atoms and molecules gradually dies down, so the whole system might be expected to freeze to an uninteresting condition of complete inertia. On the other hand, we have already seen that random temperature motion prevents the establishment of order. For example, in a paramagnetic substance, the alignment of the atomic magnets in a perfect order parallel to the direction of a magnetic field is disturbed so that the susceptibility varies inversely as the absolute temperature. The study of the properties of matter at very low temperatures is therefore very fruitful for the investigation of ordering forces too weak to be effective at ordinary temperatures. It could be then that some unusual states of a high degree of order should appear at sufficiently low temperatures. Both superconductivity and superfluidity are examples of this.

Before describing these states in more detail we shall present a few remarks about the attainment of very low temperatures.

Attainment of Very Low Temperatures

To avoid confusion it is necessary to begin by enlarging a little on the idea of temperature. The absolute temperature T of a body is a measure of the mean energy of random motion associated with each degree of freedom within the body. It is not possible here to explain in full detail the meaning of 'degree of freedom' but we can illustrate it by considering the case of a gas whose molecules are composed of single atoms. We suppose further that the gas is very rarefied so the atoms interact very weakly with each other. In that case each atom is free to move in any direction in space. As space is three-dimensional this means that each atom has three degrees of freedom. At an absolute temperature T the mean energy of motion of an atom in each degree of freedom is $\frac{1}{2}kT$ where k is the universal constant, known as the Boltzmann constant, already referred to on p. 75. If there are N atoms in the gas the total energy of random motion is therefore given by $\frac{3}{2}NkT$. If the gas molecules contain diatomic molecules further degrees of freedom arise because the molecules can rotate and the atoms within them can vibrate about their equilibrium positions. In dense systems, such as solids and liquids, many other possibilities arise and the situation is much more complicated. Nevertheless, the concept of absolute temperature remains quite definite. At absolute zero of temperature all random motion has ceased but it must be remembered that, according to quantum mechanics, there must still be zero point energy due to the requirements of the uncertainty principle (Chapter 2 p. 60).

We next introduce the concept of *entropy*. A body at an absolute temperature T, exposed to specified external influences, possesses a definite amount of entropy which is a measure of the degree of order, or rather of disorder, within the body. Increase of order, as for example in a transformation from a liquid to a crystalline solid at the freezing temperature, leads to a decrease of entropy. Any such increase of order involves, in a sense, the 'freezing' of some degrees of freedom which are unable to take a full part in random motion. The reduction in the number of degrees of freedom is proportional to the decrease in entropy. Since the energy per degree of freedom is proportional to the absolute temperature it follows that a change ΔS in entropy, due to some change in the degree of order at a temperature T, leads to a change in energy of random motion proportional to the product $T\Delta S$. As the total energy of random motion is the heat content it follows that, with appropriate choice of units, the change ΔQ in heat content is given by

$$\Delta Q = T\Delta S. \tag{A}$$

The entropy content, or degree of disorder, within a body depends not only on the external influences to which the body is subjected but also on the temperature – the higher the temperature the greater the disorder and hence entropy.

Suppose now a body is subjected, at a constant temperature, to an external influence which reduces its entropy. According to the relation (A) this will lead to a reduction in heat content – the body will give out heat, which can be taken up by some other bodies which are in thermal contact with it. Once this is done the thermal contact can be broken, the body remaining in the state of lowered entropy. If the external influence which produced the lowered value of entropy within the body is suddenly removed, the body finds itself with an entropy less than it possessed at the initial temperature before the ordering influence was applied. In the absence of such influence the lowered entropy is that which would be possessed at a lower temperature, so that once the ordering influence is removed the temperature falls. The cycle of events is illustrated in Fig. 3.13. The vital part played by entropy depends on the fact that the entropy of the body depends only on the temperature and any external influences acting on the body. It does not depend on the previous history of the body.

In one of the earliest methods for lowering the temperature of a gas, the ordering influence is increased pressure. The gas is compressed and the heat thereby generated is removed, after which the gas is cooled by expansion through a nozzle into a region of low pressure. This is used in the liquefaction of oxygen and nitrogen and, with certain modifications, of hydrogen and helium. At atmospheric pressure helium does not liquefy until a temperature of 4.2° absolute is reached. Liquid helium was first produced by Kamerlingh Onnes in 1908.

Once temperatures as low as those of liquid helium are available, it becomes possible to use weaker ordering influences effectively, to lower the temperatures still further. One method which is particularly effective is known by the somewhat forbidding title of adiabatic demagnetization. It utilizes the ordering influence of a magnetic field acting on a paramagnetic substance to lower its entropy. At liquid helium temperatures the degree of order achievable in this way is quite high. Switching on the

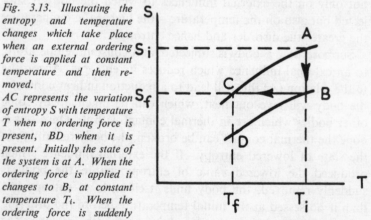

Fig. 3.13. Illustrating the entropy and temperature changes which take place when an external ordering force is applied at constant temperature and then removed.
AC represents the variation of entropy S with temperature T when no ordering force is present, BD when it is present. Initially the state of the system is at A. When the ordering force is applied it changes to B, at constant temperature T_i. When the ordering force is suddenly removed, at constant entropy, it changes to C at the lowered temperature T_j.

field leads to production of heat which is removed as explained above. The material is then thermally insulated and a drop of temperature results when the field is switched off. In this way temperatures within 0.001° of absolute zero have been attained.

Superconductivity

In 1911 Kamerlingh Onnes, in his laboratory at Leiden, was investigating the variation of the electrical resistance* of mercury with temperature, down to very low temperatures. At first it was found to decrease in the normal, quite gradual, way as the temperature fell but suddenly, below 4.2° absolute, it disappeared completely. Even with the most refined techniques of measurement at present available it is not possible to observe any electrical resistance below this temperature. It is certainly less than 10^{-11} of that possessed at a slightly higher temperature and this extraordinary change occurs within a temperature range of less than 0.001° centigrade!

This phenomenon, known as superconductivity, is found to occur with many metals but not with all, at least down to the lowest attainable temperatures. The transition temperature is highest, 11.2° absolute, for the metal technetium and is as high as 7.2° absolute for lead. Oddly enough, the metals which are the best conductors at ordinary temperatures, copper, silver and gold, do not exhibit superconductivity.

Many remarkable effects are associated with superconduction. Thus current flow in a superconductor is not accompanied by any detectable heating. Also, if an electrical current is started in a ring of superconducting material it goes on flowing indefinitely without application of any further E.M.F. This can be done by cooling a ring of metal, such as lead, in a magnetic field to below the transition temperature and then switching off the field. Electric currents induced in the ring by the change in magnetic field persist as long as the ring is kept below the transition temperature. In one such experiment a lead ring carried a steady current of several hundred amperes for more than a year.

Apart from its astonishing conducting properties a superconductor also possesses remarkable magnetic characteristics.

* The resistance is the reciprocal of the conductivity.

In particular a superconductor is a perfect diamagnetic (see p. 85) – no magnetic field can exist within it.

The superconducting state is destroyed if the material is subjected to a sufficiently strong magnetic field. The minimum field necessary to achieve this is greater the lower the temperature.

We are still far from understanding how superconductivity arises. It seems to be well established that the electric current in a superconductor is carried by electrons but how it is carried without friction, with no resistance whatever, is still very mysterious. The fact that the transition temperature for a given metal differs for different isotopes (see Chapter 1 p. 39) shows that in some way the atoms, or rather positive ions, of the metal crystal lattice must play some part and attempts have been made, with very limited success, to develop an interpretation on these lines. On the whole it is probable that the phenomenon is in some way a bulk manifestation of quantum mechanics.

Liquid Helium and Superfluidity

Liquid helium is peculiar in two main respects, one which is explicable in general terms while the other is no more deeply understood than is superconductivity.

Following on the successful liquefaction of helium attempts were made to solidify it but this proved to be impossible at atmospheric pressure. Helium remains liquid down to the very lowest temperature unless it is subjected to a pressure greater than 25 atmospheres. Even as a liquid it has a very low density, 0.15 times that of water. In classical mechanics it is inconceivable that a substance could remain liquid at absolute zero of temperature. It is only possible through the operation of the uncertainty principle of quantum mechanics (Chapter 2 p. 59). The mean zero point energy of a helium atom, because of its relatively small mass, is comparable with that arising from the very weak attraction exerted on it by its neighbours. In terms of the model of the particle in the bowl which we discussed on p. 60, the helium atom possesses such high zero-point energy that it spends most of its time near the top of the bowl. Once this is realised it is not difficult to understand how the aggregate of atoms can remain liquid down to absolute zero.

A far more remarkable phenomenon manifested by liquid helium is that of superfluidity, which occurs when it is cooled below 2.1° absolute, a temperature known as the *lambda-point*. We shall not attempt to give an historical account of the discovery and study of this phenomenon but describe something of the present position.

It had been known for a long while that small leaks in a vessel containing liquid helium became very noticeable when the liquid was cooled below the lambda-point but it was some time before it was realised why this was so. The viscosity of the liquid, which is a measure of the internal friction involved in flow, was investigated by two standard methods. One involved the determination of the resistance to rotation of a solid disc in the liquid and the other the measurement of the rate of flow of the liquid through fine capillary tubes under a definite pressure head. Results obtained by these two methods are quite contradictory when dealing with the liquid below the lambda-point. According to the first method the viscosity falls considerably as the temperature decreases below the lambda-point but is still quite measurable. On the other hand, at these temperatures, the liquid flows through fine capillary tubes as if it possessed no viscosity at all. Furthermore, the rate of flow, instead of being proportional to the pressure head as for any normal liquid, is quite independent of it. An equally abnormal result is that the liquid flows with ease through the finest capillaries.

These results are now interpreted in terms of the two-fluid theory, according to which, at temperatures below the lambda-point, liquid helium is a mixture of two fluids, one with normal flow characteristics and the other a superfluid which possesses no viscosity at all, at least for flow rates slower than a critical value. The resistance to the rotating disc is due to friction with the normal fluid while, in the capillary flow method, all the flow is due to the superfluid, which exhibits no viscosity. As the temperature falls the proportion of superfluid increases.

A remarkable experiment, which not only strongly supports the two-fluid theory but also measures the fraction of the liquid in the superfluid form, was carried out by Andronikashvili in

1946 at the suggestion of Landau, one of the proposers of the two-fluid theory. Consider the liquid suspended in a bucket which is set spinning about its axis. Before very long friction will cause the normal component of the fluid to rotate with the bucket. The superfluid, on the other hand, will not be set rotating because it is quite frictionless. There is no difficulty in measuring the total mass rotating so the proportion of the liquid which is normal can be determined. This is the principle of Andronikashvili's experiment and Fig. 3.14 illustrates the results obtained, showing how the fraction of liquid in the normal condition decreases from unity at the lambda-point as the temperature falls.

Many remarkable effects can be produced because of the decrease of the fraction of superfluid as the temperature rises. If two vessels containing liquid helium below the lambda-point (usually referred to as liquid helium II) are connected by a fine

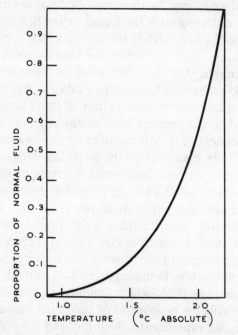

Fig. 3.14. Illustrating results obtained in Andronikashvili's experiment, giving the proportion of normal fluid in liquid helium at different temperatures below the lambda point (2.1° C absolute).

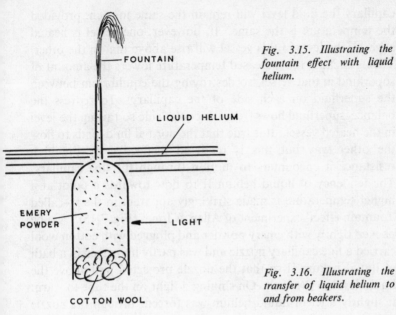

FOUNTAIN

LIQUID HELIUM

Fig. 3.15. Illustrating the fountain effect with liquid helium.

EMERY POWDER

 LIGHT

COTTON WOOL

Fig. 3.16. Illustrating the transfer of liquid helium to and from beakers.

(a)

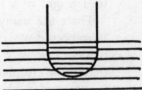

(b)

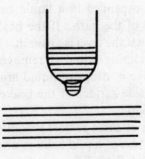

(c)

capillary the fluid level will remain the same in each, provided the temperature is the same. If, however, one vessel is heated slightly, the level in this vessel will rise above that in the other. This is because the increased temperature lowers the amount of superfluid in that vessel, so destroying the equilibrium between the superfluid on each side of the capillary. To redress the balance, superfluid flows from the cooler side so raising the level in the heated vessel. It is true that the normal fluid tends to flow the other way but this is rendered ineffective by the high resistance it encounters to motion through the fine capillary. The tendency of liquid helium II to flow towards a point at a higher temperature is made strikingly apparent in the so-called 'fountain effect' experiment of Allen & Jones (Fig. 3.15). A tube packed tightly with emery powder and plugged with cotton wool carried a fine capillary nozzle and was partly immersed in a bath of liquid helium II so that the nozzle projected well above the liquid level in the bath. On shining a light on the tube to warm it slightly a jet of liquid helium was forced through the nozzle to a height of a foot or more.

There are many other properties of liquid helium II which have been discovered and interpreted in terms of the two-fluid model. One very remarkable effect which we must mention is that of the creeping helium film. If a beaker of liquid helium II is immersed in a bath of the same liquid at the same temperature so that the level in the beaker is initially different from that of the bath (Fig. 3.16(a)) it is found that, in a short time, the levels equalise in apparently miraculous fashion (Fig. 3.16(b)). Even an empty beaker suspended in a liquid helium bath will soon fill up to the level of the bath. If the beaker is raised a little, liquid leaves it so that the level is again that of the bath. Finally, if the beaker containing liquid is removed entirely from the bath and held above it, drops of liquid are seen to form at the bottom of the outside surface of the beaker and fall back into the bath (Fig. 3.16(c)).

The explanation of these remarkable effects has been traced to the spread of a film of liquid helium, about 10^{-6} cm. thick, over the surfaces of the confining vessels. There seems little doubt that the effective spread of this film over large distances is made possible by superfluidity. If a local hot spot causes evaporation the loss is very quickly made up because of the unimpeded flow of the superfluid component.

Although the two-fluid description of liquid helium II assists in the interpretation of the wide variety of unusual effects associated with it we still do no know how it arises. The original idea of the two-fluid picture sprang from a suggestion by F. London which was on the following lines.

We have already pointed out how the Pauli exclusion principle pp. 73) affects profoundly the behaviour of a dense concentration of electrons. Helium atoms behave in exactly the opposite sort of way. Because they possess no net spin, in contrast with the half integral spin of an electron (see p. 63), they do not satisfy the exclusion principle. Instead, if a quantum state is occupied by one helium atom this tends to increase the chance of a second atom occupying the same state. At very low temperatures the atoms in dense helium gas tend to condense in the lowest state. London suggested that it is these atoms which constitute a superfluid component. Although it is far from certain that London's idea is correct it, nevertheless, did suggest the twofluid model, which was developed by Tisza. Independently, in Russia, Landau also proposed a two-fluid model but on a somewhat different basis.

One recent investigation has, however, lent some support to London's model. Normal helium consists almost exclusively of atoms of mass number 4. It is possible now to produce helium in which the atoms are those of the lighter isotope, of mass number 3. This may be done in a nuclear reactor (Chapter 7 p. 180). The interest in the present context is that light helium atoms have a half integral spin and therefore satisfy the Exclusion principle. Hence light liquid helium, liquid helium 3 as it is called, should not, according to London's model, exhibit superfluidity or possess a helium II phase. In fact it has been shown that, down to temperatures as low as $0.25°$ absolute, it still behaves as a normal liquid. There seems to be a definite connection between superfluidity and the spins of the atoms involved.

On the other hand there are analogies between superfluidity

101

and superconductivity. Both are characterised by bulk flow without friction and both are almost certainly examples of order associated with quantum effects. And yet electrons obey the Exclusion Principle, the atoms of the helium which exhibits superfluidity do not. Here we have a most intriguing mystery, the understanding of which is bound to be of the greatest interest.

Automatic Calculation and Control

Inasmuch as the original idea and design of an automatic calculating machine dates back to the middle of last century it may seem strange that we should include mention of developments in this field in a chapter devoted largely to phenomena which depend on the behaviour of electrons. It is not difficult to justify this. Although Babbage had a clear conception of the design of an automatic calculator as early as 1840, long before the days of electronic devices, it is because of the high speed and flexibility which the availability of these devices provides that we are now witnessing major developments, not only in automatic calculation but also in process control, the beginning of the age of automation.

To see in what way an automatic calculating machine differs from a desk calculator such as a Brunsviga or Marchant machine it is best to examine what is involved in the carrying out of an extensive calculation with such a calculator. The only processes which it can perform mechanically are the simple mathematical ones of addition, subtraction, multiplication and division. A vital role must be played by the human who operates the machine. He will have the task of carrying out systematically a set of arithmetical operations prescribed by the instructions issued to him in the form, say, of algebraic formulae with prescribed ranges of numerical values which the variables involved are to take. Except in the simplest tabulations the operator must carry out many arithmetical operations at intermediate stages before obtaining final results. This involves entry of results of these intermediate operations on data sheets in such a way that the numbers can be used again, when required, in further operations. In other words, the human operator exercises the functions of storage of data and of control of the sequence of operations. He must also exercise judgment such as deciding when a series of approximations has been carried far enough.

An automatic calculating machine is one which carries out automatically, not only simple arithmetical operations, but also the storage of data obtained in intermediate stages of a calculation and the control of the whole operation. Provision must be made for feeding in a programme of instructions for carrying out a particular set of calculations as well as for some means of supplying the final results in printed or other suitably recorded form.

There is no difficulty in arranging for simple arithmetical operations involving 15 figure numbers to be carried out, using electronic devices, in times considerably below 1/1000th of a second but, to take advantage of this, it is necessary that the other operations which the machine performs can be carried out with comparable rapidity. These include the time to transmit signals carrying instructions from control to store or arithmetical unit, the time taken to find the correct number in the store, and the time involved in reading instructions and data from the input mechanism and in making available the final results in some suitable form. Apart from the need for high speed of access to the store, and for rapid transfer of a number from the store elsewhere, it is important that the store should have a high capacity.

The Binary Scale

To obtain an idea of how this may be achieved it is best to begin by recalling how it is possible to express a number in the binary scale instead of the usual scale of ten. We may then see how the scale may be used to denote other kinds of information so that instructions as well as numbers may be stored. The flexibility of a machine may thus be increased by making it possible, in suitable cases, to work with a complicated set of instructions and relatively small number storage or with simple instructions and many stored numbers. Further, instructions may be altered within the machine by purely arithmetical operations for which

103

facilities are already provided. This may be used to simplify the programme for a given calculation.

When we express a number in the usual way, such as 337, we are adopting a shorthand method of denoting that the number is

$$3 \times 10^2 + 3 \times 10^1 + 7 \times 10^0 = 300 + 30 + 7.$$

This involves the use of 10 digits ranging from 0 to 10. There is no reason why 10 should be specially chosen as the base of this system. If instead we choose 2 as a base then we need only two digits 0 and 1 to express any number. Thus in terms of this binary scale the number 337 is expressed as

$$101010001.$$

This means that the number is equal to

$$1 \times 2^8 + 0 \times 2^7 + 1 \times 2^6 + 0 \times 2^5 + 0 \times 2^4 + 0 \times 2^3 + 1 \times 2^2 + 0 \times 2^1 + 1 \times 2^0 = 256 + 64 + 16 + 1 = 337.$$

Although this method is cumbersome for ordinary manual arithmetic it has great advantages for automatic machines. As there are only two digits required it is possible to represent numbers by combinations of units which have two positions such as *on* or *off*. We shall see, for example, how this may be utilised in magnetic storage devices. Alternatively, we may represent the digits 1 and 0 by the presence or absence of a hole in a punched card or tape.

Amount of Information

Representation on the binary scale may be used to provide a measure of the amount of information contained in any particular record or store. This is based on the representation of a distinct piece of information by a number which may then be expressed in binary scale. With two binary digits we can construct 4 numbers 00, 01, 10 and 11 and so represent 4 pieces of information. With three we may represent 8, with four, 16 and in general with n, 2^n. A decimal digit 0, 1, ..., 9 can be represented with 4 binary digits. It is convenient to take a binary digit as a unit of information and we may then say that a decimal digit is equivalent to 4 units of information. In the same way a table containing 1,000 numbers each of 5 decimal digits is equivalent to 20,000 units of information. This means that to store the information contained in such a table 20,000 'on-off' units would be required.

The quantity of information contained in a printed book may be estimated in a similar way. Thus, if printed in English, the information will be expressed in terms of about 80 symbols,

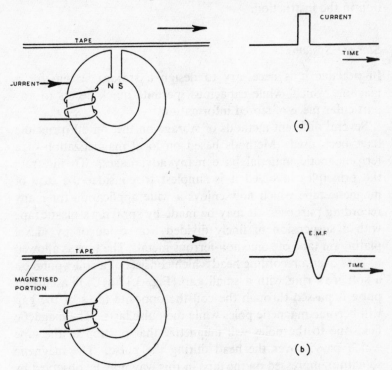

Fig. 3.17. Recording and reading with a magnetic tape
(a) Recording– the input current pulse to the recording head is shown on the right
(b) Reading – the output EMF pulse generated in the reading band is shown on the right.

comprised of 52 capital and small letters, 10 numerals and 18 punctuation and other marks. To represent any one of these, 7 binary digits are required so we can say that 7 units of information are required for every symbol. On this basis, a large reference book contains about 10^8 units of information per cubic foot, and a large reference library as much as 10^{12} units in all. For comparison it is estimated that there are something like 10^{10} nerves in the human brain so that, if used in some way as 'on-off' units, they could store 10^{10} units of information.

The instructions which must be issued in appropriate sequence from the machine control can be coded in the binary scale just as are numbers, one digit corresponding to one unit of information in the instruction.

Storage Systems

In practice it is necessary to design a storage system for a machine which, while capacious, permits quick access to any particular piece of stored information.

Several different methods of storage on the 'on-off' principle have been used. Methods based on local magnetization of a ferromagnetic material have many advantages. To illustrate the principles involved it is simplest to consider the case of magnetic tape which now enjoys a wide application for many recording purposes. It may be made by spraying a plastic tape with a suspension of finely divided iron oxide or by nickel plating on tape of some non-ferrous metal. The tape is allowed to pass over a recording head which consists of a coil wound on a soft iron ring with a small gap (Fig. 3.17(a)). If a current pulse is passed through the coil the opposite faces of the gap will become magnetic poles while the pulse lasts. The magnetic field due to the poles will magnetize that portion of the tape which passes over the head during the pulse. The magnetic signature impressed on the tape in this way may be observed by allowing the tape to pass over a reading head which is exactly similar to the recording head. As the magnetized portion passes over, an E.M.F. is induced in the coil and a current pulse flows. Fig. 3.17(b) illustrates the shape of the recording current and reading E.M.F. pulses. By means of a suitable shaping circuit the output pulse from the reader can be changed to have the same shape as the input to the recorder. At regular intervals along the tape, impression of a magnetic signature represents a binary digit 1 while absence of such a signature denotes the

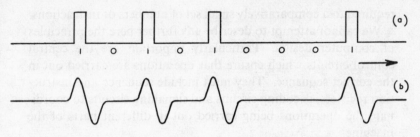

Fig. 3.18. Sequence of pulses representing, in binary scale, the number 337.
(a) Input current pulses.
(b) Output EMF pulses.

digit 0. Thus the input and output pulses corresponding to the number 337 would be as shown in Fig. 3.18.

Magnetic tape can be used not only for storage but also for the input and output of information. As many as 9,000,000 units of information may be stored in a reel of tape 1,000 feet long and ½ inch wide. This tape is between 2 and 3 thousandths of an inch thick so that it has a storage capacity of about 10^9 units of information per cubic foot. The chief disadvantage is the relatively long access time which is of the order of 1/10 sec.

Greater speed of access, of the order of 1/1000 sec. may be achieved by using a rotating magnetic drum instead of a reel of tape. A typical drum is 10 inches in diameter and 9 inches long and can represent 500,000 units of information.

Much faster access stores have been developed, some depending on the use of a square array of small rings or cores of magnetic material which may be magnetized, either in one sense or the opposite, to represent the two binary digits. A typical store of this kind may have a capacity of only 40,000 units but access to any number is possible in one millionth of a second! Recording a number takes less than one hundred thousandth of a second.

Because it is difficult to combine high storage capacity with high access speed it is usual to work with a high access speed store together with an auxiliary high capacity store to which the access is much slower. The programme of instructions can usually be so arranged that at each stage rapid access is only required to a comparatively small set of numbers or instructions.

We cannot attempt to describe any further here the principles of computer design. Particularly important are the central control circuits which ensure that operations are carried out in the correct sequence. They must include sequence and instruction registers, decoding circuits and signalling circuits to coordinate the operations being carried out in different parts of the machine.

A Typical High Speed Computer

The Ferranti Mercury Computer, which we may take as a typical example of a computer of high speed and capacity, is capable of adding two numbers of nine decimals in 1.8×10^{-4} seconds and of multiplying them in 3×10^{-4} secs. Most programming instructions can be carried out in only 6×10^{-5} seconds which is important because, during normal operation of the machine, there are between 5 and 10 times as many of these instructions as actual arithmetical ones.

The rapid access computing store can handle 40,960 units of information and is of the magnetic core type (see Plate 3.4) while there are high capacity magnetic drum backing stores capable of storing 327,680 units of information per drum (see Plate 3.5). Up to four of these drums may be fitted. Additional storage capacity can be supplied by fitting reels of magnetic tape. These, which are of plastic tape coated with iron oxide, are available in spools $\frac{1}{2}''$ wide and 3000 feet long with six information tracks. Each spool may hold 25,600,000 units of information.

There are 4779 thermionic valves and 3314 crystal rectifiers in the machine.

As an indication of performance, the machines can solve simultaneous linear algebraic equations, with 80 unknowns, in a few minutes. Even larger machines are in operation and the limit is not yet in sight.

The Maser

We have described very briefly on pp. 79-82 some of the principles involved in the design of amplifiers – devices to magnify electrical power, voltage or current. There would seem at first sight to be no difficulty, in principle, in detecting extremely weak electrical signals merely by amplifying them until they become strong enough for observation. Unfortunately, a limit exists due to what is known as *thermal noise*. At any temperature T above absolute zero, radiations of all frequencies, including radio waves, are present in any region of space. Current will therefore be generated by this radiation in a receiving aerial in the region. The power which may be received by the aerial in this way can be shown to be kT per unit frequency range, where k is Boltzmann's constant (see p. 89). At ordinary temperatures this amounts to about 4×10^{-21} watts per unit frequency range. This thermal noise cannot be reduced except by lowering the temperature of the whole enclosure surrounding the aerial.

Because of the background of thermal noise, it is not possible to distinguish signals which generate in an aerial power much less than the thermal noise. Amplification will magnify both the thermal noise and the wanted signal so that no discrimination is gained. In practice, if the mean noise level is steady, something may be done to detect an additional signal which is also of nearly constant mean strength (see Chapter 10, p. 258).

The problem is made more difficult, however, because, in addition to the thermal noise, an amplifier itself introduces further noise so that the total noise background is relatively worse after amplification than before. The noise factor of an amplifier is defined by the ratio of the output of noise power from the amplifier to the product of the input thermal noise power and amplification factor (this is the ratio of output to input power for a signal of steady amplitude at the frequency concerned). If the amplifier were to generate no additional noise its noise factor would be unity. With thermionic valve amplifiers, on the other hand, the noise factor is about 3 for wavelengths about 1 metre, rising to 12 or so for centimetre wavelengths. In the last few years a new technique of amplification has been devised which, while still in an early stage of development, bids fair to provide amplifiers with noise factors very close to unity. This involves the *maser*, which is an abbreviated way of referring to 'microwave amplification by stimulated emission of radiation'. Masers are important not only as amplifiers with very low internal noise but also for very reliable frequency standards, as accurate atomic clocks.

The principle on which a maser operates is simple. Suppose that a molecule, as for example the ammonia molecule (NH_3), has an excited state with energy E_1 lying just above the ground (lowest) state of energy E_0. If radiation of frequency $v_{10} = (E_1 - E_0)/h$ falls on an assembly of these molecules in the ground state, some of the radiation will be absorbed in producing transitions to the excited state. On the other hand, if the molecules in the assembly are predominantly in the excited state when the radiation is incident, the radiation will stimulate transitions to the ground state in which further radiation is emitted. The net result in this case is that more radiation is given out than is incident. In other words amplification has occurred.

These considerations become of practical usefulness for frequencies characteristic of short wave radio and radar. This is largely because, at these frequencies, it is possible to maintain a large fraction of the molecules in a gas or solid in an excited state for useful periods of time, the rate at which spontaneous transitions occur back to the ground state being quite low.

The first operative device of this kind was the ammonia maser. In the ammonia molecule the frequency v_{10} is 23,870 megacycles/sec. corresponding to a wavelength of 1.26 cm. At ordinary temperatures a considerable fraction of the molecules are in the excited state. To separate these, a beam of ammonia molecules is passed through a suitable electric field which deflects ground state and excited state molecules in opposite sense. The beam issuing in a particular direction therefore contains, almost exclusively, molecules in the excited state suitable for use as a maser.

In this device the noise factor is very nearly unity. The internal noise arises from the fact that the radiant energy is not continuous but consists of quantum bundles of size hv_{10}. This introduces energy fluctuations of the same order. The thermal noise fluctuations, on the other hand, are of order kT_0 where

T_0 is the wall temperature of the container through which the ammonia beam passes. Hence the noise factor is approximately $(kT_0 + h\nu_{10})/kT_0 = 1 + h\nu_{10}/kT_0$. Putting in the numbers we find that this factor is about 1.02 which is very satisfactory.

We must realise, however, that amplification will only occur at, or very close to, the frequency ν_{10}. The range of frequency about ν_{10} which will be amplified is determined, in fact, by the time t during which an excited ammonia molecule is exposed to the radiation. This is because a molecule cannot in this time tell what frequency is acting on it more accurately than to within $1/t$. t is given by l/v where l is the length of the beam within the cavity in which it is exposed to radiation and v is the mean speed of the molecules. On substitution of reasonable numerical values we find the frequency range within which amplification occurs, the amplifier band width, is only about 3×10^{-7} of the central frequency. This low band width is a disadvantage for an amplifier but, if the maser is used to generate oscillations by suitable feedback arrangements (see p. 81), it has the effect of providing a very pure frequency and so may be used as a very accurate standard clock (see Chapter 12, p. 308).

The ammonia maser is only the first of a number of devices which operate in a variety of ways. Among these and future inventions will be found low noise amplifiers with useful bandwidth as well as oscillators of very pure frequency. Once amplifiers with low external noise are available further reduction of noise background may be achieved by enclosing the whole receiving system within a cavity cooled to low temperatures so that the thermal noise is also reduced.

CHAPTER 4

THE WONDERLAND OF RELATIVITY

'Where you hide in the cellar and then look down
On the poets that live in the attics
For the whole of the house is upside down
In the Higher Mathematics'.

G. K. CHESTERTON, 'SONGS OF EDUCATION'

In Chapter 2 we have discussed the revolution in physical thought which was brought about by the introduction of the quantum theory. A no less remarkable and far reaching modification of our ideas about the physical universe has come from the theory of relativity. The motion of 'ordinary' objects with 'ordinary' speeds is well described by the mechanics of Newton, the so-called classical mechanics. It is necessary when describing phenomena on the atomic scale to go further than this to allow for the quantum of action h. Relativistic modifications become important in mechanical phenomena when the bodies concerned, whether large or small, are moving at high speeds, comparable with that of light, 186,000 miles per second, usually denoted by c. The concepts of relativity, which are firmly based on experimental verification, involve a drastic revision of our concepts of space and time. For dealing with subatomic phenomena in which the particles concerned are moving with speeds comparable with c, both quantal and relativistic modifications must be fully included in a relativistic quantum mechanics. Even today, the correct form which this must take has not been fully discovered but, notwithstanding this, some very remarkable manifestations of it are now known. As neither the quantum theory nor relativity are common sense conceptions it is not surprising that their consequences are sometimes most extraordinary. The adjectives 'unnatural' or 'unreal' must never be applied to them, however, as they rest firmly on a foundation of experimental test.

In the next few Chapters we shall be discussing subatomic phenomena in which relativistic concepts are vital. We begin

112

now by giving a short account of the special theory of relativity and then, without further delay, proceed in the next Chapter to a discussion of the creation and annihilation of matter and the remarkable concept of matter and antimatter.

Absolute Velocity and the Luminiferous Aether

The Aether

The velocity of a particle, as usually thought of, is a relative quantity. Thus, when we say that a train is travelling at 60 miles per hour we mean that it is travelling at this speed relative to the earth. We take no account of the fact that the earth is revolving in its orbit round the sun or that the sun in turn is moving relative to the so-called 'fixed' stars. The question naturally arises as to whether there is any reference system which is absolutely fixed so that any speeds given relative to it could be regarded as absolute speeds. It seemed, towards the latter half of the 19th century, that such a reference system was available in the luminiferous aether.

The existence of the aether was postulated to overcome one of the apparent difficulties of Maxwell's electromagnetic theory of light. According to this theory, light consisted of waves of electromagnetic disturbance which, in empty space, travel with the velocity c. All other known wave motions involved the propagation of fluctuations in a definite material medium. Thus we have the ripples spreading from a disturbance on the surface of a pond or sound waves which involve fluctuations in density of the solid, liquid or gas through which they pass (Chapter 2 p. 45). It seemed necessary that the electromagnetic waves must also represent disturbances in some medium. This was called the luminiferous aether and was supposed to pervade all matter while being itself immaterial – that is to say it produced no dynamic effect.

The Experiment of Michelson and Morley

If the aether were to fulfil the role of an absolutely fixed reference system it is clearly necessary that some experimental means should be found for measuring the speed of the earth relative to the aether. An ingenious way of doing this was proposed by

113

Michelson and Morley. It depended on the phenomenon of interference (Chapter 2 p. 49) to determine whether the time taken for light to pass over two equal paths at right angles was indeed different, as it should be if the earth were moving relative to the aethereal medium through which the light travelled.

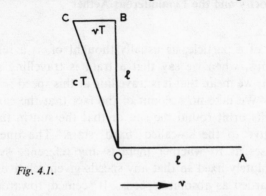

Fig. 4.1.

Thus suppose, as in Fig. 4.1, that the earth is moving with a speed v relative to the aether, in the sense OA. A light wave, proceeding from O to A will be travelling with the speed c relative to the aether but, because the earth is moving in the same direction relative to the aether, the speed of the light relative to the earth should be $c-v$. If OA is of length l the time the light will take to reach A from O is thus $l/c-v$. If it is now reflected back from A its speed on the return journey should be $c+v$ relative to the earth and the time taken to reach O from A is $l/c+v$. The total time from O to A and back is therefore

$$\frac{l}{c-v} + \frac{l}{c+v} = \frac{2cl}{c^2-v^2}. \qquad (1)$$

Consider now the corresponding time for a light wave from O to reach a point B and be reflected back to O. Here the situation is rather similar to that of a ship moving in a cross current. The motion of the light wave relative to the aether must be in such a direction that, combined with the cross current due to the earth's motion, the resultant direction of motion is along OB. Suppose the direction of the light wave relative to the aether is along OC and that CB is parallel to the direction of

114

motion of the earth. Then if T is the time taken for the light to reach B, $OC = cT$ and $CB = vT$. Since OB is perpendicular to OA and hence to BC we have

$$OB^2 = OC^2 - CB^2 = (c^2 - v^2)T^2.$$

As OB and OA are both equal to l this gives

$$T = \frac{l}{\sqrt{(c^2 - v^2)}},$$

and the total time from O to B and back is

$$2T = \frac{2l}{\sqrt{(c^2 - v^2)}}. \tag{2}$$

which is different from (1)

Michelson and Morley devised a very precise optical method of measuring the difference between the times of travel over two perpendicular paths such as OA and OB. Any small differences between the lengths OA and OB in the actual apparatus could be eliminated by swinging the apparatus as a whole about an axis perpendicular to the plane of OA and OB so that the direction of OA and OB could be changed relative to the direction of the earth's absolute motion.

Despite the high accuracy of the experiment, first carried out in 1881, no effect at all due to the earth's motion through the aether was found. This was a staggering result at the time. It seemed as if the aether were dragged along by the earth but, if this were so, its status as an absolute reference system was gone for ever. Apart from this, there were other difficulties which made the hypothesis of aether drag untenable.

Fitzgerald suggested that the reason for the null result is that a material system contracts in the direction of its motion through the aether so that a rod, of length l when at rest in the aether, contracts to a length

$$l \sqrt{(1 - v^2/c^2)}$$

when moving with a velocity v in its own direction relative to the aether. If this were so then l in (1) should be replaced by $l/\sqrt{(1 - v^2/c^2)}$ and the time from O to A and back becomes equal to that from O to B and back, as observed.

Einstein's Theory

At this point it is best to turn our attention to another line of approach to the problem. This involves the very important question of the relation of physical laws to the reference system in which they are expressed. We consider a set of reference systems which differ only in that they are moving with uniform speed relative to each other. They are usually referred to as *inertial systems*. The laws of motion of the classical mechanics of Newton take exactly the same form no matter to which of these systems they are referred – the uniform motion of the earth does not affect the form of the laws of mechanics as observed on the earth. In realizing this, we must, of course, remember that we only refer to uniform motion. The earth's rotation and its accelerated motion around the sun will produce effects which are not now in question, effects which are the province of the general rather than the special theory of relativity which we are now discussing.

Returning now to the original set of inertial reference systems it is natural to enquire whether the invariance of form of the laws of mechanics, which is preserved for all such systems, also holds for the other laws of physics. The question becomes particularly acute when the laws of electromagnetism are considered. As we have already mentioned, Maxwell's electromagnetic equations involve the velocity c of light. If this is to be the same for all our inertial systems we need to revise very drastically the concept of relative velocity as applied to light. It is also noteworthy that this is just what is required to interpret the result of the Michelson-Morley experiment. If the velocity of light is the same in all inertial systems then there will be no effect arising from uniform motion of the earth relative to the aether.

Lorentz, working on these ideas, came very close to the formulation of the special relativity theory but it was not until 1905 that Einstein realised the full implications and took the epoch-making step involved.

He postulated that the laws of physics take the same form for all inertial systems. It is then impossible to assign any significance to the concept of absolute velocity as there is no means of distinguishing one inertial system from any other. The velocity of light is an absolute constant the same for all inertial systems.

The implications of these postulates are very wide. The relegation of the luminiferous aether to the dust-heap of disproved hypotheses is of minor importance compared with the revision required of our concepts of space and time. It is obvious that such revision is necessary because of the breakdown of the classical idea of relative motion as applied to light.

New Ideas about Length, Time and Simultaneity

In pre-relativistic days it was thought that space and time were quite independent so that time measurements bore no relation to those of position in space. It is easy to see, however, that the constancy of the velocity of light in all inertial systems implies that events which are simultaneous in one are not necessarily so in another. Thus, suppose A and B are two points which are fixed in one inertial system S. Events occurring at A and B will be judged as simultaneous by S if light signals, emitted from each point at the instants the events occur, meet at a point C midway between A and B. Consider now a second inertial system S′ moving along AB with respect to the first. When the events occur the points A′, B′ fixed in S′ are coincident with A and B respectively. Since the velocity of light relative to S′ is the same as that relative to S, the light signals emitted when the events occur will still meet at a point coincident with C in S but this will not be at the centre C′ of A′B′ because C′ will have moved relative to C in the time taken for the light signals to meet. Hence the events will not be simultaneous as judged by S′.

The postulates of Einstein's theory also imply the Lorentz contraction but give it a deeper significance. It is no longer to be thought of as a mechanical effect due to motion of the matter through the aether but as an intrinsic feature of length measurement. A rod which is of length l, as measured in a reference system S in which it is at rest, will necessarily have a length $l\sqrt{(1 - v^2/c^2)}$ when measured in the system S′ moving relative to S in the direction of the rod, with speed v. If, on the other hand, the same rod were fixed in S' it would appear to S to have the contracted length $l\sqrt{(1-v^2/c^2)}$. It is the reciprocal nature of this effect which is at first most surprising. Because the speed of light is so great contraction effects are not observable in everyday life. We can imagine, however, a spaceship travelling at a speed of say 160,000 miles a second with respect to the earth. To an observer on the ground the passengers would appear to be foreshortened to about $\frac{1}{2}$ their normal extension in the direction of motion. The observers on the ground would appear similarly foreshortened to passengers in the spaceship!

No direct experimental verification of the contraction has so far been possible although there are certain observed phenomena which depend very closely on it. There is, however, a corresponding effect on time measurement which follows in an exactly similar way from Einstein's postulates and which has received a direct experimental check. The effect can be broadly stated as follows – a moving clock goes slow. In more detail, if t is the time interval between two events which occur at a point fixed in the system S, as measured by a clock fixed in S, the time interval as measured by a clock fixed in S' will be $t/\sqrt{(1-v^2/c^2.)}$ Just as for the length contraction this effect is a reciprocal one. Experimental verification is possible because of the existence of unstable subatomic particles. These have a characteristic mean life time which is equal to that which would be measured when the particle is at rest in the laboratory. The mean life of a particle moving with a speed v with respect to the laboratory should, according to relativity theory, be $1/\sqrt{(1-v^2/c^2)}$ times longer. This elongation of life time has been observed for the particles known as pi-mesons (see Chapter 8 p. 209) and provided the explanation of an anomaly observed in the absorption of cosmic rays in the atmosphere (see Chapter 8 p. 207).

Space-Time

These unfamiliar features of space and time measurement can be included in a world picture in which space and time together form part of what is known as a four-dimensional continuum.

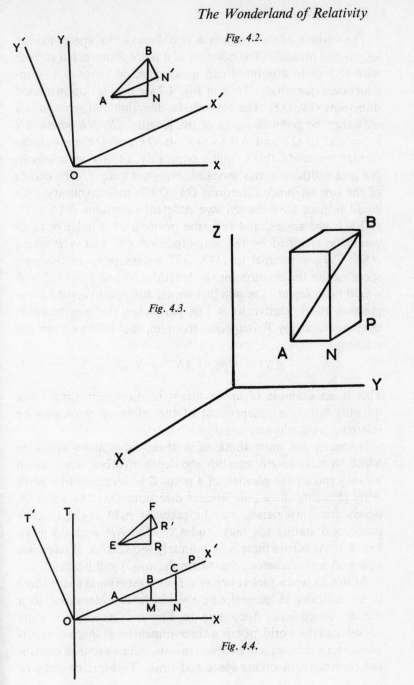

Fig. 4.2.

Fig. 4.3.

Fig. 4.4.

The surface of this page is a two-dimensional space, having length and breadth. The position of a point B on such a surface with respect to a point A can be specified in terms of two independent quantities. Thus in Fig. 4.2 we may set up two fixed directions OX, OY. The magnitude, direction and sense of AB may then be given in terms of the lengths AN, NB where AN is parallel to OX and NB to OY. If OX and OY are perpendicular we could think, quite arbitrarily, of AN as a length, NB as a width. But this specification is not unique. The choice of the two reference directions OX, OY is quite arbitrary. We could instead have chosen two different directions OX', OY', still at right angles, and then the position of A relative to B would be specified by the magnitude of AN' and $N'B$ where AN', $N'B$ are parallel to OX', OY' respectively. In this new specification the division into a 'length' AN' and a 'width' $N'B$ would be different. Despite this we are still specifying the same position of B relative to A. In particular, the length AB is unaltered and, by Pythagoras' theorem, this follows from the relation

$$AN^2 + NB^2 = AN'^2 + N'B^2. \tag{3}$$

This is an example of an invariant relation expressing some quantity which is independent of the reference directions, or reference axes, chosen.

Normally we must think of a three-dimensional space in which we have length, breadth and depth involved. Once again we may specify the position of a point B with respect to a point A by choosing three independent directions OX, OY and OZ, which, for convenience, may be taken at right angles to each other, and stating the magnitudes of AN, NP, and PB as in Fig. 4.3. As before there is an infinitely wide choice of reference axes and an invariance relation similar to (3) still holds.

Although we cannot conceive a four-dimensional space there is no difficulty in generalizing the above considerations to a further dimension. According to Einstein's theory we must conceive of the world, not as a three-dimensional space continuum with an independent progress in time, but as a four-dimensional continuum involving space and time. To examine some of the consequences of this we can ignore two of the space dimensions and just consider one space and one time dimension. Our two reference axes are now OX and OT (Fig. 4.4). A point A in the plane is now associated with a definite position and a definite time, i.e. it represents an event. All points on a line through A parallel to OT occur at the same time, i.e. are simultaneous with A. Points on a line through A parallel to OX occur at the same place at different times. Consider now points on a line such as OAP which is inclined to OX. If B is such a point the time interval between A and B is given by MB and the distance by AM. Similarly, for a point C, the corresponding quantities are NC and AN. Because OAP is a straight line

$$\frac{AM}{MB} = \frac{Distance}{Time} = v, \text{say.}$$

A particle, whose position and time are represented by points on the line OAP, is therefore moving with a constant speed given by v.

Consider now a second reference system moving with a speed v, along the direction OX', with respect to the first. A particle at rest in this system will also be moving at a speed v with respect to the first. Hence the line OAP must be the space-axis OX' for this system and the perpendicular OT' the time axis.

Let us discuss now the specification of the space-time separation or *interval* between two events E, F. According to the S reference axes OX, OT, they will be separated by a distance ER in space and RF in time. However, for the S' reference axes OX', OT' the distance will be ER' and the time $R'F$. This shows in a general way how space and time measurements become intermingled, but there is a further complication.

With the space-time system we have been discussing it would follow that, if s is the separation in distance and t that in time, then, for all reference systems.

$$s^2 + t^2 = \text{constant.} \qquad (4)$$

Apart from the fact that time and length are measured in different units which may be changed independently, the relation (4) does not give the constancy of the velocity of light. For this to hold we must have

$$s^2 - c^2 t^2 = \text{constant.}$$

Comparison with (4) shows that we must replace t^2 in the naive discussion above by $-c^2 t^2$ so that the axes OT, OT$'$ refer to imaginary time $\sqrt{-1}\,ct$ instead of the real time t. The geometry of space-time is then not the geometry of Euclid but a different geometry, known as hyperbolic geometry. The unfamiliarity of the geometry, as well as of the space-time intermingling, is responsible for much of the difficulty encountered in understanding relativity. Formally, a change from one inertial reference system to another involves a rotation, through an imaginary angle, of a four-dimensional reference system in which the four mutually perpendicular axes represent space and imaginary time (including of course the factor c)! The fact that imaginary time and not real time is treated on the same footing as each of the three space dimensions makes it possible to distinguish an absolute past and an absolute future even though different inertial systems of reference do not agree about simultaneity.

All of the laws of physics must have the same form with respect to reference axes in the four-dimensional space-time continuum which correspond to different inertial systems. It is this requirement which led Einstein to suggest a radical revision of our ideas of other important quantities such as mass and energy. With the classical definitions, form invariance is only preserved with respect to change of reference axes in 'ordinary' three-dimensional space.

If a point is moving with respect to one inertial system with speed u and with respect to another with speed u', all in the direction of relative motion, with speed v, of the inertial systems with respect to each other then, according to pre-relativistic mechanics,

$$u' = u - v. \tag{5}$$

The relativity theory modifies this to give

$$u' = \frac{1 - uv/c^2}{u - v},$$

which reduces to (5) when u and v are small compared with c. It follows that no relative velocity can ever exceed that of light which is therefore the maximum possible velocity. An interesting consequence of this is discussed in Chapter 9 p. 238.

Mass and Energy in Relativity Theory

We have already pointed out the importance of mass, energy and momentum in the classical mechanics of Newton (see Chapter 2 p. 43). In a closed system, that is to say one which is not in interaction in any way with the outside world, all these quantities are separately conserved, i.e. the total amount of each within the system remains constant.

These three conservation laws can only be retained in the framework of relativity theory if the mass, energy and momentum are redefined. The mass m of a body is now a relative concept depending on the inertial system to which it is referred. If the body is moving with a speed v with respect to the reference system its mass, *relative to that system*, is given by

$$m = \frac{m_0}{\sqrt{(1 - v^2/c^2)}} \tag{6}$$

where m_0 is an absolute constant for a particular body. It is known as the *rest mass* and can be regarded as a measure of the amount of matter in the body as distinct from its inertial mass m which determines its reaction to a force. If v is much less than c, the inertial mass is nearly equal to the rest mass m_0 but it will be noticed that m becomes indefinitely large as the speed approaches that of light. This is consistent with the impossibility of accelerating a body by application of a finite force so that its speed exceeds that of light.

The energy of the body with respect to the same inertial system is given by

$$E = \frac{m_0 c^2}{\sqrt{(1 - v^2/c^2)}} = mc^2. \tag{7}$$

In this case, when v is much less than c, we find
$$E = m_0 c^2 + \tfrac{1}{2} m v^2.$$

This is the classical value plus an amount $m_0 c^2$ which is associated with the rest mass m_0. Einstein gave reasons why this must be taken seriously so that the possession of rest mass m_0 implies the existence of an amount of energy m_0c^2. Energy and mass are to be thought of as different aspects of the same quantity, an energy E being equivalent to a mass E/c^2 or a mass m to an energy mc^2. In classical mechanics, although the total amount of energy in a closed system is constant, transformations may occur between different kinds of energy. We must now be prepared for the possibility of these transformations involving energy of rest mass. Transformation of such energy into kinetic or radiant or other forms of energy would mean the annihilation of matter, as the possession of rest mass is the characteristic property of matter. In the same way we must contemplate the possibility of the inverse transformation – the creation of matter. This seemed unbelievable at the time when Einstein put forward his ideas on the subject but is now a commonplace in modern physics (Chapter 6 p. 143) and indeed is basically responsible for the energy released in atomic explosions or power reactors.

The first experimental verification of the formula (6) came from the experiment of Bucherer in 1908. He observed the motion of electrons in a magnetic field. Owing to their small rest mass it is possible to accelerate electrons until they are moving at speeds comparable with that of light. This means that modifications due to the relativistic mass can be made quite large. Bucherer found that the observed motion was consistent with the formula (6).

The magnitude of the momentum of our particle is given in the same reference system by

$$p = \frac{m_0 v}{\sqrt{(1-v^2/c^2)}}, \tag{8}$$

so that we have the important relation

$$E^2 = p^2c^2 + m_0^2c^4. \tag{9}$$

This is to be contrasted with the classical relation

$$E_0 = p^2/2m_0, \tag{10}$$

where E_0 is the kinetic energy. The fact that the relativistic

124

relation (9) involves the square of the energy, whereas the classical one (10) only involves the energy to the first power, turns out to be very significant, as we shall see in the next Chapter.

Collisions in Relativistic Mechanics

In Chapter 2 (p. 43) we explained how the laws of conservation of energy and momentum could be applied to the consideration of a collision between two particles. If the equations (a), (b) and (c) of Chapter 2 are applied when the colliding particles are of the same mass m we find that the angles Θ and Φ must be such that

$$\Theta + \Phi = 90°,$$

as indicated in Fig. 4.5(a). This relation no longer holds when relativistic mechanics is used. Instead, we find that the sum of the two angles is always less than 90° and gradually approaches zero as the velocity of the incident particle approaches that of light (see Fig. 4.5(b)). This is an example of a general effect of relativity, a tendency for the direction of motion of particles to persist despite the occurrence of collisions. The effect is very marked when the particles are moving with speeds such that $1/\sqrt{(1-v^2/c^2)}$ is much greater than 1. This makes it difficult to make accurate measurements of the angles involved in collisions, measurements on which one must rely heavily for information about the nature of the collision and of the colliding particles (see Chapter 8 p. 212).

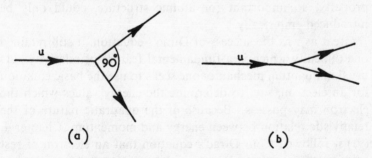

Fig. 4.5. Illustrating the effect of relativity on a collision between a particle of speed u and a particle of equal mass at rest.
(a) Case when u is much less than c
(b) Case when u is comparable with c

CHAPTER 5

WONDER UPON WONDER –
RELATIVISTIC QUANTUM THEORY

> *'Thus grew the tale of Wonderland:*
> *Thus slowly, one by one,*
> *Its quaint events were hammered out –'*
> LEWIS CARROLL, INTRODUCTION TO 'ALICE IN WONDERLAND'

Relativity and Quantum Theory – The Negative Mass Dilemma

In Chapter 4 we discussed relativity as a distinct and independent modification of classical theory but we must now consider both relativistic and quantal modifications together.

The first great step in this direction was taken by Dirac in 1928. It was soon realized that the wave mechanics of Schrödinger, while fully adequate to deal with most atomic problems, was not satisfactory from the point of view of relativity theory because it did not treat space and time (or rather $\sqrt{-1}ct$, see Chapter 4 p. 122) on an equivalent footing. The first attempts at a relativistic version of wave mechanics were not satisfactory but Dirac was successful in proposing his now famous equation for the relativistic motion of an electron, which did not suffer from the same defect and which also introduced the electron spin (see Chapter 2 p. 63) automatically. Up to that time this property, so important for atomic structure, could only be introduced empirically.

Great as was the success of Dirac's equation, it still retained one difficulty which is a fundamental feature of relativity. As usual in quantum mechanics one seeks to use the basic equation for an electron, say, to determine the energy values which the electron may possess. Because of the quadratic nature of the relativistic relation between energy and momentum (Chapter 4, (9)) it followed from Dirac's equation that an electron of rest mass m_0, moving in free space with momentum of magnitude p could possess an energy E equal either to

$$+ \sqrt{(p^2c^2 + m_0^2c^4)} \quad \text{or} \quad - \sqrt{(p^2c^2 + m_0^2c^4)}$$

If we pause a moment to examine its significance we soon see that the possibility of the negative sign is most embarrassing. A particle in free space possesses only energy of motion and energy due to its rest mass (Chapter 4 p. 123). If its total energy is negative this can only be because its mass is negative. But a particle with negative mass would be most conspicuous. If acted on by a force it would be accelerated in the opposite direction to the force. To illustrate this we may consider the case of a runaway pair of electrons (Fig. 5.1). If we have two electrons, both with negative electric charge $-e$ but with equal and opposite masses $\pm m$ then each will act on the other with a repulsive force because of their like charges. Referring to Fig. 5.1 we see that the effect of this force on the electron of positive mass will be to accelerate it to the right. If the other electron had positive mass it would be accelerated to the left and they would separate. On the other hand, as it has a negative mass, the repulsive force on it accelerates it to the right and the two electrons would move as a pair to the right with steadily increasing speed. No such fantastic situation has ever been observed in practice nor has any other case of a particle possessing negative mass. And yet we would expect that as electrons lose energy in collisions or in emitting radiation their total energy would eventually fall to one of the permitted negative values. In fact we would expect most electrons to occupy such states. Why then are they never observed?

The New Aether

Dirac made what was regarded at first as a fantastic suggestion to overcome the negative mass dilemma. He took advantage of

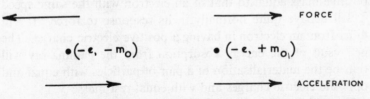

Fig. 5.1. A 'runaway' pairs of electrons of equal charge and equal and opposite mass. Because of the electrical repulsions which each exerts on the other, they are each continually accelerated in the same direction so as to chase each other indefinitely with ever increasing speed.

the Pauli principle (Chapter 2 p. 64) according to which no two electrons can occupy the same quantum state. If all the allowed states in which the electrons have negative mass are normally occupied no further electrons can drop into such states. Dirac made the bold postulate that what we regard as empty space, in that it possesses no material or other properties, is really by no means empty but is the condition in which all the negative mass states are occupied. In this way one would not normally observe an electron of positive mass to give up so much energy that its mass becomes negative. There do follow certain other remarkable consequences which should be observable and amenable to quantitative experimental test.

Creation and Annihilation of Matter – The Positive Electron

The negative mass electrons in the Dirac 'vacuum' may absorb energy from short electromagnetic radiation, gamma-rays (Fig. 2.4), provided this energy is great enough for the electron to jump to an unoccupied state, i.e. a state in which the electron has positive mass. Under these circumstances a perfect vacuum would change to a positive mass electron plus an 'imperfect' vacuum. The imperfection would arise because not all the negative mass states would be occupied. This imperfect vacuum can be regarded as a perfect one plus an absence of a negative mass electron (compare Chapter 3 p. 15). As the perfect vacuum has no physical properties any properties of the imperfect one must stem from this absence of a negative mass electron, i.e. of a particle of charge $-e$ and mass $-m$. This will be manifest as the presence of a particle of charge $-(-e) = +e$ and mass $-(-m) = +m$. As this apparent particle has a positive mass equal to that of an electron with the same speed it will behave quite normally in its response to force. It will differ from an electron in having a positive electric charge. The net result of the energy absorption from the gamma-ray will thus be the materialisation of a pair of particles with equal and opposite electric charges and with equal rest masses.

From the point of view of energy conservation we suppose that the energy possessed initially by the vacuum electron before it absorbs the radiation is given by

$$E_1 = -\frac{m_0 c^2}{\sqrt{(1 - v^2/c^2)}}.$$

If the energy absorbed from the gamma-ray is E, then the speed u of the electron which materialises in a positive energy state will be given by

$$\frac{m_0 c^2}{\sqrt{(1 - u^2/c^2)}} = E - \frac{m_0 c^2}{\sqrt{(1 - v^2/c^2)}},$$

since energy is conserved. This may be rewritten as

$$\frac{m_0 c^2}{\sqrt{(1 - u^2/c^2)}} + \frac{m_0 c^2}{\sqrt{(1 - v^2/c^2)}} = E. \qquad (1)$$

The second term now appears as the energy of the vacancy particle and the equation is of exactly the form which would be expected if the energy of the gamma-ray were used up in producing two particles of rest mass m_0, one with speed u and the other with speed v.

The least energy which must be absorbed to produce a pair in this way is obtained from (1) by putting $u = v = 0$. It is thus $2m_0 c^2$, just enough to provide the rest mass energy of each particle.

Actually a gamma ray of sufficient quantum energy cannot materialise in this way unless it collides at the same time with some particle (with positive rest mass) already present. This may, for example, be an atomic nucleus. The reason is that, otherwise, the conservation of momentum cannot be satisfied.

The remarkable thing is that this incredible series of events does occur in nature. Gamma rays with frequency v, such that hv is greater than $2m_0 c^2$, do materialise when passing through matter to produce pairs of positive and negative electrons with the properties indicated above. The positive electrons are now usually referred to as *positrons*. Pair creation is indeed one of the major processes leading to absorption of high energy gamma rays in matter.

The existence of positrons was first established by Anderson in 1932 and confirmed shortly afterwards by Blackett and Occhialini. They observed the particles among the products of the interaction of cosmic rays with matter, using the cloud chamber technique described in Chapter 6. Plate 5.1 is a reproduction of one of the early photographs showing the formation of an electron-positron pair.

Another possibility arises from the nature of a positron. It is essentially a vacancy into which an electron of positive mass may drop. If this occurs the hole is filled up, restoring a perfect vacuum into which both the positron and electron will have disappeared without trace. The occurrence of the process will be marked by the liberation of energy in the form of radiation or otherwise. This is because the rest mass and kinetic energy of both particles must be transformed to other kinds of energy. In short, the process is the inverse of the pair creation process we have discussed above.

Once again experimental confirmation of this possibility has been forthcoming. If, on collision between a positron and an electron, they annihilate each other, then two gamma-rays must be emitted in order to conserve momentum. It is possible to observe that two gamma-rays are indeed given out by using coincidence counting methods (see Chapter 6 p. 163 and Chapter 8 p. 219) and to confirm that they possess quantum energies consistent with the conservation of energy in the annihilation process.

Polarization and Field Fluctuations in the Vacuum

There are other more subtle consequences of Dirac's conception of the vacuum which have also yielded to high precision experimental tests.

An electron in so-called empty space can no longer be regarded as completely free but will act on, and be acted on by, the negative mass electrons of the vacuum which surround it. Since electrons repel each other, the 'free' electron will reduce the density of vacuum electrons in its neighbourhood below that which prevails in its absence. This is just as if a positively charged region is established round an electron and this it must carry with it as it moves through space. Here we have essentially a polarization effect in which the vacuum acquires a net positive charge around the electron and a net negative one at greater distances. The fact that the electron digs out a space around it will naturally change the potential energy of the electron from the value which it would have if it were 'bare', that is to say if there were a truly empty vacuum. As, however, a 'bare' electron in this sense is physically unrealisable, we must suppose that the properties of an actual electron, including its rest mass energy, include contributions from vacuum polarization.

Nevertheless, the possibility of some experimental test is not excluded. So far we have talked only of an electron in a field-free space, no other source of force being present (apart from the vacuum electrons). It is to be expected that the interaction of an electron with a field of force, when such is present, will be modified slightly because of the vacuum polarization by the electron. Two ways in practice in which this might occur are in the interaction of an electron with a magnetic field or with a proton as in a hydrogen atom. In both cases it is possible to calculate the magnitude and nature of the modifications to be expected. Considerable ingenuity must be exercised in carrying out these calculations. They must take the form of a strict evaluation of the modification, by the presence of the inter-acting field, of the energy changes due to vacuum polarization. In practice, with the present incomplete state of our under-standing of the source of rest mass energy, the energy contribu-tion from vacuum polarization, with and without the interacting field present, is infinitely great. It is possible, however, by use of certain subtle arguments, to determine the small difference between these two infinitely large quantities, unambiguously and to a high degree of accuracy.

Before considering these effects further we must consider another, rather larger, effect which in a sense is due to the presence of a different kind of vacuum population. We have already discussed in Chapter 2 some of the aspects of quantum theory and particularly the uncertainty principle (p. 59). Because of this principle we encounter the curious situation of an oscillator possessing vibrational energy even when it is not oscillating – the oscillator can never be regarded as at rest in its equilibrium position. A somewhat similar situation arises when we apply the principles of quantum theory to the electromagnetic field. In the absence of any electric charges the quantization of the field can be done in a similar way to that of the harmonic oscillator in which the frequency of vibration is independent of its amplitude. The allowed energies associated with a frequency v of electromagnetic waves are given by

$$E_v = (n + \tfrac{1}{2})hv$$

where h is Planck's constant. When $n = 0$ for all frequencies, we have the quantum equivalent of a vanishing electromagnetic field as no frequencies are excited at all. But this field does contain zeropoint energy (Chapter 2 p. 60) associated with each vibration. In terms of the usual electromagnetic field quantities this means that, at any one time, the electric and magnetic field intensities E and H can never be zero everywhere in the field – there will be field fluctuations so that the mean values of E^2 and of H^2 are not zero. Since the energy in unit volume of an electromagnetic field is given, in appropriate units, by $(E^2+H^2)/8\pi$ it follows that the fluctuations are associated with a non-vanishing mean energy per unit volume.

An electron in 'empty' space will be affected by the field fluctuations just as by the vacuum polarization. The rest mass energy will include a contribution from this source but again this cannot be calculated in the present state of our theoretical knowledge – just as for vacuum polarization, it comes out to be infinite. However it is again possible to calculate, unambiguously and accurately, the small *difference* between the effects with and without an independent source of interaction.

If field fluctuation and vacuum polarization effects are ignored, an electron, possessing a charge e, rest mass m and a spin quantum number $\tfrac{1}{2}$, behaves in a magnetic field as if it were a small magnet of moment $eh/4\pi mc$, c being the velocity of light (see Chapter 3 p. 89). Allowance for the two effects leads to multiplication of this moment by 1.0011454.

According to the theory of the hydrogen atom based on Dirac's equation (see p. 126), but ignoring the field fluctuation and vacuum polarization effects, the lowest energy level of the atom is a single (1s) level. The first excited level is two-fold consisting of two states, distinguished as $2s_{\frac{1}{2}}$ and $2p_{\frac{1}{2}}$, which have *exactly* the same energy. When the vacuum effects are allowed for the energies of these two states become slightly different, the $2p_{\frac{1}{2}}$ state lying below the $2s_{\frac{1}{2}}$ by 4.3712×10^{-6} e.volts. Of this -0.1227×10^{-6} e.volts is due to vacuum polarization and the remainder to field fluctuations and certain other, smaller, effects.

Although the modifications are so small, the uniquely remarkable precision with which measurements of frequency may be carried out has led to a detailed check of the theory, fantastic as the latter seems to be. Actually the fact that the $2s_{\frac{1}{2}}$ and $2p_{\frac{1}{2}}$ states of the hydrogen atom have not got exactly equal energy was discovered, and the separation measured accurately, before the theory of the effects was worked out! These remarkable measurements were first made by Lamb and Retherford in 1947 and we shall now describe them briefly.

The Lamb-Retherford Experiment

This experiment makes use of the resonance principle applied to the effects of very short electromagnetic waves, or microwaves, on hydrogen atoms in $2s_{\frac{1}{2}}$ states.

If an energy difference ε exists between the $2s_{\frac{1}{2}}$ and $2p_{\frac{1}{2}}$ states then it is to be expected that the application of an electromagnetic field of frequency ε/h to atoms in $2s_{\frac{1}{2}}$ states will produce transitions to the $2p_{\frac{1}{2}}$ states quite readily (c.f. Chapter 3 p. 110). A hydrogen atom, if left alone in a $2s_{\frac{1}{2}}$ state, will stay in that state for a very long time because the chance of a transition to the ground $1s$ state is very small – the $2s_{\frac{1}{2}}$ state is metastable. An atom in a $2p_{\frac{1}{2}}$ state, however, rapidly gives out its excitation energy in the form of radiation, the transition from $2p_{\frac{1}{2}}$ to $1s$ having a high probability. Use may now be made of these features to carry out an experiment on the following lines.

A beam of hydrogen atoms issuing from an orifice (Fig. 5.2) is of such intensity that no collisions occur between the individual atoms of the beam. As the beam passes through the space X it is subjected to bombardment by electrons so that a number of the atoms are excited to $2s_{\frac{1}{2}}$ states. Any such atom, impinging on a suitable metal plate M, will give up its excitation energy to the plate with the result that an electron is emitted from the plate. The current from the plate due to these electrons is thus a measure of the number of hydrogen atoms in the $2s_{\frac{1}{2}}$ state impinging per second on the plate.

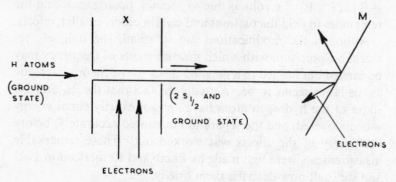

Fig. 5.2. Illustrating the principle of the experiment of Lamb and Rutherford.

Once this arrangement has been set up, the stream of metastable atoms passing beyond X can be subjected to an electromagnetic field whose frequency may be varied. The effect of this field on the electron current emitted from the plate M may then be observed at each frequency. It was found by Lamb and Retherford* that this variation takes the form shown in Fig. 5.3. This is a typical resonance curve, showing that the current has a sharp minimum at a certain frequency ν_0, implying that at this frequency the flow of metastable atoms to the plate is also a minimum. This, in turn, must be due to the field inducing transitions from the $2s_{\frac{1}{2}}$ to the $2p_{\frac{1}{2}}$ state. Atoms in this state, if they reached the plate M, would also eject electrons but, on the average, they give out their surplus energy as radiation before reaching it.

According to the most accurate measurements the resonance frequency is found to be 1057.77 ± 0.10 megacycles per second. The theoretical value is 1057.19 ± 0.2 megacycles per second, −27.35 of which is due to vacuum polarization, the remainder to field fluctuations, apart from one or two other small con-

* In practice the situation is somewhat more complicated than we have described because the $2p_{\frac{1}{2}}$ state is double and a magnetic field must be applied to separate this doublet. The resonance effect is obtained then by maintaining the frequency fixed and varying the magnetic field.

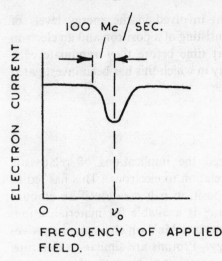

Fig. 5.3. General form of the variation of the electron current emitted from the plate M (Fig. 5.2) with frequency of the applied electromagnetic field.

tributions. It will be seen that the accuracy of the experiment is great enough to confirm the reality and magnitude of both effects.

It must be pointed out that we have given only the bare outlines of the experimental method. Many difficulties had to be overcome and the successful outcome is an experimental *tour de force*.

The Anomalous Magnetic Moment of the Electron

It has been possible, by a further application of this technique, to confirm the effect of field fluctuations and vacuum polarization on the magnetic moment of the electron (see Chapter 3 p. 89). The method involves use of the astonishingly accurate magnetic resonance method which is discussed in connection with nuclear applications in Chapter 6 p. 144. The observed ratio of the magnetic moment to that in the absence of the two vacuum effects is

$$1.001146 \pm 0.000006$$

which is to be compared with the theoretical value

$$1.0011454$$

Another very remarkable example of vacuum effects which

have been observed is that involved in the energy levels of positronium, the duplex consisting of a positron and an electron bound together for a short time before they annihilate each other. Some idea of the way in which this has been investigated is given in Chapter 8 p. 219.

Matter and Anti-Matter

Protons and Anti-protons

So far we have considered the implications of relativistic quantum theory solely in relation to electrons. This has led to the possibility of electron-positron pair creation if an amount of energy greater than $2m_0c^2$ is available for materialisation. This is about 1,000,000 e.volts or 1 MeV which is a comparatively modest amount of energy. Protons are similar to electrons in having a spin of $\frac{1}{2}$ a quantum unit and we would expect that they should obey a similar equation to the Dirac equation for electrons. The same line of argument would then lead us to expect that there is a particle, an *anti-proton*, which bears the same relation to the proton as the positron to the electron. Thus the anti-proton should have the same mass as a proton but possess a negative charge $-e$, the same as that of an electron.

To materialise a proton-antiproton pair an energy greater than $2Mc^2$ is required, where M is the proton mass. This is 1837 times larger than for electron-positron pairs so that nearly 2,000 MeV must be available. This has only been realised in the last few years during which it has been definitely established that anti-protons exist and have the expected properties (at least as far as necessary to identify them). An outline of the method used to verify that they may be produced is given in Chapter 8 p. 221.

Antineutrons

Apart from electrons and protons there is a third building stone in matter, the neutron. This again is a particle with spin $\frac{1}{2}$ a quantum unit so we can expect it also to have a corresponding anti-particle. We might at first have some difficulty in seeing how the two could be distinguished as a neutron has no electric charge. Actually, as we noted in Chapter 3 p. 69 (see also

Chapter 6 p. 148), the absence of charge does not mean absence of all electromagnetic properties. Neutrons possess a magnetic moment comparable with, but of opposite sign to, that of a proton. An anti-neutron has a magnetic moment equal and opposite to that of a neutron.

The production of anti-neutrons in very high energy reactions has been confirmed (Chapter 8 p. 223) so we may think of anti-matter in which electrons, protons and neutrons are replaced by positrons, anti-protons and anti-neutrons respectively. One can go further and consider even an anti-universe. There is no reason why there should be a particular emphasis on one choice of building stones as against the other. The way in which the anti-particles have been introduced has been based naturally on the universe around us but we must regard matter and anti-matter as on the same footing in general. Coexistence of matter and anti-matter is not possible because mutual annihilation between particles and anti-particles would take place. This does not exclude the possibility that anti-matter may exist at very great distances from our universe.

Anti-gravity?

One curious question arises. Particles and antiparticles are produced in pairs. How could matter and anti-matter ever separate? Electrical forces could not be responsible as charged particles necessarily attract the oppositely charged anti-particles. One possibility, which cannot be ruled out at the present stage, is that of a repulsive force of gravity between matter and anti-matter. Any piece of matter attracts any other piece of matter with a gravitational force which, while very small compared with electrical forces between particles, becomes important for large masses of matter. We cannot say yet whether a piece of matter exerts a gravitational attraction or repulsion on a piece of anti-matter – we do not know whether anti-protons tend to fall downwards or upwards! The nature of the force of gravity is still so obscure that no reliable answer can yet be given from theory and it will be some time before any experimental tests will be practicable. Gravitational control of the motion of such tiny particles as anti-protons is so very weak compared with that due to electrical effects that the nature of its influence cannot be sorted out.

The New Aether – Some Final Comments

We see that, after having disposed of the luminiferous aether, relativity taken together with quantum theory has replaced it by a new, far more complex one, in the densely populated vacuum. Apart from the negative mass electrons and the electromagnetic field oscillators it includes negative mass protons, neutrons and, as we shall see later (Chapter 8 p. 209), mu-mesons. There are even more mysterious denizens such as anti-neutrinos (Chapter 9 p. 239). The lack of symmetry between particles and anti-particles, which are regarded as holes in an otherwise fully populated vacuum, leads one to hope that eventually we may be able to dispose of the new aether from the conceptual point of view. Already it plays no explicit role in the mathematical theory, although it is true that this theory is greatly complicated by the fact that one can never think of isolated particles in truly empty space. All problems essentially involve many bodies so the situation may often be even more unfavourable for detailed analysis than, say, the three-body problem in astronomy.

We shall return to related subjects in Chapters 8 and 9.

CHAPTER 6

EXPLORING THE ATOMIC NUCLEUS – THE TOOLS AND SOME OF THE RESULTS

> *'And now I see with eye serene*
> *The very pulse of the machine;'*
> W. WORDSWORTH

Survey of Problems and Methods

In Chapter I a brief historical account was given of the developments which led up to the concept of the nuclear atom in which the nucleus is composed of protons and of neutrons. These particles, which we shall refer to as *nucleons*, have approximately equal mass whereas protons alone possess electric charge. The atomic number of an atom determines the chemical, and much of the physical, behaviour of an atom since it is equal to the number of electrons in the atom. As this in turn is equal to the number of protons we obtain this latter number immediately from the atomic number. On the other hand the mass number is equal to the sum of the numbers of neutrons and protons.

Many major problems arise when the structure of the atomic nucleus is concerned. There is the fundamental one – what is the force which binds nucleons together so firmly in nuclei, and how does it arise? It clearly cannot be electrical in character as neutrons have no charge. The elucidation of the nature of nuclear forces is still a leading problem although much work, both experimental and theoretical in character, has been devoted to it. However, it is not necessary to know the answer to this before studying the ways in which nuclei may interact and exploiting these interactions for human purposes. After all it is only since 1927 that we have had any real understanding of the forces which lead to chemical reactions yet man has exploited these reactions in the form, for example, of fire ever since palaeolithic times. It is not surprising then, that the energy residing in nuclei has been put to use before we fully understand its nature and source.

The exploration of the nucleus and of nuclear reactions has reached its present highly developed state only because of the extraordinarily powerful methods of experiment which have been developed. Thanks to the use of high precision methods it is possible to measure the physical properties of nuclei, such as their masses and magnetic moments, to a very great accuracy. This is essentially the subject of nuclear statics in which the properties of nuclei in equilibrium are investigated. A great deal more work is concerned with the study of nuclear reactions. A chemical reaction takes place when molecules collide and a rearrangement of atoms occurs between them. This results in the production of new molecules and the liberation or absorption of energy. A nuclear reaction is quite analogous, involving collisions of nuclei during which nucleons are redistributed. There are, however, such very marked differences in the magnitudes involved that the techniques for studying the two types of reaction are wholly different.

First of all there are the great energy differences. Nucleons are very much more firmly bound to each other in nuclei than are atoms in a molecule. To break up the most strongly bound diatomic molecule, carbon monoxide CO, 11.1 e.volts of energy is required. This is to be contrasted with 2.2 million e.volts (2.2 MeV) necessary to disrupt the deuteron, one of the least firmly bound nuclei. We must expect, therefore, that the energy changes produced in a nuclear transformation will be very much larger than in any chemical change.

An even more important difference, from the practical point of view concerns the *activation energy* required to initiate the reactions. Many chemical reactions will not begin until some energy is supplied. Thus an explosive mixture of hydrogen and oxygen will not explode if left alone but it will do so if a lighted match is applied to supply the small amount of initial activation energy. In all nuclear reactions, except those in which neutrons are involved, a large activation energy is necessary because the force between two nuclei is repulsive until they approach very closely. If the nuclei have atomic numbers Z_1 and Z_2 they will repel each other, when at large distances R apart, with the electrical force $Z_1 Z_2 e^2 / R^2$. This means that, for the two nuclei to approach to within the distance R, they must possess kinetic energy of relative motion greater than $Z_1 Z_2 e^2 / R$, at least according to classical mechanics. As the repulsive force prevails until the nucleon separations are of the order of nuclear radii (10^{-12} cm.) this energy is large. It is true that the so-called tunnel effect in quantum mechanics allows some degree of pentration even when the kinetic energy is classically inadequate, but the chance of this occurring falls very rapidly as the kinetic energy falls below the classical minimum. A simple numerical calculation shows that the relative kinetic energy required to initiate a nuclear reaction is of the order of millions of electron volts except when the lightest nuclei are involved. Whereas the energy of random motion at accessible temperatures (say up to 2,000°C) is adequate for the initiation of chemical reactions, requiring only a fraction of an e.volt activation energy, this is not possible for nuclei, as the temperatures required are of the order of 100,000,000°C or higher (see, however, Chapter 7 p. 195). The only way to produce a nuclear reaction in which charged nuclei are concerned is to speed up a stream of nuclear missiles to the necessary energy and bombard material containing the target nuclei. The technique of accelerating charged particles for this purpose has become a major branch of experimental physics. Accelerators are now available which provide nuclear missiles with kinetic energy far in excess of that necessary to overcome the electrical repulsive forces between, say, protons and the heaviest nuclei. The energies attainable are so large that reactions leading to materialisation of new particles are possible and are observed. It is convenient to use the symbols MeV and GeV (or BeV in the U.S.A.) to denote respectively one million and one thousand million electron volts and we shall adopt this shorthand henceforward.

The one reservation about energy requirements is that they do not apply when the bombarding missiles are neutrons. This is because these particles, being uncharged, encounter only attractive forces in nuclear interaction. This has given rise to the possibility of large scale nuclear power reactors which provide, not only power, but also intense streams of neutrons which can be used, among other things, to produce nuclear reactions of many kinds. We shall discuss these large scale applications in the next Chapter.

Even when the problem of producing nuclear missiles energetic enough to initiate nuclear reactions is solved, there is a further necessary development of experimental technique. The number of missiles which can be speeded up to bombard a target material is quite limited and both the target and missile nuclei are extremely small. Very few nuclear reactions can therefore be produced in a reasonable time. It follows that the methods used to observe the nature of the reactions which occur must be extraordinarily sensitive, far beyond the best achievable in micro-chemical analysis. This has led to some of the most remarkable and effective developments of modern experimental physics which enable single fast particles to be detected and identified. Because of this, the nuclear physicist is able to observe individual nuclear reactions and to make quantitative measurements of the properties of certain strange atoms (see Chapter 8 p. 218) which are only available in thousands. The most sensitive of microchemical methods are only operative if at least several billions of molecules are available.

We shall in this Chapter concentrate our attention mainly on the experimental procedures which have proved so vital and so fruitful in nuclear physics. Opportunity will be taken to describe some of the results obtained, particularly in the concluding sections. The following Chapter will describe further results, particularly in relation to the full scale release of nuclear, or as popularly known, atomic energy. Many more results, obtained especially in very high energy reactions, will be described in Chapter 8.

Measuring Nuclear Properties

We shall content ourselves here by discussing the measurement of two properties only, to give some idea of the principles involved and the accuracy attainable.

The Masses and Binding Energies of Nuclei

We first consider the determination of nuclear masses. Comparison of masses may be made by means of a mass spectrograph, the principle of which has already been described in Chapter 1 p. 39. There have been very great advances in technique since the pioneering work of Aston and it is now possible to compare the masses of two nuclei of similar mass number to about 1 part in 10^7. In fact, with the largest mass spectrographs now being constructed, it is nearly possible to detect the mass difference between a normal and a metastable helium atom due to the possession by the latter of 19.77 e.volts excitation energy! According to the Einstein relation (Chapter 4, (7)) between mass and energy this is equivalent to a relative mass difference less than one part in 10^8.

The validity of this relation for nuclear reactions has been verified to a high degree of precision and it may now be used, in connection with measurement of the energy released in appropriate nuclear reactions, to determine the mass differences between nuclei.

It follows also that the Einstein relation can be used, in conjunction with the measured masses of nuclei, to determine the nuclear energies. The energy required to break up a nucleus into individual free nucleons is known as its binding energy. If $M(Z, A)$ is the mass of a nucleus of atomic and mass numbers Z and A respectively, then the binding energy is given by

$$E = [ZM_p + (A-Z)M_n - M(Z,A)]c^2,$$

where M_p is the mass of a free proton and M_n that of a free neutron.

The masses of the two nucleons are clearly of great importance. That of a proton can be derived from accurate measurement of the ratio of its charge to its mass, using essentially the same principles, but much more refined technique, as that of J. J. Thomson in his pioneering study of the electron (see Chapter 1, p. 28). Naturally, the mass of the neutron cannot be determined in this way. It has been obtained, quite accurately, by quantitative study of certain reactions involving deuterons. Thus, if M_d is the mass of a deuteron, its binding energy is given by

$$E_d = [M_p + M_n - M_d]c^2.$$

M_p is known, M_d/M_p and hence M_d can be obtained by mass spectrographic methods, so if E_d can be measured M_n follows. One way of measuring E_d is to determine the energy released as gamma radiation when a very low energy neutron combines with a proton to form a deuteron. The frequency ν of the gamma rays can be measured and hence the energy $h\nu$ derived.

The mass of a neutron is slightly greater than that of a proton. In terms of the mass n of an electron

$$M_p = 1836.13 \pm 0.04 \, m, \; M_n = 1838.66 \pm 0.04 \, m.$$

It is noteworthy (see Chapter 9, p. 226) that M_n exceeds M_p by more than the mass of an electron.

Great practical as well as theoretical significance is attached to the form of the variation of nuclear binding energy with atomic or mass number. The observed relation is illustrated in Fig. 6.1 where the binding energy per nucleon (E/A) is plotted as a function of A. It will be seen that this rises rather irregularly for the light nuclei, then more smoothly to a maximum for nuclei with A about 60 (those of iron, cobalt and nickel) and then falls gradually as the mass number increases. The existence of this maximum is of great importance as we shall see in the next Chapter (p. 174).

For the lighter nuclei the binding energies are as follows –: deuteron (one proton + one neutron) 2.2 MeV, triton (one proton + two neutrons) 8.5 MeV, helium isotope of mass 3 (two protons + one neutron) 7.7 MeV, normal helium (two protons + two neutrons) 28.3 MeV.

Magnetic Moments of Nuclei

We have already remarked in Chapter 5, p. 133 that the measurement of frequency is the most accurate possible in physics. The ratio of the magnetic moments of two nuclei can be measured in terms of the ratio of two frequencies and so can be obtained with astonishing precision. Thus the ratio μ_d/μ_p of the magnetic moment μ_d of the deuteron to that μ_p of the proton is known to be

$$\mu_d/\mu_p = 0.30701219 \pm 0.00000003$$

from the measurement made by Wimett.

Although it is not easy to describe the principles of these

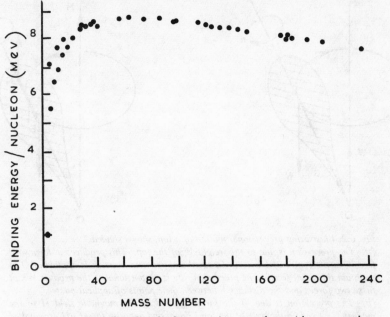

Fig. 6.1. Variations of nuclear binding energy per nucleon with mass number.

remarkable experiments in non-technical terms, it is worthwhile attempting to give more idea of what is involved. We start from the notion of the precession of a spinning nuclear magnet in a magnetic field, a phenomenon quite analogous to the familiar precession of a top under gravity. Thus in Fig. 6.2(a) the heavy top is spinning about its axis which passes through a fixed point O. The angular momentum of the top about this axis is the product of the rate of spin n (the number of revolutions per second) and a quantity C, known as the moment of inertia, which is determined by the distribution of mass in the top with respect to the axis. When the top is released it does not stay with its axis fixed. Instead the axis precesses about the vertical as shown so that a point of the top, such as its centre of gravity G, describes a horizontal circle. The rate of precession depends only on the angular momentum Cn, and the product Wh of the weight W of the top and the distance h of its centre of gravity G from O. This product appears because it is a

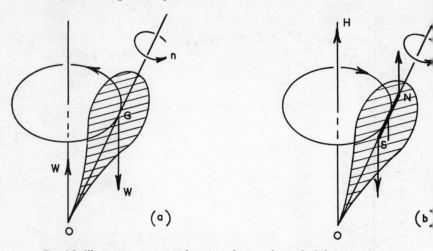

Fig. 6.2. *Illustrating precessional motion of a top, shown shaded.*
(a) The precession is due to the weight W of the top. This produces a downward free W at the centre of gravity. An equal and opposite force W is applied at O to maintain this point fixed. The precession rate is proportional to the product Wh of these two forces and the distance h between their points of application.
(b) The precession is due to the forces applied by the magnetic field H to the magnet NS fixed on the axis of the top. Equal and opposite forces pH are applied to the poles of this magnet, p being the pole strength. The precession rate is proportional to the product pHh of these forces and the distance h between their points of application .pH is the moment μ of the magnet so that the situation is as in (a) with Wh replaced by μH except that the sense of precession is opposite. This is because the equal and opposite forces tend to produce rotations in opposite senses in the two cases.

measure of the tendency of the weight to rotate the axis of the top about a horizontal axis – a tendency which is rendered ineffective by the angular momentum of the top which directs it, so to speak, to produce precession.

Consider now the analogous precession which occurs if we have a weightless top but one which includes a magnet along its spin axis. If this top is set spinning about the fixed point O with angular momentum I about its axis, it will not precess because there is no force tending to tilt the axis. The situation becomes quite similar to the heavy top if a magnetic field of strength H is applied in the vertical direction. The magnet in the top tends to align itself with its north pole pointing in the field direction. The strength of this tendency is measured by the product $H\mu$

of H with the moment μ of the magnet (see Fig. 6.2(b)). Precession will occur about the direction of the field at a rate depending on the angular momentum I and the product $H\mu$. If this rate can be measured and H and I are known, μ may therefore be obtained.

A nucleus in general possesses a spin angular momentum I which, according to quantum mechanics is restricted to values $\sqrt{\{i(i+i)\}}\ h/2\pi$ where h is Planck's constant and $i = 0, \frac{1}{2}, 1, \frac{3}{2}, \ldots$. In general the allowed values will be known for a nucleus under investigation. Thus for protons $i = \frac{1}{2}$, for deuterons $i = 1$. Hence, if the frequency of precession of a nucleus in a known magnetic field can be measured, its magnetic moment may be obtained.

The principle used for measuring the precession frequency is illustrated in Fig. 6.3. When the precession is established a disturbing magnetic field is applied at right angles to the main field. If this magnetic field oscillates in magnitude and sign with a frequency ν it will have no important effect on the precession unless this frequency is close to that of the precession.

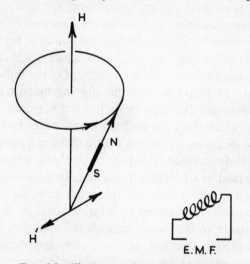

Fig. 6.3. *Illustrating the principle of the magnetic resonance method. H' is the oscillating magnetic field which disturbs the precession when its frequency is close to that of the precession.*

147

Once this condition is satisfied the effect becomes large and the angle of inclination of the top axis changes rapidly. It is only necessary to vary the frequency ν^* and to devise means of detecting the change when it occurs. This may be done by placing a coil so that, when the inclination of the top axis changes, there is a change in the magnetic field pervading the coil. By the familiar laws of Faraday, this will set up an electromotive force in the coil which may be detected by a suitable electrical system.

For absolute determination of a magnetic moment the main magnetic field H must be measured. This limits the accuracy as compared with relative measurement which depends only on comparison of precession frequencies for the same value of H.

The magnetic moment of the neutron cannot be determined by this technique as it is not possible to confine free neutrons in sufficient concentration within the apparatus. An alternative method has been devised and operated with success, but it is not possible to describe it in detail here. Fig. 6.4 illustrates the general principles, which depend on the fact that, if a beam of neutrons passes through magnetized iron, the neutron magnets tend to align themselves parallel to the direction of magnetization in the iron. The degree of alignment of a beam may be analysed by observing the ease with which the beam passes through a second sheet of iron magnetized in the same direction as the first. In Fig. 6.4, A is the aligning magnet and B the analysing magnet. Between these the beam passes through a region C in which there is a uniform magnetic field which causes the aligned neutrons to precess with a definite frequency. This frequency is determined as before by applying a perpendicular perturbing field of adjustable frequency. In this case the sudden effect which occurs when this frequency is equal to the precession frequency is manifest by a sudden change in the degree of transmission of the beam through the analysing magnet B.

It is surprising that the neutron, although electrically uncharged, nevertheless possesses a magnetic moment. This is equal to $- 0.68500 \pm 0.00003$ times that of the proton. The

---

* In practice it is often more convenient to keep ν fixed and vary the frequency of precession by varying H.

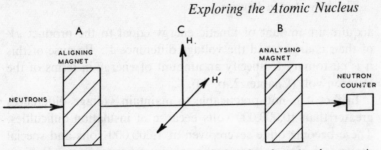

Fig. 6.4. Illustrating the principle of the method used to determine the magnetic moment of the neutron. H is a uniform magnetic field and H' an oscillating magnetic field of adjustable frequency.

moment of the latter particle is also anomalous. If it is regarded simply as a spinning charge with angular momentum quantum number $\frac{1}{2}$, the moment should be $eh/4\pi Mc$ where h is Planck's constant, c the velocity of light and e and M the charge and mass respectively of a proton. The measured value is 2.79276 ± 0.00006 times greater, an anomaly first observed as early as 1933 in some remarkable experiments by Frisch and Stern.

These unexpected results are now considered to arise from the same source in the two cases. This is concerned with the meson theory of nuclear forces which is discussed in Chapter 8, p. 210.

Accelerators

We now discuss the development of methods for speeding up charged particles to very high energies so they can be effective in producing nuclear reactions and even in the creation, from kinetic energy, of the rest masses of new particles. These developments have been, and are continuing to be, extraordinary in many ways. It is remarkable how new ideas have been introduced just when the limit for one method was reached. It is equally remarkable that equipment so expensive as the modern high energy machines is now being used for strictly fundamental research, there being no application in mind but simply a search for new knowledge about the basic laws of matter and energy.

The most obvious way of accelerating a beam of charged particles is to allow the beam to pass between two points across which a voltage difference is maintained. The particles then acquire an amount of kinetic energy equal to the product eV of their charge e and the voltage difference V. Because of this it is customary to specify an amount of energy in terms of the electron volt (Chapter 2, p. 43).

In fact it is not practicable to maintain voltage differences greater than 10,000,000 volts because of insulation difficulties. These become quite severe even at 1,000,000 volts and special designs of high voltage generator must be used to go higher. For the study of nuclear reactions it is necessary to have proton beams available with energies of at least this order, comparable with those of the alpha particles from naturally radioactive substances. When it is realised that, to produce a proton anti-proton pair (see Chapter 5 p. 136) an energy of at least 1,900 MeV must be available, it will be seen what a great gap exists between the energies obtainable by direct application of a steady high voltage and those necessary for the experimental study of anti-matter. And yet this gap has been bridged, since the war, by the introduction of ingenious indirect methods, the full scope of which is probably still not exploited.

The Cyclotron

The parent of all these indirect devices is the cyclotron or rather, in view of later developments, the fixed-frequency cyclotron. This was invented by E. O. Lawrence, the first one being brought into successful operation in 1934. The principle is as follows.

We have already seen (in Chapter 1, p. 29) that a particle of charge e and mass m projected in a magnetic field of strength H with a speed v in a direction perpendicular to the field, will describe a circle in a plane perpendicular to the field (see Chapter 1, Fig. 1.4). The time of a complete revolution in the circle is given by $2\pi mc/He$ where e is the charge and m the mass of the particle and c is the velocity of light. Provided the speed v is much less than c, the mass m, and hence the time of revolution, is independent of v. This opens the possibility of a synchronised accelerating procedure.

If a steady voltage difference V is maintained between the two halves of the circular path of a particle, no matter how large the radius may be, we have the situation illustrated in Fig. 6.5. While circulating within ABC the particles experience no electrical force but on passing from this region to the half DEF their energy increases by an amount eV. Continuing their journey within DEF they experience no further force until they pass across the gap to ABC once more. In doing so they lose exactly the same amount of energy eV as they gained in the last crossing of the gap in the opposite direction so there is no net gain in energy per revolution. Suppose now that the voltage V is made to oscillate with the period $T = 2\pi mc/He$ i.e. it reverses its sign every $T/2$ seconds. A particle which crosses the gap from CBA at a time when the sign of the voltage is such as to accelerate it, will arrive at the return gap $T/2$ seconds later, as before. In this interval, however, the voltage difference will have reversed so as to be in the correct sense to accelerate the particle again as it crosses the gap to CBA. By the time the particle is about to return across the gap to DEF the voltage will again be in the sense to accelerate it and so on. Thus, when the particle has made n revolutions it will have gained an energy $2neV$. We thus have the possibility of accelerating a particle indefinitely by application of an oscillating voltage V.

In practice, the particles are accelerated within an evacuated

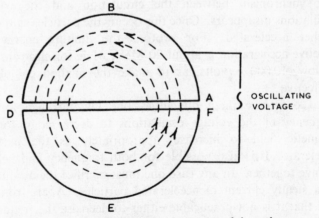

Fig. 6.5. Illustrating the principle of operation of the cyclotron. Typical paths of accelerated particles are indicated by the broken curves.

151

chamber which is placed between the poles of an electromagnet. The halves ABC, DEF are insulated metal discs, or dees, between which the oscillating voltage difference is maintained.

As the speed increases, the radius r of the circular path increases according to the relation $r = mvc/eH$ so the track of an accelerated particle is an unwinding spiral as shown in Fig. 6.5. The uniform magnetic field must cover the area of the outermost circle which represents the path of the most energetic particles. The maximum attainable value of the field strength H is limited so that for protons of 10 MeV energy the radius r is about 1 foot. This requires large pole faces, as well as a large mass of iron to provide the necessary field strength. The voltage V must perform a few tens of millions of oscillations per second between extreme values which are usually chosen to be a few tens of kilovolts.

The energy attainable by use of the cyclotron principle is limited by the relativistic increase of mass with velocity. Thus the mass m which appears in the formula $2\pi mc/He$ for the period of revolution is strictly the relativistic mass

$$m = m_0/\sqrt{(1 - v^2/c^2)}$$

where m_0 is the rest mass (Chapter 4, p. 130). Eventually, as v increases, the period begins to increase to such an extent that the synchronism between the circulation and the voltage oscillations disappears. Once this occurs the particles cannot be further accelerated. For protons the limiting energy for effective acceleration is about 20 MeV, while for electrons it is so low, 10,000 e. volts, as to make the method completely ineffective.

To overcome these difficulties one may arrange for the frequency of the voltage oscillations to decrease, or for the magnetic field to increase, appropriately as the particles accelerate. It is also possible for both frequency and field to change together. In any case one must sacrifice the attainment of a steady current of accelerated particles. Apart from the fact that it is not practicable either to decrease the frequency, or increase the magnetic field, indefinitely it is not possible to continue to feed in particles if either or both the frequency and the magnetic field are changing. Instead, both the magnetic field and the change of frequency must oscillate. The particles can then be fed in at appropriate moments in the cycle and ejected as soon as the variation of field and/or frequency begin to reverse to the wrong sense for further acceleration. This means that the current of accelerated particles appears as a pulse once in each oscillation of field or frequency variation. The higher energy is achieved at a sacrifice of current strength.

The practicability of these machines which operate with variable frequency and/or magnetic field is due to an inherent stability of the motion of the particles which so adjusts itself that particles continue to arrive, at the point where the oscillating voltage difference is applied, at the right moments to be further accelerated.

The Frequency-Modulated or Synchro-Cyclotron

In these accelerators a periodical variation is impressed on the frequency of the oscillating voltage. Charged particles are injected at the beginning of the decreasing phase of frequency. Conditions are so arranged that, when this phase is completed, the particles have reached the outermost orbit.

With these machines very much higher energies may be reached. The first to be put into operation was that at Berkeley, California, which accelerated protons up to 345 MeV energy. By introducing suitable modifications, this will be extended to 750 MeV. Meanwhile, the most energetic machines are those at Dubna in the U.S.S.R. (660 MeV) and at the C.E.R.N. (Centre Européénne pour la Recherche Nucléaire) at Geneva (600 MeV). Plate 6.1 illustrates the latter machine. The magnet pole-faces are 2.27 metres in diameter and the total mass of iron used is 2500 tons. The oscillating voltage is of magnitude 12 kilovolts and the frequency varies from 28.7 Mc/s* to 16.6 Mc/s in a period of 1/110 sec.

There are many other synchrocyclotrons in operation, including the 450 MeV machine at Liverpool and the 150 MeV

* We shall use henceforward the standard notation Mc/sec for megacycles (10^6 cycles)/sec.

machine at the Atomic Energy Research Establishment at Harwell.

The limitation to the energy attainable in these frequency modulated cyclotrons is a practical one imposed by the increase in the weight of iron used as the energy increases.

The Proton Synchrotron

The great weight of iron required in a high energy cyclotron is due to the fact that, throughout the acceleration, the radius of the orbit increases and the magnetic field must be uniform over the whole range covered. Great economy in the amount of iron required could be realised if, in some way, the acceleration could be achieved while the particles continued to revolve in an orbit of fixed radius. The magnetic field would only have to be maintained uniform over an annular region surrounding the circulating path. This principle is employed in the proton synchroton. Machines of this type provide protons with the highest energy yet attainable artificially.

If the particles are circulating with speed v approaching that c of light, in an orbit of fixed radius r, the frequency of the oscillating voltage which accelerates them has the constant value $c/2\pi r$ but the magnetic field H must be increasing as $1/\sqrt{(1-v^2/c^2)}$ to hold the radius fixed. If the speed v is considerably less than that of light, the frequency of revolution in the fixed orbit increases as the particle accelerates so that, in addition to the increase of magnetic field, the frequency of the oscillating voltage must also increase. This situation applies in the acceleration of heavy particles such as protons. Both the magnetic field and the voltage frequency are pulsed so that acceleration of the particles occurs during the phase when both are increasing. The necessary range of variation of the frequency is reduced by injecting particles of a considerable energy (10 MeV or higher) at the beginning of this phase. When this phase terminates it is necessary to expel the circulating particles so that they do not suffer deceleration during the decreasing phase. This is done by sudden distortion of the frequency so the orbit expands or contracts and the protons strike a target or some other ejection device at the periphery of the magnet ring.

The first proton synchrotron in operation was the cosmotron at Brookhaven providing protons of 3 GeV energy and a similar machine is now operating at Saclay in France. The largest machine of this kind at present in full operation is the bevatron at Berkeley, California, which provides 6.5 GeV protons. In this machine, a picture of which is illustrated in Plate 6.2, the radius of the annular magnet is 50 feet and it includes 10,000 tons of iron. 10 MeV protons are injected into the machine at the beginning of an accelerating cycle of 1.85 secs. duration during which the voltage frequency increases from 0.364 Mc/sec. to 2.460 Mc/sec. About 1,500 e.volts are added in each revolution so that, during the accelerating pulse, a proton travels about 300,000 miles. A similar machine is being constructed at the Rutherford Laboratory of the British National Institute for Research in Nuclear Science at Harwell, while a 10 GeV machine is coming into operation at Dubna in the U.S.S.R.

Even with the economy of iron achieved in the proton synchrotron the weight required in a machine such as the bevatron is already formidable and, to go much higher, some further new principle must be introduced. This is afforded by the idea of a strong focussing magnetic system. The mass of iron cannot be reduced below a certain level if the magnetic field encountered by the particles is to be uniform, because the uniform field must extend over a wide enough region on each side of the mean orbit to allow for fluctuations in the motion of the particles. It is possible to reduce these fluctuations, to make the orbit more rigid, by arranging for the magnetic field to vary across the radius of the orbit in an alternating fashion. That is to say, over one small section it increases outwards while in the next it increases inwards and so on round the whole circumference. This principle is being used in the great machine now coming into full operation at the C.E.R.N. Laboratories, Geneva.

The C.E.R.N. alternating gradient proton synchrotron is designed to produce protons of 25 GeV energy. 100 magnets arranged in a circle of 330 feet radius provide an alternating gradient magnetic field through which the particles circulate (see Plate 6.4). The arrangement of these magnets needs to be very accurately carried out and maintained – the radius of the

155

circle must not deviate by more than 1/400 of an inch from the designed value. This imposes extremely severe restrictions on the choice of foundations for the machine as well as such matters as the temperature variations over the magnet array etc. Much preliminary investigation had to be carried out on the chosen site before work could begin. The accuracy required was such as to extend to the limit available methods of surveying. Special designs of support for the magnet ring had to be developed to minimize effects of earth movement and temperature change. In addition, the magnets themselves must all conform very closely to the required properties and special methods of selection of the magnetic material had to be adopted to ensure sufficient uniformity.

The protons are injected into the machine after acceleration to 50 MeV by a linear accelerator (see p. 157 and Plate 6.5). At the moment of injection the mean magnetic field required for circulation on the chosen path is quite small and must increase to about 80 times this value during the accelerating phase of the machine. This lasts about 1 second during which time the frequency of the accelerating electric field must increase by a factor of 3.3 from 3 to 10 Mc/sec. The protons gain about 54 keV* energy per revolution and so make about 500,000 revolutions, travelling about 150,000 miles, during each accelerating phase. These phases are repeated 20 times a minute. Despite the high energy to be reached the total amount of iron required is only 3,200 tons, testifying to the effectiveness of the alternating gradient principle.

Plates 6.3 and 6.4 show some features of the C.E.R.N. machine in course of construction. A similar machine is being constructed at the Brookhaven National Laboratory in the U.S.A. while a somewhat smaller one, designed to give 7 GeV protons, is being built in the U.S.S.R., partly to serve as a model from which to gain experience before designing a 50 GeV machine of the same type.

Acceleration of Electrons

We have already noted that it is not possible to use the cyclotron

* 1 keV = 1,000 e. volts.

156

principle to accelerate electrons. The very reason which is responsible for this makes it easier to apply the synchrotron method to electrons than to protons – electrons circulating in an orbit of fixed radius with energies of 1 MeV or more have velocities so close to that of light that there is no need to vary the frequency of the oscillating voltage.

Many electron synchrotrons have been built and provide electrons with energies of 300 MeV or more. Thus the machine at the Massachusetts Institute of Technology, which accelerates electrons to 330 MeV, has a 50 ton magnet, the radius of the orbit is 40 inches and the frequency of the oscillating voltage is 46.5 Mc/sec.

The limitation in the energy which may be reached with these machines arises from the increasing rate of loss of energy by the circulating electrons, due to radiation. An accelerated charged particle radiates electromagnetic waves. Since the electrons pursuing circular paths in a synchrotron are continually changing their direction of motion they must lose energy in this way (see Chapter 1 p. 32). The rate of loss increases as the fourth power of the energy. At sufficiently high energies this loss will balance any gain from the applied voltage and no higher energy can be reached. This limits the attainable energy to about 1000 MeV.

An alternative, very successful, method of accelerating electrons, which does not suffer from this difficulty, is that of the linear accelerator.

The principle of this machine was well known before the war but it was not put to practical use to any extent because sufficiently high frequency electrical oscillators were not available. Fig. 6.6 shows how synchronized acceleration is achieved. Oscillating electrical fields are applied across the gaps between the coaxial hollow cylinders shown. Particles passing along the axis are screened from any electrical effect while within the cylinders but are either accelerated or retarded as they travel across the gaps between them.

Those particles which arrive at a gap when the oscillating field is at its maximum value in the accelerating sense receive an extra energy eV. It is possible to choose the lengths of the

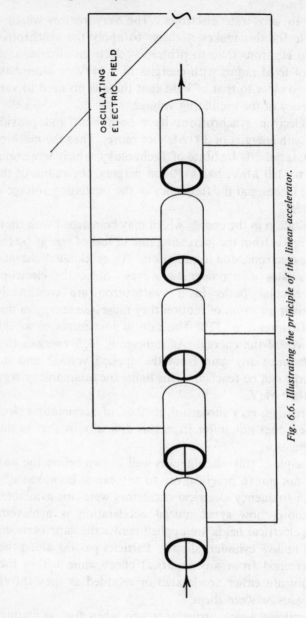

Fig. 6.6. Illustrating the principle of the linear accelerator.

OSCILLATING ELECTRIC FIELD

cylinders so that particles accelerated to this extent at each gap spend the same time T within each cylinder. Synchronism is then achieved if the electric fields across the gaps oscillate in phase with the same period T (or a period nT where n is a whole number). Once again the small rest mass of electrons is an advantage because they are soon travelling at a speed close to that of light after which the hollow cylinders can all be of the same length. The higher the available frequency of oscillation of the electrical field the shorter this length can be.

Many successful linear accelerators for electrons are in operation. The most energetic at present is that at Stanford University in California, providing electrons with 650 MeV energy. This machine is 220 ft. long, the operating frequency being 2856 Mc/sec. Larger machines are being constructed in France and in the U.S.S.R., to give 2 GeV electrons, while authority is being sought by Stanford University to proceed with the construction of a truly vast accelerator, 2 miles long, for the energy range 15 to 25 GeV!

The linear accelerator principle may also be applied to protons. Thus, before injection in the CERN proton synchrotron, the protons are accelerated to 50 MeV in this way (see Plate 6.5). Other proton linear accelerators in the same energy range are in operation at Minnesota and at the Rutherford Laboratory, Harwell.

Detecting Fast Particles

The possibility of detecting fast charged particles depends on the fact that, in passing through matter, these particles collide with the atoms of the matter and many of these collisions lead to ionization, i.e. electrons are knocked off the atoms leaving residual positively charged ions. On the average a particle of energy E MeV produces about $3 \times 10^4 E$ ions before it is brought to rest. The production of such a large number of electric charges can be observed in many different ways, some of which we now describe.

We can distinguish those methods which depend on the observation of an image of the track of the particle from those which essentially record the arrival of a particle. The latter devices are particle counters although in practice it is often possible, from a study of the signal in a counter, to obtain more information about the particle than the simple fact that it has passed into the counter.

Counters for Fast Particles – The Geiger-Muller Counter

The best known counter is one which was first introduced by Geiger over 47 years ago. It consists essentially of a wire which is placed along the axis of a thin-walled metal cylinder but is insulated from it. The cylinder is filled with a suitable gas at a pressure of about ⅕th of an atmosphere and the wire is charged to a positive voltage, with respect to the cylinder, not quite large enough to produce an electric discharge between them. If a fast particle enters the cylinder the ions and electrons which it produces in the gas cause an electrical breakdown so that a discharge does take place. The pulse of current which occurs can be amplified and recorded. Soon after the particle has passed through, or been brought to rest, the discharge stops and the counter is once more in a condition to record the passage of a further particle. By varying the nature and pressure of the gas and the dimensions and wall thickness, the sensitivity of a counter may be varied so that it responds to particular kinds of particles with a particular range of energies. In this way, to a limited extent, selective counting may be carried out.

The Scintillation Counter

Many of the classical experiments carried out by Rutherford made use of the fact that fast charged particles produce flashes of light when they impinge on screens coated with suitable materials such as zinc sulphide. In Rutherford's day the separate flashes or scintillations had to be counted by eye. This was an exhausting, frustrating and often subjective technique and for a long while the method was superseded by the Geiger-Muller counter and variants thereof. It has come into its own again in recent times because of the introduction of automatic methods of counting the flashes and even of recording their individual intensities.

All this has become possible because of the development of the photo-multiplier, an extremely sensitive device for the detection of light quanta. Fig. 6.7 illustrates the principle employed. Light quanta impinging on the first plate A produce electrons from it by the photo-electric effect. These electrons are accelerated by about 100 volts to fall on a second electrode B with sufficient energy to produce further electrons from it. These in turn are accelerated to the next plate C producing still further electrons and so on. In this way a very few incident quanta can lead to the production of a large number of electrons from the final plate Z. The current pulse can be further amplified by electronic techniques so as to be finally recorded on a suitable screen, or simply in a mechanical counter.

A typical scintillation counter consists of a material known as a phosphor which will emit light when the fast particles concerned pass into it. This light is piped into a photomultiplier the signal from which can be displayed to give the intensity of the pulse, if desired, as well as merely recording its occurrence.

Considerable flexibility is available with a scintillation counter, by choosing the nature and dimensions of the phosphorescent material (see Chapter 9, p. 232 for an extreme case). The intensity of the light pulse, or pulse height as it is called, also provides additional information which is often very valuable.

Scintillation counters can be used to detect not only fast protons and heavier nuclei, but also electrons and gamma rays. The crystal phosphor should be large enough to stop the fast particles being studied and this may pose quite difficult problems because it is necessary that, no matter how large, it must still be transparent towards the light emitted. The growth of perfect crystals of this size is a highly skilled technique. For proton counters plastic scintillators are usually employed.

Čerenkov Counters

Another counting method which depends on the observation of light emitted as fast particles pass through matter is the Čerenkov counter. The light observed arises in a quite different way from that which is utilised in a scintillation counter.

A body such as an aeroplane or bullet, moving at supersonic speed through air, produces a shock wave similar to the bow wave associated with a boat moving over a smooth sea. Plate 6.6

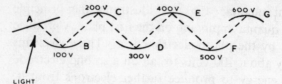

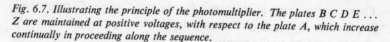

Fig. 6.7. Illustrating the principle of the photomultiplier. The plates B C D E ... Z are maintained at positive voltages, with respect to the plate A, which increase continually in proceeding along the sequence.

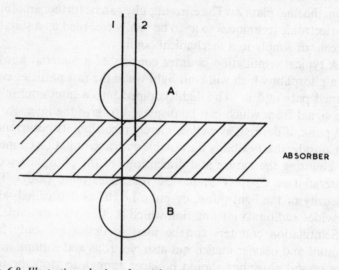

Fig. 6.8. Illustrating selection of particle records by coincidence counting. Particle 1 passes through and hence operates both counters but particle 2 is stopped in the absorbing material between A and B so it only activates counter A.

162

shows the shock wave, at the nose of a bullet, which is visible because, at the wave front, there is a sharp discontinuity of air density. The angle Θ the wave front makes with the direction of motion of the bullet is given by the relation

$$\sin \Theta = v/u,$$

where v is the speed of sound and u of the bullet through the air.

An electromagnetic shock wave, which includes visible light, is produced in an exactly analogous way by a charged particle moving through matter at a speed greater than that of light in the matter. The light can be observed by using photomultipliers and it is possible to determine the direction of the wave front and hence the ratio of the speed of the particle to the speed of light in the matter. This device can be used as a discriminator between particles of different speeds. It has already been used very effectively (see Chapter 8, p. 223) and it is likely to become of even greater importance in experimental work concerned with ultra-high energy particles.

Coincidence and Anti-Coincidence Counting Systems

It is possible to combine counters in many ways to obtain information about the nature and direction of motion of the particles being counted or to select for record only counts due to particles, in a mixed beam, which have particular properties. In the latter connection, signals due to wanted particles may be selected from an otherwise dominating background of signals due to stray particles of various kinds.

Thus, suppose a beam containing two kinds of particle is incident on a counter A (Fig. 6.8). This will be actuated by either kind of particle but we wish to record only the arrival of particles of one kind. One way in which this may be done is effective if the ranges (or path lengths before coming to rest) of the two kinds of particle in some material are different. A plate of this material, thick enough to stop one kind but not the other, is placed after A. Only one kind of particle will penetrate the plate and these will actuate a second counter B. If these particles are the wanted ones, we only record coincident operation of both A and B, if they are the unwanted ones we only record operation of A which is not coincident with B. In the latter case A and B are said to be operated in anti-coincidence.

Examples of the operation of counter systems are described below in connection with the verification of the existence of the anti-proton (Chapter 8, p. 223) and of the neutrino (Chapter 9, p. 231).

Track-observing Devices – The Wilson Cloud Chamber

This famous technique, invented and developed by C. T. R. Wilson, has been in operation for over 40 years and has been most fruitful.

At a particular temperature a vapour is in equilibrium with its own liquid at a definite vapour pressure. If the system is suddenly cooled, the equilibrium is disturbed and will only be restored at a lower vapour pressure – in other words condensation must occur. However, if the vapour is completely free of dust and no charged particles are present, this readjustment to a new equilibrium will not take place for a very long time unless the degree of supersaturation is high. If, for example, gas containing vapour in equilibrium is suddenly expanded, its temperature will be lowered so the original vapour pressure will be above the new equilibrium value. Droplets of condensed vapour will not form unless the expansion ratio is quite high, but if, while in the supersaturated condition, a fast charged particle passes through, the ions which it produces in the gas act as centres for condensation so that drops condense along the track of the particle. To use this in practice it is necessary to arrange for the gas to be illuminated at the moment of expansion and for a photograph to be taken to show up any tracks which appear as droplet trails. Typical tracks obtained in this way are illustrated in Plates 5.1, 6.8, 6.9, 8.2 and 8.5.

There is considerable flexibility in the design of Wilson chambers. The size may be varied within wide limits – as an example of a large chamber one may cite the one in use at the CERN laboratories at Geneva, which has an internal volume of about one cubic metre. Again, the nature of the main gas may be changed at will and it is possible to operate at gas pressures as high as 100 atmospheres. Plate 6.7 illustrates an automatically operated cloud chamber of this type constructed and operated by University College, London. It is also possible to introduce heavy metal plates into cloud chambers, thereby increasing greatly the chance of interesting reactions occurring within them.

Another very useful feature is that a trail of ions persists for an appreciable time after the fast particle has passed through. It is therefore possible to arrange for a coincidence counter system to record the passage of a particle through a chamber and then to trigger off the operation of the chamber. A counter-controlled chamber of this kind is economical in operation as it only functions when, as judged by the counter system, an event of interest has occurred within it.

Wilson chambers have played a vital part in the discovery of the positron (see Chapter 5, p. 129) of the mu-meson and of other strange particles (see Chapter 8, p. 212), among many other important investigations.

The Bubble Chamber

Although this instrument is a comparative newcomer, it is a very lusty child and is now regarded as one of the most important tools for research in ultra-high energy physics. We describe it next because in some ways it operates on the inverse principle to the cloud chamber. Instead of depending on the phenomenon of supersaturation it relies on superheating.

When subjected to a particular external pressure a liquid will boil at a definite temperature. The higher the pressure the higher is this temperature. Suppose now a liquid is maintained, under a pressure considerably greater than atmospheric, at a temperature which is below the boiling temperature for that pressure but is considerably greater than that for boiling at atmospheric pressure. Nevertheless, if the pressure is suddenly reduced to atmospheric the liquid will not boil immediately if dust and charged particles are absent. There will be a delay of several seconds before boiling occurs. During this period the system is sensitive to the passage of fast particles because vapour bubbles begin to form immediately around the ions produced in the liquid by the particles. These bubbles define the tracks of the particles which may be photographed in a similar way to cloud chamber tracks.

The usual way a bubble chamber is operated is in connection with an accelerator which releases regular pulses of high energy particles. At the instant of release into the chamber containing the hot liquid, the pressure is reduced so the liquid becomes sensitive and a photograph is taken. The liquid can then be brought back quickly to the high pressure condition ready for the next pulse. In this way an enormous number of tracks may be obtained very quickly (up to 10,000 a day, for example, with the bevatron in Berkeley, California).

One of the main advantages of the bubble chamber is the high density of the liquid, which increases the chance of particles interacting within it, together with the fast rate at which it can operate.

Perhaps the most remarkable development in this field has been the successful operation of large bubble chambers containing liquid hydrogen. The advantage of doing this is manifest, as the nuclei of hydrogen are themselves fundamental particles and their reactions with other particles are of basic importance. It is equally clear that the technical difficulties are very great. Liquid hydrogen boils at $-246°C$ and it is necessary to work between pressures of 1 and 7 atmospheres. Apart from the problems involved in operation at these very low temperatures, there is the risk of explosion due to leakage of oxygen into the system. Nevertheless, these difficulties have been overcome. At the Radiation Laboratory in Berkeley, California, a chamber containing liquid hydrogen is in operation which is of dimensions $72'' \times 20'' \times 15''$. It uses several gallons of liquid hydrogen per hour so it is necessary to couple a full scale hydrogen liquefier to the chamber to maintain this supply. A chamber of comparable dimensions is in operation in the U.S.S.R. and one is being constructed in Britain. The great size is required in order that very energetic particles will react within the chamber and further that some, at least, of the products, before leaving the chamber, will themselves react in some way which will assist in identifying them.

Naturally these large liquid hydrogen chambers are very

expensive and it is more usual to employ a liquid such as propane which operates at a temperature of 60°C and a pressure of 22 atmospheres. Attention is also being concentrated on the use of dense liquids such as the freons. These have the advantage that reactions involving the production of gamma rays can be studied. This is because the high density ensures that many of the rays produced within the liquid will, before escaping, materialise as electron-positron pairs which produce visible tracks.

The high rate of operation of a bubble chamber makes it necessary to develop methods of comparable speed for analysis of the photographs. Automatic means for doing this have been put into operation already at Berkeley and this combination is likely to prove one of the major tools of future research in very high energy physics.

Some typical bubble chamber photographs are illustrated in Plates 8.6, 8.7 and 8.9.

The Nuclear Photographic Emulsion

A fast particle passing through suitably sensitized photographic emulsions produces silver granules along its path, due to the action of the ions. By a suitable developing and fixing procedure, the track is photographed. Owing to the small thickness of the emulsion the tracks are short (only a few millimeters at most) and must be viewed by a suitable microscope. Plates 8.1, 8.3, 8.8 and 8.10 illustrate micrographs of tracks obtained in this way. They are not continuous but made up of a number of grains which may or may not overlap.

For the study of very fast particles which can penetrate several thicknesses of emulsion, stacks consisting of a pile of emulsions stripped from their glass backings may be used. As an example, in certain cosmic ray experiments, a stack of 250 sheets of emulsion each 0.6 mm. thick and of superficial dimensions 37×27 cm. was used. This weighed as much as 300 lbs.

Many very important discoveries have been made, and are being made, using photographic emulsions, particularly in the field of cosmic rays. One need only point to the discovery of the pi-meson (Chapter 8, p. 207) and certain of the *K*-mesons (Chapter 8, p. 212).

Identification of Fast Particles

The rest mass of a particle, which is perhaps its most important characteristic, can be determined if any two of the three quantities, energy, momentum and velocity, are known for the particle.

The energy can be obtained if the range of the particle is known. This requires that the track should end in the chamber or photographic emulsion (or stack of emulsions). If this does not occur and the speed of the particle is not close to that of light, information about the energy may be obtained from the concentration of ionization along the path. For a cloud chamber this is determined from the drop density, in a bubble chamber from the bubble density, and in a photographic emulsion from the grain density, along the track. For particles moving with velocities near that of light, ion density does not vary sufficiently with energy to be useful.

The momenta of particles producing cloud chamber tracks may be measured by enclosing the chamber within a large uniform magnetic field. This causes charged particles to pursue circular paths with radii inversely proportional to their momenta. For this to be accurate the curvature due to the field must be much greater than that due to the many chance scattering events which occur with atoms in the medium. The density of a photographic emulsion is so high that the scattering curvature can only be made negligible if an excessively large magnetic field is applied. One of the advantages of a liquid hydrogen bubble chamber is the fact that the magnetic field required for momentum measurements is not impracticably great and this applies even with a propane chamber.

When the density of the medium is too high for magnetic fields to be used, the curvature of tracks due to scattering may be measured and this gives a measure of the product of momentum and velocity which, however, is not of high accuracy.

The speed of a particle may be measured by using Čerenkov counters or simply by timing the flight of the particle between two points a measured distance apart. As it is possible, with modern electronic techniques, to measure times of order 10^{-10} seconds, this apparently fantastic procedure is actually quite practical. Both methods have been used very effectively in the discovery of the anti-proton (Chapter 8, p. 221).

So far we have been referring to charged particles. As uncharged particles produce no ionization, their tracks cannot be made visible and one must rely on interactions of the particles in the medium to produce charged and identifiable secondary particles, or on transformations into charged particles, as for example in the materialisation of gamma rays to produce electron-positron pairs.

It must be understood that we have not attempted to deal exhaustively with the important question of identification but have only aimed at giving some idea of the lines of attack. Examples will be discussed in the succeeding chapters.

Some Nuclear Reactions

Rutherford, in 1919, was the first to observe a nuclear transformation. The alpha particles emitted by radium C all possess the same energy and hence have the same range in air. Rutherford allowed these alpha particles to bombard nitrogen gas and observed the ranges of the issuing particles, using the original scintillation method of detection. He found that, in addition to particles of the normal range, there were also a few of much longer range. He suggested that these were energetic protons produced in collisions between alpha particles and nitrogen nuclei. In terms of the rearrangement of neutrons and protons involved we have

$$\text{Alpha particle} \begin{pmatrix} 2 \text{ protons} \\ 2 \text{ neutrons} \end{pmatrix} + \text{Nitrogen nucleus} \begin{pmatrix} 7 \text{ protons} \\ 7 \text{ neutrons} \end{pmatrix}$$

$$\rightarrow \text{Proton} + \text{Nucleus of oxygen isotope} \begin{pmatrix} 8 \text{ protons} \\ 9 \text{ neutrons} \end{pmatrix}.$$

Energy given out in this reaction, in which neither neutrons nor protons are destroyed but merely rearranged, is carried away in energy of motion of the proton. In modern notation the reaction is written

$$_2He^4 + _7N^{14} \rightarrow {}_1H^1 + {}_8O^{17}$$

in which the chemical symbol is used for the nucleus, the upper suffix gives the mass number and the lower the atomic number. The sums of each of these numbers must be the same on both sides of the reaction equations.

Plate 6.8 is a reproduction of a now classical cloud chamber photograph taken by Blackett, which illustrates one of these events.

Until 1932 no other missiles in the form of fast particles were available except the alpha-particles from natural radioactive materials. The culmination of all investigations of this type was the discovery of the neutron by Chadwick in 1932. He examined the products of the reaction between alpha particles and beryllium nuclei,

$$_2He^4 + _4Be^9 \rightarrow {}_6C^{12} + {}_0n^1.$$

in which $_0n^1$ is a neutron. Although a neutron is not directly detectable, Chadwick established its existence by allowing the reaction products to pass into hydrogen gas. Some of the neutrons collided with hydrogen nuclei, protons, to which they communicated considerable kinetic energy. These projected protons, being charged particles, could be detected and their energy measured. From this the mass of the neutral particles, which communicated the energy to them, could be determined.

Shortly afterwards, Cockcroft and Walton used a beam of protons, accelerated by direct application of an electrical potential of 250,000 volts, to bombard lithium and observed the reaction

$$_3Li^7 + _1H^1 \rightarrow 2_2He^4,$$

in which the alpha particles were produced with as much as 8.6 MeV energy. This first nuclear transformation produced by artificially accelerated nuclear missiles marked the beginning of what is now a very extensive series of investigations which have provided detailed and accurate information on nuclear binding energies, have produced many new isotopes of various elements,

170

and indeed new elements altogether. Many types of transformation, including nuclear fission which first made possible the controlled release of nuclear energy on a large scale, have been discovered. Extension of the work to higher incident energies led to the artificial production of new particles of various kinds, including the anti-proton and anti-neutron. We cannot hope to say much about this immense field of research but many examples will be described and discussed in the next three Chapters. Here we shall conclude by referring to a few reactions which were produced with comparatively low energy missiles and which are of special interest and importance.

The isotopes $_1H^3$ and $_2He^3$, of hydrogen and helium, each of mass 3, were discovered as products of the reaction between two deuterons (see Chapter 1 p. 42) namely

$$_1D^2 + {}_1D^2 \to {}_2He^3 + {}_0n^1, \tag{A}$$

or

$$\to {}_1H^3 + {}_1H^1. \tag{B}$$

Both isotopes may now be manufactured in nuclear reactors (see Chapter 7, p. 183), thereby making possible the detailed study of the reaction

$$_1H^3 + {}_1D^2 \to {}_2He^4 + {}_0n^1,$$

in which 17.6 MeV of energy is released.

Plate 6.9 illustrates a cloud chamber photograph of tracks of the proton ($_1H^1$) and triton ($_1H^3$) produced in a reaction of the type (B).

As explained on p. 141, even very slow neutrons are effective in producing nuclear transformations and the study of such reactions began shortly after the discovery of the neutron. A very useful reaction is that with boron

$$_5B^{10} + {}_0n^1 \to {}_3Li^7 + {}_2He^4. \tag{C}$$

This makes possible the production of slow neutron counters consisting of tubes filled with boron trifluoride. Neutrons produce ionization in the chamber through the reaction (C) and this may be detected by standard methods.

In other cases a slow neutron is absorbed by the struck nucleus, the surplus energy being released as gamma radiation. The behaviour of different nuclei in this respect varies very widely. Some, such as those of cadmium, are extremely effective absorbers of slow neutrons; others, such as deuterons or oxygen nuclei, have very little absorptive power. The behaviour of a given nucleus also depends very strongly and irregularly on the energy of the colliding neutron. Similar effects are found for collisions in which the incident particle is a proton or an alpha particle, but because of the long range repulsive forces between such particles and nuclei, the reactions are only observed when the energy of the particles is high enough. At sufficiently high energies, usually above a few MeV for target nuclei of medium mass number, the irregular behaviour disappears and the effects vary smoothly with energy for a given nucleus and, at a given energy, from nucleus to nucleus.

Artificial Radioactivity

In 1934 Curie and Joliot made a discovery of the greatest importance. They were studying the effects of bombardment of aluminium by alpha particles. Among the reaction products they identified not only protons and neutrons but also positrons. Furthermore, it was found that emission of positrons continued for some time after bombardment had ceased. Curie and Joliot correctly interpreted this as indicating that radioactive nuclei had been produced from aluminium by the bombardment, nuclei which decayed by emitting positrons in a similar way to those natural radioactive nuclei which emit beta-rays (or electrons). In fact the following reaction occurs on bombardment

$$_{13}Al^{27} + {_2}He^4 \rightarrow {_{15}}P^{30} + {_0}n^1,$$

producing an isotope of phosphorus which is radioactive (the stable isotope is $_{15}P^{32}$).

Radioactive isotopes of most stable nuclei may now be produced artificially by bombardment with suitable missiles. The isotope of hydrogen referred to on p. 171 is an example as it is beta-radioactive (Chapter 1, p. 30, Chapter 9, p. 226). Many applications may be made of these radioisotopes, some of which will be described in Chapter 7.

We shall conclude with these few examples of nuclear reactions. Further examples will be discussed in the next three Chapters.

CHAPTER 7

EXPLOITATION OF THE NUCLEUS

'I sought the fount of fire in hollow reed,
Hid privily, a measureless resource
For man, and mighty teacher of all arts'
AESCHYLUS, 'PROMETHEUS BOUND'
(TRANSLATED BY G. M. COOKSON)

It is our aim in this book to discuss developments of a purely scientific character with applications considered only incidentally. In this Chapter we shall depart from this aim to discuss the widespread applications which have been made, mainly in postwar years, of phenomena associated with the atomic nucleus. These provide a very striking example of the way in which research work, conducted for its own sake, leads unexpectedly to major and, indeed, revolutionary applications. Until 1940 nuclear physics was a very 'pure' branch of physics, of the greatest scientific interest but of no obvious or likely practical value. As late as 1937, Lord Rutherford, in an address to the British Association, said that the large scale release of nuclear energy for practical purposes might never be possible. It was most certainly not a goal towards which the famous Cavendish Laboratory directed its activities. Now we find a major industrial effort in the United Kingdom based on the development of nuclear power, nuclear-powered submarines voyaging under the polar ice-cap, the shadows of the conventional (sic!) atomic and hydrogen bombs falling across world activities and the more pleasing prospect of unlocking the enormous power potential provided by the heavy hydrogen in the world's oceans. In addition to these dominating aspects there is a host of ways in which industry, medicine and research are being assisted by the availability of radioactive materials in quantity and variety. It is often forgotten in this wealth of novelty that, in the course of these activities, the alchemist's problem of transmuting one metal into another has been solved. Plutonium, utilised in bulk for atomic weapons and of great potential value as a fuel in nuclear reactors, is a man-made metal. The possibility of making other metals is with us though it may not be economical to do so at this stage.

We shall discuss the more scientific aspect of these developments, including an account of the principles and problems involved in the controlled economic release of nuclear power.

Fission and Fusion as Sources of Nuclear Energy

In Fig. 6.1 the variation of the binding energy of a nucleus per nucleon is illustrated as a function of the mass number. As pointed out on p. 144 a maximum is reached at the nickel nucleus for which the binding energy is 8.8 MeV per nucleon. The presence of this maximum for nuclei of intermediate atomic and mass number means that there are, broadly speaking, two kinds of nuclear transformation which can lead to release of energy. One is by the break-up or fission of heavy nuclei into lighter fragments, the other by the building up of heavier nuclei from very light nuclei.

To see this we note that, for a heavy nucleus such as uranium, the binding energy per nucleon is about 7.5 MeV. If the uranium nucleus were to break up into two nearly equal fragments, each of mass number 119, the binding energy per nucleon in each would be 8.4 MeV. This means that the two fragments would contain 0.9 MeV *less* energy per nucleon than the parent uranium nucleus. As there are 238 nucleons involved the surplus energy which could be released in principle by the break-up would be about 200 MeV.

Turning now to very light nuclei, we note that the binding energy of the helium nucleus, or alpha particle, is 28 MeV, so that, if 2 protons and 2 neutrons could be fused to form an alpha particle, this amount of energy would be released. It is not necessary to proceed as far as this, for the combination of two deuterons to produce a triton and a proton (see Chapter 6, p. 171) already leads to release of 4.1 MeV energy.

The fission process is at present the sole source of nuclear power. Fusion is responsible for the heat of the stars, and adds the extra power to the hydrogen bomb. Modes of application to controlled power generation are being eagerly sought, but many years will probably pass before this is achieved. We turn first to discuss the way in which nuclear fission has been utilised in practice.

Nuclear Fission and Chain Reactions

Discovery of Nuclear Fission

Neutrons are unique among nuclear projectiles in that they possess no electric charge so that even very slow neutrons may produce nuclear transformations when they strike suitable target nuclei. As described in the preceding Chapter, the study of neutron-induced transmutations began quite soon after the discovery of the neutron. Until 1939, however, no definite evidence had been found of a fission process of the type we have discussed hypothetically above. In all transformations brought about by impact of neutrons, protons or light nuclei, a small fragment only of a target nucleus was struck off. It is true that Fermi and his collaborators, who were largely responsible for the initiation of the study of the interactions of slow neutrons with nuclei, had observed some peculiar features when the target nucleus was uranium. The elucidation of these peculiarities and the discovery of nuclear fission was left to Hahn and Strassmann who, in 1939, showed chemically that a nuclear fragment of intermediate size, that of barium (mass number 137, atomic number 56) was formed as a result of slow neutron bombardment of uranium. Further investigations confirmed and extended these results.

The fission process is analogous in many ways to the break-up of a drop, when disturbed, into two smaller droplets and it is amusing to note that Bohr and Wheeler, in developing their theory of the process, were able to refer back to the work of Rayleigh in 1879 on the oscillation of droplets under the influence of surface tension and gravity.

In a nucleus such as uranium, which possesses a high nuclear charge, there is a rather delicate balance between the disrupting forces due to the electric repulsions between the many protons, and the attractive nuclear forces. As the latter are of much shorter range than the former, any disturbance of the nucleus from a spherical form will tend to favour the repulsive forces.

175

This is because any such departure will tend to increase the mean distances between nucleons. If the disturbance is great enough, the nuclear attractions will lose control and the nucleus will break up, usually into two comparable fragments. In the fission processes we have been discussing, the disturbance is produced by capture of a slow neutron.

As natural uranium contains two isotopes of mass number 238 and 235, the heavier being 140 times as abundant as the lighter, it was important to determine which of the two isotopes was concerned. It was found that it is only the light, rare isotope which is fissile under impact of slow neutrons, though neutrons with energy greater than 1 MeV can also produce fission of the heavier isotope. No other naturally occurring nuclei were found to be fissile by slow neutrons, although thorium and proto-actinium are fissile by fast neutrons.

Possibility of a Chain Reaction

Although the discovery of fission excited much interest in scientific circles and there was an instinctive feeling that this was the threshold to vast new developments, there still remained no possibility of utilising the energy released in fission processes for practical purposes. The missing link was supplied a little later when Joliot, Halban and Kowarski established that, on the average, in the fission of the U 236* nucleus, which results when a slow neutron is captured by U235, more than one neutron is emitted. As each fission thereby provides the where-withal for the production of further fission, a chain reaction, leading to fission of a bulk of uranium by a single external neutron, became an early prospect.

It is natural to enquire why any uranium still exists as there are plenty of neutrons available from cosmic radiation (see Chapter 8 p. 202) or natural radioactivity, to initiate chain fission. Actually, it is quite impossible to produce such a chain reaction in natural uranium. Suppose that, on the average, fission of a U235 nucleus produces x neutrons which are capable of producing further fission. Between their production and

* We use the notation U236 to denote the isotope of uranium of mass number 236.

utilisation in this way, the neutrons will have a chance of under-going other reactions which destroy their effectiveness. If such reactions remove on the average more than $x-1$ neutrons from the roll of those effective in producing fission, a chain reaction cannot be set up. In natural uranium, one of the chief parasitic sources of neutron removal arises from absorption by the main constituents, the $U238$ nuclei. They are particularly effective in absorbing neutrons in an intermediate energy range (between 6 and 200 eV) but do not absorb slow neutrons appreciably. Neutrons emitted in $U235$ fission possess an average energy of 2 MeV. On the average they make 140 encounters with $U238$ nuclei before encountering a second $U235$ nucleus and are therefore absorbed before being able to produce fission. They are not energetic enough to cause any appreciable fission of $U238$.

The reactions which ensue on capture of a neutron by U238 are of great practical interest, apart from their parasitic character in a chain reaction. The $U239$ nucleus first formed, is beta radioactive and decays with a half-life of 23 minutes to produce neptunium (Np 239). This is also betaradioactive, with a half-life of 2.3 days, producing plutonium (Pu 239), a nucleus which has the important property of being fissile by slow neutrons. As compared with $U235$ it is at a slight disadvantage in that it is somewhat more prone merely to absorb slow neutrons without undergoing fission. This tendency is less apparent for higher energy neutrons.

One obvious way of producing conditions suitable for the propagation of a chain reaction is to separate the less abundant isotope from natural uranium. Pure $U235$ absorbs neutrons only to a very slight extent so that a chain reaction will be set up within a lump of the material, provided this exceeds a certain critical size, depending on its shape. Neutrons produced by a fission must not be able to leave the material before initiating a further fission. If the lump of material is small enough they will certainly do so, and this is the reason for the existence of a critical size.

The chief difficulty in the use of this method is the great cost of isotope separation. It must be remembered (see Chapter 1,

p. 42) that isotopes do not have different chemical properties so that other methods of separation must be used. Before the last war no large scale separation of any isotopes except those of hydrogen had been achieved. To separate those of uranium, to obtain in reasonable purity the rare isotope present to a concentration of only 0.7% and differing in mass from the abundant one by only 1.5%, is an enormous enterprise to carry out on a big scale. Nevertheless this was done during the war, in the course of the Manhattan Project in the United States, to produce atomic bombs in the shortest possible time. Even for bomb production this method is not necessary, as we shall see.

Although the separation of nearly pure $U235$ is very costly it is less expensive to produce uranium enriched to some degree in the lighter isotope. Such material can be of much use in power applications as will be seen below. The most effective method of isotope separation is to use the difference in the diffusion rate of uranium hexafluoride (UF_6) according as the uranium is the heavier or lighter isotope. Diffusion is allowed to occur from one side of a leaky barrier to the other between which a pressure difference is maintained. As the lighter molecules will move on the average a little faster than the heavier ones, the relative concentration of the former will be a little higher on the far side of the barrier. The maximum enrichment for a single diffusion stage is only 1.0043, so that it is necessary to pass the fluoride through a great number of stages in series to secure a useful enrichment. The vast size of a plant necessary to produce complete separation will now be apparent.

Chain Reaction with Natural Uranium

Fortunately, an alternative possibility exists for the initiation of a chain reaction in natural uranium. This depends on the fact that, whereas $U238$ nuclei very readily absorb neutrons in a narrow intermediate energy range, they are almost completely ineffective towards slow neutrons. The trick then is to ensure that, on the average, the neutrons emitted in a $U235$ fission, which have mean energies of 2 MeV, do not encounter a $U238$ nucleus until they have been slowed down to energies below a few e.volts. This can be done by distributing natural uranium in chunks of suitable size in a material, known as a moderator, which, while being effective in slowing down neutrons, does not absorb them appreciably.

The most effective moderator from the point of view of slowing down is a material rich in hydrogen, for the smaller the masses of the nuclei of the moderator, the more effectively they take up the energy from a neutron in an elastic impact. On the other hand, protons absorb neutrons with an appreciable probability to form deuterons. Because of this it is not possible to initiate a chain reaction in natural uranium with water as a moderator. If the uranium is enriched in $U235$, more loss of neutrons by absorption in the moderator is acceptable and then water may be used.

Next in order of effectiveness from the point of view of slowing down is deuterium and this is also the least absorbing of all substances. Heavy water is therefore a very good moderator, the only disadvantage being its expense. It can certainly be used with natural uranium.

The only other commonly occurring substance, which is effective, is carbon in the form of graphite. This is much less effective in slowing down than heavy water so that neutrons from a fission must pass through a much greater thickness of graphite than of heavy water before their energy is sufficiently reduced. As very little neutron absorption occurs, even in these thicknesses of graphite, it is possible to develop a chain reaction with natural uranium and a graphite moderator. Historically, the very first chain reaction ever initiated by man was produced by Fermi and his colleagues at Chicago on 2 December, 1942, using a pile of uranium rods embedded in graphite blocks. Although it is bulky, the graphite-moderated, natural uranium combination has many economic advantages for power production and has been adopted for the first full scale nuclear power stations in the United Kingdom.

Another substance which may come into large scale use as a moderator is beryllium. As the metallurgy of this element has not yet been developed, it is expensive at present but it has the advantage of greater effectiveness than graphite in slowing down neutrons.

Fission Reactors

General Remarks

We must now look a little further into what is required to make practical use of a fission chain reaction. Once such a reaction is initiated, it will provide heat because of the redistribution of the high kinetic energy of the fission fragments among the surrounding materials. If uncontrolled, the temperature will rise so high as to melt the solid materials and possibly produce an explosion, not as violent as that of an atomic bomb but destructive enough. To prevent this, control rods may be automatically inserted into the reacting system to maintain the rate of heat generation at a desired level. These rods are made of materials such as cadmium which absorb slow neutrons very easily. They extract neutrons from the fission chain so that the reaction simmers at the required level of temperature or is damped out altogether, as required. A system supplying heat through a nuclear fission chain reaction is known as a *nuclear reactor* or *pile*.

In addition to the control rods and moderator, it is also necessary to remove the heat generated. This involves the circulation throughout the reactor of a coolant which, while being effective in heat removal, is not a strong absorber of neutrons. If it is desired to use the heat to generate electrical power it is necessary, for high efficiency of conversion, to extract the heat at a high temperature, certainly above a few hundred °C. This means either the use of gases such as carbon dioxide or helium which do not react chemically with the hot materials of the pile, or water under high pressure or liquid metals such as sodium or bismuth. The latter have the advantage that they need not be operated under pressure – even the gaseous coolants require high pressures to operate above a few hundred °C.

The operation of a reactor provides, in addition to a source of heat energy, an intense concentration of neutrons, and a wide variety of fission products. The initial fragments produced in a fission process are highly radioactive as may readily be seen from the following considerations. As the mass number increases, the proportion of neutrons relative to protons in a stable nucleus increases. Hence the fission fragments will have a much greater proportion of neutrons than is required for stability. To readjust, a number of neutrons must be transformed to protons and this takes place by successive processes of beta-decay (see Chapter 9, p. 226). As the reactor operates it therefore accumulates an increasing amount of intensely radioactive ash. The disposal or utilisation of this material is an important problem which must be solved in large scale application of fission reactors.

Because of the intense production of neutrons, as well as of gamma and other nuclear radiations, it is necessary to enclose a reactor in a thick shield of concrete and other materials so that the intensity outside the reactor is reduced to a level harmless for living beings. This biological shield may in turn be enclosed with an outer pressure shell so as to maintain the high pressure under which the reactor operates.

Many other difficult technical problems arise in the design of reactors. The effect of the intense bombardment of the materials in the structure on their mechanical properties is often serious and has to be investigated by exposing substances to such radiation in reactors, known as Materials Testing Reactors, built specially for this purpose.

An example of one of the effects of bombardment is the Wigner effect in graphite. Fast neutrons on collision with the carbon atoms in the graphite may displace them from their normal position in the crystal lattice. They do not spring back immediately unless the graphite is at a temperature well above 100°C. The result is that the graphite in a reactor working at a low temperature gradually stores up energy due to the displaced carbon atoms, each of which is poised like a catapult to spring back to its normal position when the small amount of energy necessary for release becomes available. To prevent too great accumulation of energy, it is usual to anneal the graphite at regular intervals by warming to a temperature about 50°C above that at which it is bombarded, so that the displaced atoms spring back to their normal places. This is done, for example, with the

British plutonium-producing reactor at Windscale and it was in the course of annealing on 8th October 1958 that the accident occurred which led to combustion within the reactor.

Uses of Reactors

The most obvious application of reactors is to produce heat for electricity generation. In these cases the role of the reactor is the supply of high temperature heat, usually by production of steam under pressure. Conversion to electrical energy then follows by more or less conventional procedures.

The initial full scale reactors were constructed for a quite different purpose, the manufacture of an alternative material, plutonium, for atomic bombs. In a natural uranium reactor, the absorption of neutrons by $U238$ is brought down to a level which makes it possible for the chain reaction to build up. At this level, sufficient absorption nevertheless occurs to produce plutonium at a useful rate (see p. 177). As plutonium is fissile by slow neutrons, it may be used as an atomic explosive in a similar way to $U235$. The large reactors were built at Hanford during the war, as part of the Manhattan project, to produce plutonium for this purpose. As no attempt was made to utilise the heat generated, extraction could take place at low temperature. In a similar way the first large-scale reactors were built in the United Kingdom at Windscale, for the same purpose. They operate with air cooling at quite low temperatures.

The fact that plutonium is produced in a natural uranium reactor, or in fact in any reactor which contains $U238$, is of great importance, not only for the production of atomic explosives but also for power production. Plutonium may be burned as a nuclear fuel in a reactor as well as in a bomb. Thus a uranium reactor, as it operates, breeds new fuel which may be extracted at a suitable stage and used in a further reactor. With suitable neutron economy it might even be possible to replace every nucleus of the initial fuel by one of the new fuel. Thus, if sufficient neutrons are generated per fission of $U235$, not only to produce a further fission and make up for those neutrons lost in other ways, but also to produce a plutonium nucleus through absorption by $U238$, operation of the reactor will breed as much fuel as it uses up. Such a reactor is known as a *breeder reactor*.

It is possible to breed new reactor fuel not only from $U238$ but also from the relatively abundant element thorium (*Th* 232). Capture of a slow neutron by the thorinm nucleus converts it into a further isotope $U233$ of uranium which does not occur in Nature, and which is fissile by slow neutrons. We shall have more to say about breeder reactors on p. 186.

Apart from the supply of heat for electricity generation, the possibility arises of using the heat for propulsion of ships, aircraft, etc. Although again the prime function of the reactor is to supply heat at a high temperature, there are further limitations, particularly of size and safety, which do not arise with a reactor for large scale generation of electric power.

The production of radioactive material in bulk, though incidental to reactor operation, may be used in a variety of ways which we shall discuss in more detail below. In addition to the fission products, it is possible to manufacture specific radioactive materials by inserting a suitable inactive substance into a reactor – in other words the large scale manufacture of radioisotopes. As we shall see, radioisotopes are of special importance because, although they behave in an exactly similar way chemically to the corresponding normal materials, they can be detected in extremely minute quantities from the radiation they emit. The manufacture of radioisotopes is now an important industry.

Finally, the intense concentration of neutrons produced in a reactor may be used for research purposes, as for example in examining the structure of solids by neutron diffraction (Chapter 3, p. 68), or in investigating the properties of neutrons (Chapter 6, p. 171, Chapter 9 p. 226) etc.

Reactors may be designed primarily for any one of these uses, and this accounts for the wide variety which are already in operation. We shall now discuss the present state of development in the different directions.

Large Scale Primary Reactors for Electric Power Generation

The chief advantage of a nuclear reactor as a source of heat is the very low rate of fuel consumption. This is due to the fact that each fission releases nearly 200 MeV of energy, more than 20 million times greater than that released per atom in any chemical reaction. 1 pound of uranium can generate as much heat as 1,500 tons of coal. Whether or not it is possible to produce electric power competitively with other more conventional methods nevertheless depends strongly on local conditions. In the United Kingdom there is a grave shortage of power for industrial developments and the urgency for introduction of new sources of power is great. Political factors such as the increasing dependence on oil from the Middle East enhance this sense of urgency. It is not surprising that the most advanced development of large scale power reactors has taken place in Britain. Great attention is also being paid to this matter in Western Europe where the International Consortium known as Euratom has been set up. In both cases very large power requirements are involved. The problem is economically somewhat different in smaller, under-developed countries where a much lower capacity is required. In the United States, where there is abundant power from conventional sources, there has been much less emphasis on the development of power reactors, although the importance of export trade in this branch of manufacture is now stimulating much activity in that country also. The U.S.S.R. has a considerable nuclear power programme under development, both for internal use and for export.

The British programme is based on the use of the graphite-moderated, natural uranium reactor. This is a natural choice under the circumstances as it is the only combination which employs relatively cheap raw materials. Thus the only other alternative as a moderator of natural uranium is expensive heavy water, while ordinary water moderation is precluded unless the uranium is enriched by an expensive isotope separation process. To extract the heat carbon dioxide is used. As the working temperature is at least 300°C for the effective conversion of heat to electrical power, the gas is at a pressure of 7 atmospheres. This requires the construction of a huge pressure vessel to enclose the whole reactor, including the biological shield.

The first full scale plant of this kind to come into operation is at Calder Hall in Cumberland, generating 70 megawatts of electrical power. It employs two reactors each of which includes 130 tons of natural uranium embedded in an approximately cubical block of pure graphite of 27 ft. edge, weighing 1,200 tons. The uranium fuel elements are in the form of rods 1.15 inches in diameter, protected from chemical attack by enclosure within cans made of magnesium alloy. The biological shield is of concrete 7 feet thick and the whole is enclosed in a pressure vessel $37\frac{1}{2}$ feet in diameter and 70 feet long, made of steel 2 inches thick. Plate 7.1 reproduces a photograph of this plant.

The next generating stations to be built will be of higher capacity, the first three being rated at 300 megawatts and the fourth at about 500 megawatts. It is aimed to produce 5-6000 megawatts of electrical power by 1965, saving thereby the equivalent of 18 million tons of coal per year. By 1975 this may well be increased by a factor of 3 or more.

Quite different problems arise when the question of supplying smaller amounts of power, of the order 20-30 megawatts, in industrially under-developed areas is considered. The high capital cost of the Calder Hall type of reactor makes it economically unsuitable for these purposes. A smaller reactor employing heavy water as a moderator, with gas cooling, is a possibility which is being investigated.

Reactors for Marine Propulsion

The problem of utilising nuclear energy for ship propulsion is quite a difficult one, particularly if it is desired to work on an economic basis. Apart from anything else, one must take into account the need for safety, not only as regards the personnel on the ship, but also in the event of collision in a port or harbour. The biological shield is necessarily quite large and heavy so that attention should be restricted to large ships. This makes it possible to counterbalance the weight of the reactor with the great saving in weight of fuel. It is reasonable then to contemplate the use of nuclear-powered engines in large merchant vessels and liners. For naval vessels the strategic and tactical advantages are paramount. A particularly suitable case is that of a submarine. The virtual elimination of the need for refuelling means that a nuclear-powered submarine may travel vast distances underwater.

In the United States much attention has been concentrated on the design of nuclear-powered submarines. To reduce the reactor size to a minimum an enriched uranium, water-moderated and water-cooled reactor was first developed. The submarine 'Nautilus' was fitted with an engine powered by the heat generated from one of these reactors. It is now a matter of history how this remarkable vessel completed the first voyage under the north polar ice cap in August 1958. Other submarines of this type have since been built and many are on order. Projects are also under way for the provision of reactors to provide the power to propel an aircraft-carrier and a cruiser. A contract has also been let in the U.S.A. for the manufacture of a reactor for installation in a merchant ship.

It is natural that, in the Soviet Union, developments in this field have been directed particularly towards the propulsion of icebreakers and one powerful nuclear-propelled vessel of this kind is in operation.

The problems associated with the economic use of nuclear power for ship propulsion are also being studied actively in Great Britain with the particular possibility in mind of a nuclear-propelled tanker.

Fast Breeder Reactors

It is possible in principle to build reactors without moderators by using pure $U235$ as a fuel. They are known as fast reactors because the neutrons within them are not reduced to thermal energies before producing fission. The first experimental fast reactor to be put into successful operation was in November 1946 at Los Alamos using pure plutonium as fuel and liquid mercury as coolant.

As the large scale primary reactors will produce plutonium in the course of normal operation, the question of the most economical use of this new fuel becomes important. There are advantages in employing it in fast reactors, not only because unwanted absorption of slow neutrons is thereby reduced, but particularly because of the possibility of breeding further fuel from natural uranium or thorium.

Suppose that, on the average, in a fission s neutrons are emitted. If p is the chance that an emitted neutron will be absorbed without producing fission then, from the point of view of maintaining the fission chain, $s(1-p)$ neutrons are available from each fission. As one of these is necessary to maintain the chain reaction, the number available for breeding in, say a surrounding shell of $U238$ or $Th232$, is $s(1-p) - 1$ per fission. This we call the *breeding ratio*. If it is substantially greater than one the prospect opens of breeding more fuel than is used up. For thermal neutrons and plutonium $s = 2.88$ and $p = 0.33$ so that the breeding ratio is only 0.94. On the other hand, while s remains practically unchanged, p falls to 0.06 for fast neutrons giving a breeding ratio of 1.70 which allows a considerable margin for odd sources of neutron loss.

A prototype fast breeder reactor has been constructed at Dounreay in Scotland which consists of a core of highly enriched uranium (the breeding ratio for $U235$ and fast neutrons is about 1.23) enclosed within a shell of natural uranium (this may be replaced at a later stage by thorium from which to breed $U233$). Some plutonium will also be introduced in the core for test purposes. The core is quite small, consisting of a cylinder about 2 feet in diameter and 2 feet long from which over 60 megawatts of heat will be released. These small dimensions and high heat output are characteristic of all fast reactors. It is obvious that extraction of heat under such conditions presents great engineering difficulties. In the Dounreay reactor the coolant is a sodium-potassium alloy which remains liquid even at the shutdown temperature of the reactor. No surprise will be felt at the need to encase the whole assembly in a metal sphere capable of withstanding the high pressures which could build up in the unlikely event of any accident. A great many precautions are being taken to reduce the chance of accident to a very small value.

Other Experimental Reactors

A wide variety of reactor types have been, and are being, built

187

in order to study their relative advantages and disadvantages. The boiling water reactor uses enriched uranium fuel and water as a moderator. By allowing the water coolant to boil it avoids the need for operation under high pressure. One of the major technical difficulties of protecting the fuel rods is overcome in the so-called homogeneous type of reactor in which the fuel is dissolved in the moderator or coolant. One example, constructed in the U.S.A., consists of a solution of uranium sulphate in heavy water. This design raises so many new technical problems that it is still doubtful whether it will prove of practical value.

The amount of development research being carried out on reactor design is now very great and is likely to increase as the relative importance of nuclear power sources continues to grow.

Utilisation of Fission Products

Intensive research has been devoted to the discovery of practical applications for the by-products of nuclear reactors, the intensely radioactive fission products. The disposal of this ash, without causing danger to life through radioactive contamination, is very difficult and it is unlikely that it will ever be possible to find uses for it on such a scale as to render disposal unnecessary. Nevertheless, many ways have already been suggested for using the intense radiation which is available.

The radiations are of value in radio-therapy, for treatment of cancer, and there is the immediate possibility of using the fission products to supplement in bulk the supply of radium. It is not quite as simple as this but it does appear that one of the radio-active fission products, caesium 137, may be made effective and it is now being supplied to hospitals.

A very promising application is to the prevention of insect infestation of grain. Irradiation from the immensely strong sources which are now available can kill the insects in the grain or render them sterile at an early stage. Other possibilities occur in which insects which cause damage to fabrics may be killed without injuring the fabric in the process. A rather similar application is to the cold sterilization of food stuffs by irradiation. At present this cannot be done, except in a few cases, without adversely affecting the taste structure but it is not impossible that these difficulties can be overcome.

Plant breeders can make use of the fact that the rate and variety of mutations in plants can be increased considerably by exposure to intense radiation.

Another possibility, which may prove to be economically valuable, is that of initiating chemical reactions, of the type which lead to plastic production, for example, by means of radiation.

Other applications exist and are being continually sought after but we cannot devote further space to them here.

Radioisotopes in Medicine, Industry and Research

A radioisotope of an element is one which behaves in an exactly similar way chemically to an inactive isotope but it is 'tagged' by its radioactivity in the sense that it can be detected in extremely minute quantities by using radiation counters (Chapter 6, p. 160).

Exposure of an inactive element to intense bombardment by the neutrons in a reactor will normally convert it into a radioactive isotope by neutron capture. We thus have the means of producing radioisotopes of most elements, thereby opening the way to a vast amount of important applications.

In medicine, radioisotopes may be used for diagnosis. Thus it is possible to check whether a particular substance is passing normally through the body by introducing a small amount of the radioisotope, either by feeding or by injection, and tracing its course by means of counters. An example is the use of radioiodine for diagnosing disorders of the thyroid gland and so on. Limited use has also been found in the treatment of certain disorders.

The use of radioisotopes in industry is growing rapidly. Leaks in pipe lines may be traced by methods similar to those used in medical diagnosis. Other applications include the measurement of the rate of wear of bearings, the determination of the efficiency of industrial filters and so on.

Perhaps the most important use of all is in research in chemistry and the biological sciences. It will be clear that, for the study of the physiology of living organisms, radioisotopes provide a new tool of unrivalled importance. One of the most important of all is carbon 14, which can be used for the investigation of photosynthesis, the way in which plants build up organic materials from water, carbon dioxide and sunlight. This isotope of carbon has also proved to be of great value to the archaeologists in the form of a new method of accurate dating of events which took place in the last 15,000 years. We shall choose this to describe as a detailed application, in a rather unexpected direction, of radioactivity and the precise and highly sensitive techniques now available to measure it.

Dating by Radiocarbon

The earth's atmosphere is under continual bombardment by cosmic rays. We shall discuss the nature of these rays in some detail in the next Chapter. Meanwhile all that it is necessary to know about them is that the primary rays are very energetic nuclei, mainly protons. Most of these interact with the nuclei of atmospheric atoms producing, among other secondary particles, about 2.4 neutrons per sec. per sq.cm. of the earth's surface, averaged over all geographical positions. These neutrons may be measured by balloon-borne counters but hardly any are present at sea level, showing that most must suffer absorption in the lower atmosphere. The only important absorption process is that which leads to the formation of the radioisotope of carbon, C^{14}, which emits beta rays and has a half life-time of 5568 years. It follows that 2.4 C^{14} atoms are produced per second per sq.cm. of the earth's surface. If this has been going on for a time greater than the half life-time of C^{14}, the concentration of the isotope over the earth's surface must have built up so that the rate at which it is produced by the cosmic rays is balanced by the rate at which it undergoes beta decay.

We now consider how the radiocarbon will be distributed, remembering that it is chemically similar to normal carbon. The first step will be the production of carbon dioxide in the atmosphere. This will be assimilated by living plants in the process of photosynthesis and in turn by animals through feeding on plants. The total mass of carbon in living material per sq.cm. of surface on the earth is about 0.9 gm. In addition, the atmospheric carbon dioxide will be continually exchanging with that in sea water which is present as dissolved carbonates or other carbon-containing compounds. This amounts on the average to about 7.25 gm. per sq cm. of surface. Assuming that there has been no change in the cosmic radiation or in the extent and composition of the oceans, over several half life-times of C^{14}, there should occur, in every gram of normal carbon which exchanges freely with atmospheric carbon dioxide, 2.4/8.2 beta decays due to C^{14} per second, or about 16.1 per minute. The observed rate for living matter at present is 15.3 per minute and shows no dependence on latitude and longitude. This is sufficiently close to the estimated value to give confidence in the correctness of the assumptions.

The dating of organic matter now follows by making the further reasonable assumption that, once an organism dies, the matter ceases to take up any further radiocarbon. Any residual beta activity must then be due to the C^{14} present at death. By measuring this activity, it becomes possible to determine how long an interval has elapsed since death. This is because the rate at which the radioactivity falls off follows a definite law which is known accurately once the half life is known, and is unaffected by the environment.

Special precautions have to be taken in measuring the very weak activities concerned. The specimen is carbonized and this carbon is smeared over the inner wall of a Geiger counter (Chapter 6, p. 160). The counting rate due to natural radioactivity and to secondary cosmic rays would be about 100 times faster than from the radiocarbon. The former effect is removed by enclosing the counter within an iron shield several inches thick. To eliminate counts due to cosmic rays, a ring of counters in close contact is placed around the central counter and the electrical system so arranged that, if one of the former is operated, no count is recorded on the central counter. The beta rays from the radiocarbon will not activate the counters in the ring as they cannot penetrate the walls of the central counter.

Before employing this technique extensively, it was necessary to apply further checks. A number of objects of known age were tested and quite good agreement found with the age determined from the radiocarbon. Thus to choose only a few examples: wood from the deck of the funerary ship from the tomb of King Sesostris III of Egypt was estimated as 3750 years old by egyptologists, while the radiocarbon age was 3621 ± 180 years; wood from the heart of a great redwood tree felled in 1874 could be dated from the growth rings as 2928 ± 51 years old, to be compared with the radiocarbon determination of 2710 ± 130 years, and so on. The inference from this last example, that the heartwood still contains the same carbon as that deposited there when the wood formed, is in itself very remarkable. One might have thought that, in the life of the tree, more mixing would have occurred in outer layers.

Much interesting chronological information has been obtained by this very effective method. Thus the charcoal from the Lascaux caves in the Dordogne district in France shows that the fires were lit about 15,500 years ago, before the last ice sheet had retreated from Europe. A sample of charcoal from Stonehenge in Wiltshire gives an age of 3800 years. Dung of a giant sloth from Gypsum Cave, Las Vegas, Nevada must have been deposited 10,500 years ago, a date which does not differ much from that derived from the dung of another sloth from Mylodon Cave in Chile. A large log from the famous Zimbabwe site in Southern Rhodesia was found to be 1300 years old, and so on. In each instance the age is estimated to be correct within a few hundred years.

Energy from Nuclear Fusion

Survey of the Problem and the Possibilities

The excess power which a hydrogen bomb possesses over a 'conventional' atomic bomb is due to the initiation of fusion reactions. In the explosion of a conventional bomb a fast chain reaction is initiated in a pure fissile material such as $U235$, or plutonium. This, being uncontrolled, liberates an enormous amount of energy in a very short time so that the core attains a temperature of the order of millions of degrees, high enough to initiate fusion reactions in suitable surrounding material containing light nuclei. The energy released from these reactions is added to that generated by the fission chain. This is a very different situation from that we are now considering in which economical production of power in a controlled way from nuclear fusion is being considered.

The heat of the stars is provided by nuclear fusion reactions which go on in their interiors. We shall describe some of these reactions in Chapter 9, p. 243 but, as they are very different from the ones which might be utilised for large scale practical purposes on this earth, we shall not refer to them further at this stage.

The essential requirement for the generation of power by nuclear fusion on a large scale is the provision of a very high temperature within a sufficiently large bulk of reactor material, for a sufficiently long time. As the temperature required is of the order of a hundred million degrees, it is obvious that the problem is going to be a very difficult one.

The need for the high temperature arises because no nuclei can react with each other unless they possess sufficient energy of relative motion to overcome the electrical repulsion between them, which exists at distances of approach greater than 10^{-12} cm., or thereabouts. This has already been discussed in some detail in Chapter 6, p. 140. If one is concerned only with the study of nuclear reactions and not with their large scale generation, the required energy of relative motion can be obtained by using particle accelerators as described in Chapter 6, p. 149. In no case, however, could power be obtained economically in this way. Far more energy must be expended in accelerating the particle beams than can be obtained from the reactions they initiate. The only remaining possibility is to use energy of random motion, in other words, heat energy. This can only be effective if the mean energies of the particles are of the order of 1000 e.volts, which means a temperature of 100,000,000°C.

The reactions which require the lowest temperature for initiation are those between nuclei with the lowest charge, namely protons ($_1H^1$), deuterons ($_1D^2$) or tritons ($_1H^3$). As only hydrogen and deuterium exist in nature, we are restricted in the first instance to the reactions between two deuterons discussed in Chapter 6, p. 171 namely

$$_1D^2 + _1D^2 \rightarrow _1H^1 + _1H^3,$$
or
$$\rightarrow _1n^0 + _2He^3.$$

The first of these releases 4 MeV per reaction, the second 3.3 MeV. We must also allow for the triton produced in the first case to react with a third deuteron as follows: –

$$_1D^2 + _1H^3 \rightarrow _2He^4 + _1n^0,$$

releasing a further 17.6 MeV. It is to be noted that, in this way, we are considering the synthesis of an alpha particle from three deuterons, releasing 2 neutrons and 21.6 MeV.

To estimate the temperature which must be attained to utilise these reactions, we must first note that it will at any rate be so high that the deuterium gas will be in a very different state to that in which we normally find it. Not only will the molecules D_2 be broken up into single atoms but these atoms will be completely stripped of their electrons. This is already clear when we note that only 13.5 e.volts is required to remove an electron from a hydrogen or deuterium atom whereas the mean energy of relative motion in a collision will be of the order 1000 e.volts. The gas will thus be completely ionized, consisting of electrons and protons moving round freely with this high mean energy. This is known as a fully ionized *plasma* and it possesses many properties different from that of a normal gas. Many of these properties arise from the existence of the long range electrical forces between the ions and electrons, in contrast to the much shorter range interaction between neutral atoms. It is to be noted that, while the freely moving ions in a plasma possess opposite electric charges, the average electric charge in any region which includes a considerable number of ions and electrons will be zero. If it were not, very powerful electrical forces would arise to restore the neutrality.

A hot plasma will radiate energy due to the continual acceleration and retardation of the electrons and ions under their mutual interaction. The temperature must be high enough for the energy released per second by the nuclear reactions to exceed that radiated. For economic operation it must exceed it substantially to allow for the efficiency of conversion of nuclear into electrical energy. When these considerations are worked out in detail, it is found that the temperature must be greater than 2×10^8°C for the deuteron-deuteron reaction to be effective.

The Pinch Effect

We must now turn to further practical considerations. A way must be found to heat up the deuterium to these enormous temperatures. But, even supposing this to be solved, how is the hot plasma to be confined? No solid materials can withstand temperatures greater than a few thousand degrees. Furthermore, there will be a loss of heat by conduction if contact is made between the hot plasma and any containing walls.

One way of producing and heating a plasma is to pass a high current electric discharge through the gas (Chapter 1, p. 27). It is necessary to work under conditions of reduced pressure so that the electrons and ions may be able to move through sufficient distances between collisions to pick up a large amount of energy from the applied electric field. To avoid the difficulty of the walls attaining a high temperature it is desirable to operate a pulsed discharge, i.e. the discharge runs for a certain time then ceases and begins again after a suitable interval, periodically.

To initiate a pulsed discharge, one may use the transformer principle in which the gas through which the discharge passes is the secondary. The choice of shape for primary and secondary is important as we shall see when we come to consider the question of confinement.

An electric current produces a magnetic field which in turn acts on the moving charges which constitute the current. Thus, suppose a discharge current consisting of ions and electrons in a plasma is moving within the cylinder shown in Fig. 7.1. The direction of the magnetic field produced by the current is indicated, together with that of the force which this exerts on the electrons. Because of their relatively slow speeds, the ions are little affected directly by the magnetic field but they remain with the electrons because of the powerful electrical attractions between them. It will be seen that the force due to its own magnetic field tends to compress the current into a cylinder of smaller radius. Equilibrium will be attained when the pressure due

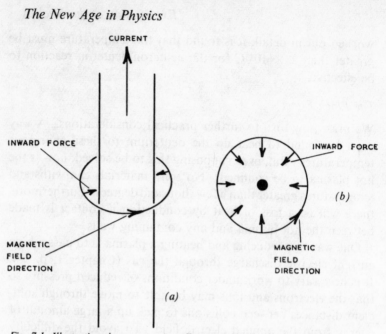

Fig. 7.1. *Illustrating the compressive effect of the self-magnetic field of a current flowing in a cylindrical plasma.*
(a) Elevation. (b) Plan through a horizontal section.

to the magnetic field balances that of the plasma particles. It may be easily shown that this requires that the current I in amperes is related to the temperature $T°$ absolute by the formula

$$I^2 = 5.5 \times 10^{-14}\ NT,$$

where N is the number of ions per unit length in the current column.

As the discharge current in a tube increases, a stage is reached when the current is pinched away from the walls by the magnetic pressure, thus meeting automatically the essential requirements of containment. The discharge and the high temperature are confined to the central region as illustrated in plate 7.2.

The use of a straight discharge tube is undesirable because one would still be faced with the problem of containment at the ends. One obvious way is to use an endless tube in the form of an anchor ring, doughnut or torus, as in the British research programme. Similar devices are also in operation in the U.S.A. and the Soviet Union.

Before describing the latest developments in this direction we must hasten to point out that, without further modifications, the pinch effect does not provide the answer to the containment problem. This is because the pinched discharge is unstable and soon begins to wriggle violently so that contact is made with the walls with consequent serious loss of heat, etc. The discharge illustrated in Plate 7.3 exemplifies this. One way of suppressing the instability is to apply a magnetic field along the axis of the torus. It is also desirable to construct the walls of the torus of some conducting material so that the eddy currents induced in it by the wriggling discharge help to damp out the wriggling.

Zeta and the Solar Corona

The largest British experimental equipment which uses the principles we have described is known as Zeta. In this machine the torus within which the discharge occurs is of aluminium, is of 3 metres mean diameter and cross sectional radius 1 metre. The gas in this torus is maintained at a low pressure, and pulsed currents up to 200,000 amperes, lasting for several thousandths of a second, may be passed through it. The pulses are initiated by discharging a bank of condensers through the primary coils wound round the torus. Axial magnetic field for stabilization is provided by winding subsidiary coils, through which current may be passed, around the torus. Plate 7.4 illustrates this machine with which ion temperatures as high as $5 \times 10^{6}°C$ have been obtained.

It is of interest to note that, apart from its importance for nuclear fusion, Zeta provides conditions very similar to those which occur in the outer mantle of the sun, the solar corona. This consists mainly of highly ionized hydrogen, at a temperature of $10^{6}°C$. A photograph of the solar corona is illustrated in Plate 7.5. The high value of the coronal temperature was only discovered in 1942 by Edlèn. He identified certain lines in the spectrum of the corona as arising from transitions between certain levels of an iron atom from which no less than 13 electrons had been stripped. It is possible to show from the relative intensities of these lines, and those involving iron atoms which have lost more or less electrons, that the emitting region

197

must have a temperature as high as $10^{6}°C$. Similar methods may be used to determine the temperature in the Zeta discharge, by introducing suitable impurity ions, but the conditions are considerably different in this case because the discharge is pulsed.

Another method for determining the ion temperature is to measure the widths of the spectrum lines emitted from the impurity ions. Because of their high mean speed the frequency range of the observed line will be broadened by the Doppler effect* which is determined by the ratio of the speed of the emitting ion, in the line of sight, to the speed of light (see Chapter 10, p. 269, Chapter 11, p. 290 and Chapter 12, p. 302).

Although Zeta works remarkably well, there is still a long way to go before controlled fusion reactions are a near prospect. Apart from the necessary increase of temperature by two orders of magnitude, the pulse duration must be increased by several hundred times to the order of 1 second.

Other Experiments

There are other methods of attacking the problem of attaining temperatures high enough to ignite a fusion fire, and of containing the fire within a small enough volume for long enough. Research is going on actively in many directions in the U.S.A., the Soviet Union and elsewhere. It is not possible here to discuss all of this work but one or two salient features can be mentioned.

So far, all methods of containment rely on the use of a magnetic field in some way. In the pinched discharge this is mainly the self-field generated by the discharge current, although external fields have to be supplied to reduce wriggling. Several experimental devices depend entirely on the use of external fields of some kind. In one of these developed at Princeton University, and known as the Stellarator, the discharge is produced in a tube which is in the form of a twisted figure of eight. Containment is achieved by applying a magnetic field of a special form, produced by passing current through coils wound on the tube.

---

* Let f be the observed frequency of waves emitted by a source which is at rest with respect to the observer. Then, if the source is moving with a speed v towards or away from the observer, the observed frequency is respectively $f(1+v/c)$ or $f(1-v/c)$. This is the Doppler effect so apparent in the pitch of a train whistl which falls as the train passes.

Others employ so-called magnetic mirrors. These are regions in which the magnetic field changes in such a way as to reflect back particles of the discharge plasma which penetrate to them.

Apart from the necessity for containment there is of course the very important question of how to heat the plasma to a sufficiently high temperature. In Zeta, for example, much of the heating arises in the same sort of way as in a hot wire electric radiator, due to resistance to the current flow. At temperatures above a few million degrees, however, the resistance of a plasma is so low that this method of heating is ineffective. One alternative is to use what is known as magnetic pumping. Thus, if the plasma passes into a region in which the containing magnetic field is greater it suffers compression and heats up in much the same sort of way as a gas at ordinary temperatures and pressures (see Chapter 3, p. 94). Even if the plasma does not move as a whole it may be compressed during the operating cycle by application of a magnetic field which increases at a suitable rate during the cycle.

A further possibility, which is being explored in both the U.S.A. and the Soviet Union, is to use artificially accelerated particles to feed in energy. In the Direct Current Experiment (DCX) at the Oak Ridge National Laboratory in the U.S.A. the accelerated particles are ions of the deuterium molecule D_2^+ accelerated to an energy of 600,000 e.volts These ions are injected into a region in which there is an intense magnetic field of the form shown in Fig. 7.2. They follow a circular path in the field so that, if otherwise uninfluenced, they would return to the point of injection. In fact, at the extremity of their path they pass through a carbon arc discharge. This breaks up the molecular ions into single deuterons D^+ and deuterium atoms. Because of their smaller masses the D^+ ions travel in circles of smaller radius than do the D_2^+ ions, as shown in Fig. 7.2. Again, if subject to no other influence, these ions would be trapped indefinitely to build up a ring of high speed deuterons from which a very hot plasma could be built up. The chief difficulty arises from the presence of residual gas in the apparatus. In collision with atoms of this gas the deuterons may lose their charge and hence would no longer be subject to the influence

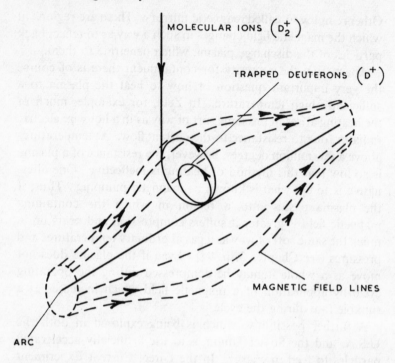

MOLECULAR IONS $\left(D_2^+\right)$

TRAPPED DEUTERONS $\left(D^+\right)$

MAGNETIC FIELD LINES

ARC

Fig. 7.2. Illustrating the principle of the direct current experiment (DCX) to obtain a very hot plasma.

of the magnetic field. If, however, the injected current of D^+ ions can be maintained for a long enough period, all the residual gas atoms will eventually have reacted with deuterons. Thereafter build-up of the ring current of deuterons and hence of the hot plasma should begin.

Although great ingenuity, as well as extensive resources in equipment and power, are being lavished on this most challenging problem, we are still uncertain as to how, if ever, the ultimate solution will be found. Enough has been done to show that further effort is well worthwhile. After all, success would mean the solution for all time of the problem of world power supply. It is quite certain that, in any case, we shall learn a very great deal of the behaviour of matter at very high temperatures, a field which seemed to be the exclusive province of astronomers.

CHAPTER 8

COSMIC RAYS AND THE STRANGE PARTICLES

'Yet all experience is an arch where through
Gleams that untravell'd world, whose margin fades
For ever and for ever when I move.'

LORD TENNYSON, 'ULYSSES'

Historical Introduction

The story of this chapter begins as far back as the beginning of the present century. At this time attention was drawn to the fact that the electric charges on bodies insulated from their surroundings steadily leak away at a rate much greater than would be expected from the small residual conductivity of any solid connections. This was attributed correctly to the presence of ionizing radiations in the air which cause it to have an appreciable conductivity. It was natural to consider the radio-active substances in the earth's crust as the source of the radiations but, in order to test the validity of this hypothesis, experiments were carried out in balloons to test whether the conductivity decreased with height. The first experiments, by Gockel, were indecisive but certainly did not show the expected decrease. Systematic observations carried out in 1910 by Hess proved conclusively that the conductivity actually increased with height. This ruled out the possibility of a terrestrial origin of the ionizing radiation so it was thenceforward referred to as cosmic radiation.

Really intensive study of cosmic rays began after the First World War and it has been one of the most fruitful in modern physics, leading to the discovery of the positron, the pi- and mu-mesons and the strange particles (as if the first three are not strange enough). The importance of cosmic rays in geophysical and cosmological research generally is also very great.

It was soon found that the cosmic rays are very penetrating and that they could be analysed broadly, at sea level, into two main components, referred to as the hard and the soft component. The latter can be stopped by about 4 inches of lead whereas nearly 20 times that thickness is required to stop the former.

The application of the Geiger counter and Wilson cloud chamber techniques to study cosmic rays marked a big step forward. It made possible the identification of the particles and electromagnetic radiations present at sea level, but still left the nature of the primary radiation unsettled. Very few of these rays reach sea level without transformation into secondary particles of some kind. However, in 1927-9, Clay made the first decisive observations in this direction. He found that the intensity of cosmic radiation at sea level decreased with geo-magnetic latitude, establishing that the charged particles were certainly included among the primary rays. It was not until 9 years later that Johnson showed, from further observations on the east-west variation of the intensity, that there is an excess of positively charged particles. The development of the nuclear emulsion technique (Chapter 6, p. 167), together with the possibility of recovering emulsions taken up to altitudes between 80,000 and 100,000 feet by balloons, has now shown that the primary particles are largely very energetic protons. A comparable, though smaller number, are bare helium nuclei, or alpha particles (see Chapter 1, p. 31), while there are present in much smaller proportion other heavier nuclei stripped completely of their usually attendant electrons. Because of their high electric charges these nuclei produce very dense ionization in passing through matter. Plate 8.1 illustrates micrographs of tracks of primary cosmic ray nuclei in emulsions, showing the very thick tracks from the heavy nuclei.

The primary particles have energies usually in excess of 500 MeV – one observed event could only have been caused by a particle possessing as much as 10^{13} MeV! During solar disturbances (see Chapter 10, p. 258) lower energy particles from the sun are sometimes added to the normal high energy radiation.

We shall not have occasion to refer further in this chapter to the primary cosmic rays. It is the remarkable variety of secondary particles which they produce which will hold our interest for some time now. Until quite recently, cosmic radiation was the only source of particles energetic enough to produce mesons and other strange particles, but very high energy accelerators capable of providing protons with energies of 10,000 MeV or more, have now become available. The beams issuing from these machines are more intense, are controllable and are more homogeneous in character. The use of cosmic rays for fundamental research in high energy physics is now restricted, after a glorious golden age, to the study of reactions occurring at extremely high energies, beyond the reach of any present designs of accelerator. As a tool for geophysical, solar and cosmological studies the importance of cosmic radiation is even greater than ever (see Chapter 12, p. 305).

Soft Showers and the Positron

The elucidation of the nature of the soft component of cosmic radiation came from a combination of Wilson cloud chamber studies with Dirac's theory of the positron (Chapter 5, p. 128). In 1932, Anderson discovered positrons, formed from the soft component, in a cloud chamber. Identification came from the density of ionisation along the tracks and the curvature produced by the magnetic field in which the chamber was bathed. Shortly afterwards, Blackett and Occhialini, using for the first time a counter-controlled chamber (Chapter 6, p. 165), independently discovered positrons (see Plate 5.1).

Among the photographs obtained in this systematic study of the soft component were a number which showed cascades or showers of particles identified as electrons and positrons. Plate 8.2 shows a typical example.

These remarkable effects can be traced to a sequence of events resulting from the formation, at some stage, of an energetic electron pair by materialisation of a very high frequency gamma ray. The fast particles of the pair, as they interact with matter, in turn initiate further gamma rays which again materialise to pairs and so on. Thus we get the sequence illustrated diagrammatically in Fig. 8.1, producing a shower of electrons and positrons. By adding up the energies of the final swarm of particles, a lower limit may be placed on that of the gamma ray which began the process. This can be very great indeed.

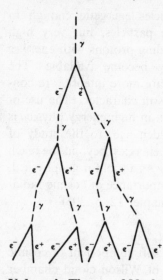

Fig. 8.1. Illustrating the development of a soft cosmic ray shower. The dotted lines are tracks of gamma rays (γ), the full lines of electrons (e^-) and positrons (e^+) formed in pairs.

Yukawa's Theory of Nuclear Forces, Mesons and the Hard Component

We now turn for a time to consider the nature of the hard component. The history of the events which led up to our present understanding of the nature of this component is quite remarkable but not untypical of the way in which scientific research progresses.

The problem of the nature of the forces which hold nucleons together in atomic nuclei is a fundamental one. We have indicated very briefly in Chapter 6, p. 139 how the empirical study of internucleonic forces is proceeding. A more basic approach was initiated in 1935 by Yukawa in a magnificent example of inductive reasoning. He noted that the force between two electric charges could be regarded as arising from the exchange, between the charges, of electromagnetic waves, or photons. In this picture, action at a distance, a very different concept, no longer occurs, the force being transmitted by the intermediary photons. It is true that no unaccelerated charge is able to radiate a photon but, as explained in Chapter 5, p. 130, no charge can ever be free from the action of the vacuum field fluctuations. Conservation of energy does not have to apply in the individual emission and absorption processes, which are not separately observable, but only as a whole. The uncertainty principle in energy (Chapter 2, p. 59) always permits a large enough energy fluctuation in a sufficiently short time for this so-called virtual emission or absorption to occur.

Yukawa now considered how the picture could be modified to take into account the chief features of nuclear forces – their great strength but short range. He showed that, if the intermediary photons, possessing zero rest mass, were replaced by particles having a suitable finite rest mass, then the apparent action between the exchanging particles would have a short range. This may be seen easily by an elementary argument based on the energy uncertainty principle.

To create a particle of rest mass μ the energy of a nucleon must fluctuate by an amount μc^2 where c is the velocity of light (see Chapter 4, p. 123). According to the uncertainty principle, (Chapter 2 p. 59) a fluctuation of this magnitude can only endure for a time T given by

$$\mu c^2 T \simeq h/2\pi$$

where h is Planck's constant. We thus have that $T \simeq h/2\pi\mu c^2$. The materialised particle cannot travel faster than light so, during the fluctuation, it will not move a distance much greater than $h/2\pi\mu c$. This means that, during the fluctuation, it has little chance of reaching another nucleon located at a greater distance. Interchange of particles of rest mass μ between two nucleons at rest is thus limited to separations of the nucleons not much greater than $h/2\pi\mu c$. No limit of this kind is imposed on electrical interactions as for photons $\mu = 0$.

Although the range of the forces between nucleons was not very well known at the time, Yukawa estimated that the intermediary particles should have a mass about 200 times that of the electron. Following the analogy with the electrical case, Yukawa suggested that, just as accelerated charges radiate photons (as for example electrons emit X-rays when impinging on a target), accelerated nucleons should radiate the corresponding intermediary particles. However, as the real radiation of one of these particles involves the creation of rest mass, it can only occur if the incident nucleons are sufficiently energetic.

Using Yukawa's estimate of this energy, it comes out to be over 100 MeV, far above that available at the time from particle accelerators but quite low for cosmic rays. A search was made for particles of this order of mass in the radiation at sea level and Anderson, followed shortly after by Street and Stevenson, did discover them in cloud chamber photographs produced by the hard component. Because their masses are intermediate between those of electrons and of protons, these particles are now called *mesons*, after the initial use of the term yukon and then mesotron.

There are one or two points which arise here. Photons are uncharged but Yukawa had suggested that this need not apply to the nuclear force intermediaries. In fact it was an advantage to suppose that positively and negatively charged, as well as neutral, varieties exist. The discovery of charged particles with the predicted mass occasioned no surprise but doubt began to grow about another feature. The particles were found in the hard component which interacts very weakly with matter and yet, to transmit the very strong forces between nucleons, their contact interaction with nucleons should also be very strong. How then could they form part of the hard component?

This mystery was not resolved until after the second world war. Meanwhile, however, another remarkable prediction by Yukawa also seemed to be verified. He suggested that mesons, if left alone, are not stable, but transform into electrons. His argument in this case is less convincing than that which led him to predict the existence of mesons. It was based on the occurrence of the phenomenon of beta radioactivity in which nuclei transform by emission of an electron (see Chapter 1, p. 31 and Chapter 9, p. 226). Yukawa proposed to regard this break-up as essentially a two stage process. A neutron, through an energy fluctuation of sufficient magnitude, transforms to a proton plus a negatively charged meson. There is a small but finite chance that, before the fluctuation is over and the neutron restored, the meson transforms to an electron. Provided energy can be conserved, the net result is a beta-decay in which a nuclear neutron changes to a proton and an electron. From the estimated strength of the contact interaction between a nucleon and a meson and the known order of the half lifetime for beta-decay, Yukawa estimated that the mean lifetime of a negative meson, before transforming to an electron, was about 10^{-8} seconds.

Remarkably enough, this suggestion cleared up an outstanding difficulty in the behaviour of the hard component which did not seem to be absorbed by matter according to the usual laws. The possibility of a further way in which the intensity would fall off, even in the absence of matter, was just what was required to clear up the discrepancy. Nevertheless, the mean lifetime of the hard component mesons, derived from absorption experiments, came out to be about 100 times longer than deduced by Yukawa from his beta-decay hypothesis.

Only one further advance was made before the second world war had put a stop to most pure scientific research. This was the observation by Williams and Pickup of the decay of a cosmic ray meson into an electron in a cloud chamber.

Resuming the story after the war, fresh and very convincing evidence was soon produced that the mesons in cosmic rays at sea level interacted very weakly with nuclei. The decisive step which resolved the difficulty was taken by Powell, Occhialini and Lattes. They exposed nuclear emulsions at high altitudes in the Bolivian Andes and, among the tracks they obtained, were several of the type shown in Plate 8.3. In these it will be seen that a fast primary particle (π^+) producing a thin track slows down, as indicated by the track thickening, but at a certain point the track ends and a new thin track begins. This suggests that the particle producing the first track, after slowing down, transforms into a lighter particle (μ^+), the residual rest mass energy being transformed to kinetic energy of the secondary. It will be seen in Plate 8.3 that the track of the secondary also thickens as this particle slows down in turn. Estimates showed that both particles had masses between 200 and 300 times that of the electron. The primary particle of the pair may be identified with Yukawa's meson while the secondary is the meson observed at sea level.

Complete confirmation of this picture is now available. Events have been observed in which two successive transformations occur, the secondary meson decaying to an electron (*e*) (see Plate 8.3).

It is worth noting how the true situation differs from that pictured by Yukawa although it was his suggestions which pointed the way. The sea level meson is an unsuspected particle, not the nuclear force intermediary. Nevertheless this intermediary does exist. Again, Yukawa's proposal about beta decay is not valid as his meson has only a very small chance of decaying into an electron. Yet the absorption anomaly of the hard component is due to decay of the constituent mesons to electrons! Progress in the fundamental aspects of physics, as indeed in all scientific research, proceeds by this jumble of brilliantly inspired but inaccurate guesses, apparent experimental confirmation and later realisation that even more complicated and unexpected phenomena have been unearthed.

One further discovery remained to complete our understanding of the sequence of transformations which result in the production of the hard and soft components from the primary radiation. This concerns Yukawa's neutral meson. It was shown theoretically by Oppenheimer and Lewis that this particle must, if left alone, transform within a very short time (less than 10^{-14} sec) to two gamma rays. Some evidence for this was forthcoming by observing electron pairs due to materialisation of the gamma rays produced from the decay of neutral mesons which had been emitted in encounters between incoming fast particles and nuclei in emulsions. Complete confirmation has been obtained by coincidence counting methods applied to neutral mesons produced by artificially accelerated particles (see p. 210).

The primary protons entering the atmosphere radiate Yukawa mesons, positive, negative and neutral, in collisions with atmospheric nuclei. The positive and some of the negative mesons decay into the weakly interacting variety before reaching sea level, so constituting the hard component. On the other hand the neutral Yukawa mesons transform very quickly into gamma rays which initiate the showers that constitute the soft components. This of course is somewhat of an oversimplification but it certainly presents the main features.

The Properties of Pi- and Mu-mesons

The mesons which are of the type predicted by Yukawa are known as pi-mesons or pions and denoted usually by the symbol π, π^+, π^- and π^0 referring to positively charged, negatively charged and neutral pions respectively. The weakly interacting mesons are called mu-mesons or muons, denoted by the symbols μ^+, μ^-.

A considerable amount of information about the properties of these mesons was obtained from photographic emulsion studies at mountain altitudes but the most precise data have been obtained in recent years since it has become possible to produce them artificially.

This was first achieved at Berkeley, California in 1948 by exposing a block of carbon to bombardment by a beam of 390 MeV alpha particles accelerated in the 184 inch synchrocyclotron (see Chapter 6, p. 153). Since then the experimental study of artificially produced mesons has become a new branch of physics.

The masses of the mesons have been measured accurately and are given in Table 1. It will be noted that the neutral meson is slightly less massive than its charged counterparts.

Considerable importance attaches to the determination of the intrinsic spins of the pi- and mu-mesons. It has been shown quite definitely that pions have no intrinsic spin. They are therefore bosons, like photons, as might perhaps be expected because of their similar roles as intermediaries between fermions (see Chapter 2, p. 64). Muons are found to be fermions possessing the same intrinsic spin, $\frac{1}{2}$ a quantum unit, as nucleons and electrons. As might be expected, pions have no appreciable magnetic moment (see p. 219) but muons have a moment of the expected magnitude for a fermion*.

The mean lifetime of the charged pions before decay into the corresponding muons is 2.5×10^{-8} sec. as shown in Table 1. It will be seen to be about 100 times smaller than for the decay of muons into electrons or positrons. There is much more to

---

* The expected magnetic moment is $e/2\mu c$ times the spin angular momentum, μ being the mass of the particle concerned (Chapter 3, p. 89).

be said about these decay processes but this will be kept until the next Chapter (see p. 228).

The experimental confirmation of the production of neutral pions in encounters between sufficiently energetic protons is a triumph of modern technique. It was carried out by observing the energies of gamma-rays, produced in coincidence, in directions determined by the dynamics of the nucleon-nucleon impact. The energies were measured by conversion of the gamma rays into electron-positron pairs whose momenta were measured separately by curvature in a magnetic field (Chapter 5, p. 129).

Pions and Nuclear Forces

Although the final discovery of pions confirms the general character of Yukawa's suggested origin of nuclear forces, we are still unable to follow the theoretical argument through in detail to derive the law of force. This is despite all the information which has been accumulated during the past few years from studies with artificial accelerators. The problem is rendered difficult by the great strength of the contact interactions between pions and nucleons. This is particularly hard to handle when it is remembered that it is never possible to work in terms of 'bare' particles (Chapter 5, p. 131) so that all problems are of a multi-body character. Enough progress has been made to show that Yukawa's ideas, taken with the observed properties of pions, provide a good description of the force between nucleons at distances apart greater than about 0.5×10^{-13} cm. At smaller distances the complications due to virtual formation of nucleon-antinucleon pairs (see Chapter 5, p. 136) become so severe that no quantitative theoretical treatment has yet proved possible.

The magnetic moment of the neutron can be traced to the fact that, for part of its time, a neutron is virtually dissociated into two charged particles, a proton and a negative pion. The magnetic moment arises from the orbital motion of the pion. In a similar way the anomalous magnetic moment of the proton (Chapter 6, p. 149) can be traced to the orbital motion of the positive pion when the proton is virtually dissociated into this particle and a neutron.

The Strange Particles

Discovery of the Strange Particles

Ignoring for the moment the unwanted and unsuspected muons, we have an effective scheme of fundamental particles. These can be divided into the building stones and the cements. The former are the fermions, the electrons, protons and neutrons. Photons are the intermediary bosons which cement electrons and protons together through electrical forces while pions are the corresponding cementing bosons for protons and neutrons. In addition to this family of 3 types of brick and 4 types of cement (photons and positive, negative and neutral pions) there are of course the anti-bricks (positrons, antiprotons and antineutrons). All of these are theoretically understandable.

The discovery of the muons is a definite complication. We can only think of them as bric-à-brac in the makeup of matter. It was soon found that they are by no means alone in this regard. We shall devote most of the next Chapter to the most remarkable piece in this collection, the neutrino, which can be thought of as the ghost in the material mansion. Here we shall describe the other so-called strange particles, known as the *K*-mesons and the hyperons.

The success of investigations at mountain altitudes in revealing the existence of pions stimulated much work in laboratories constructed and operated with some difficulty on mountains at heights 10,000 feet or more above sea level. In Western Europe such stations are snow covered throughout a large fraction of the year and, although attractive to the tourist, they are not quite so pleasant to work at in isolation for long periods at a time. For visitors they often offered a very pleasant prospect and cosmic ray physicists employed in high mountain stations were looked on with envy. Stations were operated on the Pic du Midi in France, the Jungfraujoch in Switzerland, and in Italy at Cervinia and Mt. Marmolada in the Dolomites. Plate 8.4 shows the location of the latter station – a comparatively low altitude one (7,000 feet). There were also a number of stations elsewhere, including particularly the U.S.A. Although the development of such high energy accelerators as the cosmotron and bevatron (Chapter 6, p. 155) has rendered much of this type of research obsolete, it did lead to the discovery of the remarkable family of strange particles whose detailed properties we may now study in controlled laboratory experiments.

Even before the recent war there had been some controversy about the masses of mesons and some investigators reported the observation of particles with masses as high as 800 times the electron mass. There was insufficient evidence to confirm these isolated examples and they were generally looked upon with scepticism. However, in 1949 Brown, Camerini, Fowler, Muirhead, Powell and Ritson discovered a track which came to rest in an emulsion and then produced three secondary tracks which were definitely identified as due to pions (see Plate 8.8). The particle producing the track must therefore have had a rest mass greater than 3 times that of a pion. This was the first example of a K-meson and later work has shown that the mass is 966 times that of an electron. Other varieties of decay of charged mesons of this mass have been observed in emulsions and are indicated in Table 1.

Meanwhile, cloud chamber studies of the hard component, by Rochester and Butler, revealed the existence of unstable neutral particles of more than one kind. These were first known as V-particles from the nature of their tracks, an example of which is shown in Plate 8.5 (see also Plates 8.6 and 8.7). The neutral primary produces no visible track but decays into two charged secondaries which make visible tracks branching from the point of decay. Study of the energies and momenta of the secondaries showed that in some cases one was a proton, the other a pion. This revealed the existence of a new type of unstable particle with mass greater than that of a proton. They are known as hyperons and the one discovered by Rochester and Butler is known as the lambda nought ($\Lambda°$) hyperon. It has a mass 2181 times that of an electron.

The other unstable particle observed to form V-tracks decays into two pi-mesons and is a neutral K-meson with the same mass as that observed for the charged counterpart in the emulsion experiments. It is noteworthy, however, that the latter particle decays into 3 pions (see Plate 8.8) whereas the

V-particle decays into 2. More will be said about this, which is actually a profound puzzle at the present time, in Chapter 9, p. 236.

Positively and negatively charged hyperons have also been observed. One is the so-called cascade particle or Ξ^- (xi minus) hyperon, which decays into a Λ° hyperon and a π^- meson, viz.

$$\Xi^- \to \Lambda^\circ + \pi^-. \tag{1}$$

This shows a characteristic appearance in a cloud chamber or bubble chamber. The track of the charged hyperon suddenly deviates at the point of decay, becoming that of the negative pion. Somewhat further on the Λ° hyperon produces its characteristic V track. By checking on the directions, planes and energies of motion of the particles forming the different tracks, it is possible to verify the existence of the reaction (1) and determine the mass of the primary hyperon (2577 times that of the electron).

A further pair of charged hyperons are known as the Σ (sigma) type. They differ from the Ξ^- hyperons in that they decay to nucleons and pions instead of to Λ° hyperons and pions.

Neutral counterparts of both the charged xi and sigma hyperons have also been identified. This is despite the fact that the Σ° particle lives for only about 10^{-20} secs. before decaying into a Λ° hyperon and a gamma ray. The ephemeral existence of the particle has been established from the detailed study of energy and momentum relations in certain observed nuclear reactions with very fast particles.

The Ξ° particle is the very latest addition to the family of observed particles. It was first identified as a product of reactions between K^- mesons and protons occurring in a liquid hydrogen bubble chamber (Chapter 6, p. 166) at Berkeley, California, towards the end of 1958. The reaction is

$$K^- + p \to \Xi^\circ + K^\circ.$$

The production of the K° meson was established through its decay into two oppositely charged π mesons, and that of the Ξ° from the decay

$$\Xi^\circ \to \Lambda^\circ + \pi^\circ,$$

following which the $\Lambda°$ hyperon produced its characteristic V-shaped decay track (see Plate 8.6).

The properties of the various strange particles, hyperons and K-mesons, are listed in Table 1. It will be noted that the hyperons are listed as fermions, the K-mesons as bosons. The fact that a $\Lambda°$ hyperon decays into a proton and a pion shows that it must be a fermion, for otherwise angular momentum would not be conserved in the transformation. Similar arguments may be introduced in the other cases except in those reactions in which a ? appears. This conceals the emission of a neutrino about which we shall have more to say in the next Chapter.

Production and Interaction of Strange Particles with Matter

The first observations of artificially produced hyperons were made using the secondary pi-meson beam from the cosmotron with a kinetic energy of only 1.1 GeV. This beam was passed through hydrogen gas in a cloud chamber and tracks were observed in a few photographs which could only have arisen from reactions of the type

$$\pi^- + p \rightarrow \Lambda° + K°. \tag{2}$$

The two neutral particles, the $\Lambda°$ hyperon and the $K°$ meson, decay a short distance from the point of reaction, producing the characteristic V-shaped tracks. In the reaction the rest mass of the $\Lambda°$ hyperon is not created entirely from kinetic energy but is built upon the already present mass of the proton. The minimum pion kinetic energy required is therefore much lower than it would otherwise be.

Many subsequent investigations have been made using bubble chambers (see Plate 8.7) in conjunction with the pion and proton beams from the cosmotron and bevatron and we now have a fairly definite idea of the laws which govern the various reactions. The salient features are as follows.

(a) In no case is a hyperon materialised entirely from kinetic energy. When it is produced it is built upon a nucleon already involved in the reaction.

(b) A hyperon is always produced in association with one or more K-mesons. Thus the reactions

$$\pi^- + p \rightarrow \Lambda^\circ + K^\circ, \tag{3}$$

$$p + p \rightarrow p + K^+ + \Lambda^\circ, \tag{4}$$

do occur but

$$\pi^- + p \rightarrow \Lambda^\circ + \pi^\circ,$$

$$n + p \rightarrow \Lambda^\circ + p,$$

are never observed.

(c) A positive K-meson is only produced in association with another K-meson or a hyperon.

(d) A negative K-meson is only produced in association with at least one positive K-meson.

Because of this the minimum kinetic energy which must be available to produce a K^--meson is considerably higher than for a K^+. Thus the minimum kinetic energy of a proton to produce a K^+ meson by the reaction (4) is 1.37 GeV. To produce a K^- meson the least energy required is 0.9 GeV greater, via the reaction

$$p + p \rightarrow p + p + K^- + K^+. \tag{5}$$

Baryon Number and Strangeness

Up to the present we have always assumed that, in any reaction, certain physical quantities are conserved. These are the net electric charge, the total energy (including the rest mass energy), the momentum and the angular momentum or spin. In no case are any of these conservation rules disobeyed in the reactions between fast particles and matter. The duration of a collision is of the order of 10^{-23} sec., as the distances involved are about 10^{-13} cm and the relative speed is of the order of that of light (3×10^{10} cms. per sec.). For there to be a reasonable chance of a reaction being observed in a collision, the reaction must be able to take place within a time of the same order. On the other hand the lifetimes of the pions, muons, K-mesons and hyperons, before spontaneous decay, are between 10^{-6} and 10^{-10} secs. The interactions which produce these decays must be enormously weaker than those responsible for the reactions which lead to strange particle production on interaction with matter. It is significant that for weak reactions, the decay processes, the fundamental conservation rules, with the exception of charge, do not seem to be obeyed. We shall take up this important matter in the next Chapter.

Meanwhile, we turn again to the strong interactions in relation to the further rules (a), (b), (c) and (d) outlined above. These suggested that there are additional conservation laws which must be obeyed in order that a fast reaction should be possible. It might be mentioned here that it was only after a very intensive study of the strange particles that these additional regularities have been discovered. They have recently been expressed in terms of the conservation of two additional quantities known as baryon number and strangeness.

The term *baryon* is applied to the nucleons and hyperons. As these are all fermions there will also be the corresponding antiparticles. The *baryon number* of a group of reactants is the number of baryons minus the number of antibaryons. It is conserved in all reactions. This embraces the observed rule (a) that the rest mass of a hyperon can never be created from kinetic energy alone but must be built upon that of an already existing baryon. The production of nucleon-antinucleon pairs (see Chapter 5, p. 136) by a process such as

$$\pi^- + p \rightarrow \pi^- + p + p + \bar{p},$$

where $\bar{p}$ is an antiproton, is also consistent with the rule since the baryon number of an antiproton is -1.

The rules such as (b), (c) and (d), concerning associated production of strange particles, can all be covered, as pointed out by Gell-Mann in an extension of earlier work by Pais, by assigning a further number to baryons, pions and K-mesons, known as the *strangeness* number – a very apt name as its origin is still very obscure. The total strangeness, the algebraic sum of the strangeness numbers of the individual reacting particles, must be conserved in any fast reaction.

In this scheme, the nucleons and the pions have zero strangeness number but the K-mesons and the hyperons all have strangeness number either ± 1 or -2. The actual assignments are given in Table 1 which summarizes the properties of the different particles. Associated production must now occur because the colliding particles will always have zero strangeness, so that the

Table 1

Properties of the Nucleons, Mesons and Strange Particles

Particle	Symbol	Charge (in units of the electron charge e)	Mass (in units of the electron mass)	Decay Products	Lifetime (sec.)	Spin quantum number	Strangeness quantum number
Proton	p	1	1836.6	Stable		$\frac{1}{2}$	0
Neutron	n	0	1839.0	$p + e^- + ?^*$	770	$\frac{1}{2}$	0
Muons	μ^+	1	207	$e^+ + ?^*$	2.2×10^{-6}	$\frac{1}{2}$	
	μ^-	-1	207	$e^- + ?^*$	2.2×10^{-6}	$\frac{1}{2}$	
Pions	π^+	1	273	$\mu^+ + ?^*$	2.5×10^{-8}	0	0
	π°	0	265	2γ	5×10^{-15}	0	0
	π^-	-1	273	$\mu^- + ?^*$	2.5×10^{-8}	0	0
K-mesons	K^+	1	966	$2\pi^+ + \pi^-$; $\pi^+ + 2\pi^\circ$; $\pi^+ + \pi^\circ$	10^{-8}	0	1
	K°	0	966	$\pi^+ + \pi^-$	5×10^{-10}	0	± 1
	K^-	-1	966	$2\pi^- + \pi^+$; $\pi^- + 2\pi^\circ$; $\pi^- + \pi^\circ$	1.7×10^{-10}	0	-1
Hyperons	Λ°	0	2181	$p + \pi^-$; $n + \pi^+$	3.7×10^{-10}	$\frac{1}{2}$	-1
	Σ^+	1	2327	$p + \pi^\circ$	0.3×10^{-10}	$\frac{1}{2}$	-1
	Σ°	0	2327	$\Lambda^\circ + \gamma$	10^{-20}	$\frac{1}{2}$	-1
	Σ^-	-1	2327	$n + \pi^-$	0.3×10^{-10}	$\frac{1}{2}$	-1
	Ξ^-	-1	2577	$\Lambda^\circ + \pi^-$		$\frac{1}{2}$	-2
	Ξ°	0		$\Lambda^\circ + \pi^\circ$		$\frac{1}{2}$	-2

* The ? actually denotes neutrinos and/or antineutrinos as discussed in Chapter 9.

production of some strange particle must be associated with that of another of equal and opposite strangeness.

No exceptions to the strangeness rule have been found and many examples are known where it severely limits the possibilities. It does not represent an absolutely strict law because in decay processes it is violated. Thus the decay of a K^+-meson into three π-mesons (see Plate 8.8) according to the reaction

$$K^+ \rightarrow \pi^+ + \pi^+ + \pi^-,$$

violates the rule. The total strangeness is initially $+ 1$ and finally 0. It seems that when there is a change of ± 1 in strangeness the process will occur in a time of order 10^{-8} to 10^{-10} secs. if there are no other restrictions. No reaction or decay in which there is a change of ± 2 or more in strangeness has ever been observed.

There seems now to be little doubt that the conservation of baryons and (for fast reactions) of strangeness are both of deep significance and a great deal of thought has been given to understanding what this significance really is. We are probably here on the threshold of some major new step forward, comparable with that involved in the introduction of relativity and of quantum theory. The situation about the weak interactions is also at an exciting stage but we defer consideration of this to the next Chapter.

Strange Atoms

The constituents of normal atoms may be replaced by charged mesons, strange particles or antiparticles to produce a whole new series of strange atoms. Despite the fact that these atoms can only be produced in very small numbers, the great power of particle-counting techniques makes it possible to study many of their properties.

First among them is *positronium* which can be thought of as a hydrogen atom in which the proton is replaced by a positron. The allowed energy values are, in magnitude, half those for the corresponding states of hydrogen. Of course, a positronium pair will eventually annihilate itself due to the electron dropping into the vacancy occupied by the positron (see Chapter 5, p.

130). It turns out that para-positronium, in which the electron and positron spins are opposed, has a mean lifetime of 1.2×10^{-10} sec. and annihilates with emission of two gamma rays, but ortho-positronium, in which the electron and positron spins are opposed, lives on the average over 1000 times longer and annihilates with emission of three gamma rays. By using double and triple coincidence scintillation counters for gamma rays, it is therefore possible to determine, under any particular conditions, whether a positron ends its life via ortho- or para-positronium production, or otherwise. Nevertheless, it is astonishing that the effect of field fluctuations and vacuum polarization on the lowest energy levels of positronium (Chapter 5, p. 133) has been measured with accuracy and agrees with expectation!

Mesic atoms are those in which an electron is replaced by a negative pion or muon. The allowed energy values for a mu-mesic hydrogen atom are 212 times as great in magnitude as the corresponding values for a normal hydrogen atom. Eventually the negative muon will either decay as usual or be absorbed by the proton to produce a neutron and a neutrino (see Chapter 9, p. 230). The former is much the more likely fate of the muon in mu-mesic hydrogen and indeed in mu-mesic atoms with nuclei lighter than that of carbon. In heavier mu-mesic atoms there are so many protons present that the muon is normally absorbed before it decays.

As a negative meson slows down in matter it is eventually captured into an energy level about one of the nuclei. This level will usually be an excited one so that the meson may drop to lower levels, emitting X-rays. The wavelengths of these characteristic X-rays have been measured and from these the separations between the energy levels of the mu-mesic atom can be deduced. It is found that these separations are close to what would be expected when allowance is made for the possession, by a muon, of a magnetic moment 212 times smaller than that of an electron (see footnote, p. 209). Similar observations have been carried out for pi-mesic atoms and have confirmed the expectation that in these cases there is no effect due to possession of any intrinsic magnetic moment by the pion.

An interesting effect associated with negative muons in a mixture of liquid hydrogen and deuterium has been observed. As they slow down these muons may be captured to form mu-mesic hydrogen atoms. These in turn may combine with deuterium atoms to form mu-mesic molecules μHD. In such a molecule the negatively charged meson spends much more of its time close to either nucleus than would an electron in a normal HD molecule. This reduces the repulsive electrical barrier between the proton and deuteron in the molecule so that the chance of the nuclear reaction

$$_1H^1 + _1D^2 \rightarrow _2He^3 + \gamma, \tag{6}$$

occurring is substantially increased. γ denotes a gamma ray. Plate 8.10 shows a bubble chamber photograph in liquid hydrogen, containing some deuterium, which exemplifies this sequence of events: namely, the slowing down of a meson followed at a little distance by the occurrence of the reaction (6).

There are many other possibilities, such as hydrogen atoms with protons replaced by positive muons, pions or K-mesons, protonium in which a proton and antiproton are combined, and so on. It is likely that, from a study of strange atoms, we shall learn more about the structure of ordinary matter – for example positrons are proving valuable as tools for studying the solid state.

Strange Nuclei

Just as we produce strange atoms by replacing electrons or protons by mesons, strange particles or antiparticles, we find also strange nuclei in which a nucleon is replaced by a hyperon.

The first example to be observed was a hypertriton. The track of a fragment, of charge e, from a nuclear disintegration in a nuclear emulsion was found to branch at the end of its range into two collinear tracks. These were identified as due to a He^3 nucleus (of charge $+ 2e$) and a π^- meson. The fragment must therefore have been a complex of charge $+ e$ containing three baryons. These could not have been nucleons as the energy of an H^3 nucleus is less than that of He^3. The most likely interpretation is that the complex differed from H^3

through the replacement of one neutron by a Λ° hyperon. Further evidence for this is provided by the fact that the energy released in the decay of the fragment is slightly greater than for the process

$$\Lambda^\circ \rightarrow \pi^- + p.$$

This would be expected because of the additional energy available due to the binding of the hyperon with the neutron and proton.

Since this first discovery, many other hypernuclei have been identified, including those corresponding to H^3, He^3, He^4, Li^7 and Be^8 (Plate 8.10). No stable hyperdeuteron exists but, on the other hand, the hypernuclei corresponding to H^4 and He^5 are stable, unlike their normal equivalents. This is not difficult to understand. H^4 composed of three neutrons and a proton is not stable because the Pauli Principle (Chapter 2, p. 64) prevents the third neutron from occupying the same energy level as the other two. Instead it is forced into the first excited level which has too high an energy for the system to be stable. If the third neutron is replaced by a Λ° hyperon the Pauli Principle no longer applies so and the hyperon is not forced into an excited state.

Discovery of the Antiproton

We conclude this Chapter by giving a brief description of the way in which the antiproton was discovered, as an illustration of the technique used in this type of identification. It must be remembered, however, that in a sense the problem was a special one, that of searching for particles with certain clearly defined properties, charge $-e$, rest mass equal to that of a proton, stable in the absence of matter but capable of releasing more than 900 MeV of energy in collision with a target nucleus. Furthermore, they can only be created as pairs together with normal protons so that the minimum kinetic energy required of a proton beam, in order to produce them on bombardment of a target, is at least 1800 MeV. The first machine capable of providing sufficient energy is the bevatron (Chapter 6, p. 155) and it was with this that the discovery was made.

Fig. 8.2 is a schematic diagram illustrating the arrangement employed. The beam of 6.2 GeV protons circulating in the

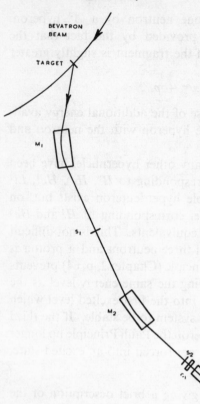

Fig. 8.2. Illustrating the arrangement of apparatus in the first experiments which verified the existence of the antiproton.

M_1 and M_2 are analysing and focussing magnets which ensure that only particles of a selected momentum pass through the scintillation counters S_1 and S_2 and Čerenkov counters C_1 and C_2.

The total length of path from the target T to the first scintillation counter S_3 was about 80 feet.

bevatron was caused to bombard a copper target thereby producing a variety of secondary particles. By means of a suitable set of analysing magnets, the negative particles among these secondaries which possessed a definite momentum were collimated to issue as a beam into the detecting and identifying equipment. This beam included antiprotons but only among about 40,000 times as many negative pions. Other negatively charged unstable particles would all have decayed before reaching the detecting equipment. To identify the antiprotons against the intense pion background use was made of the fact that, at the momentum chosen, the antiprotons were moving with a speed only about 0.78 times that c of light whereas that of the pions was as much as 0.99 c.

Two ways of using this difference in speed to advantage were employed. The first consisted in timing the particles across a stretch of 40 feet along the beam by noting the time delays between coincidences in two scintillation counters (S_1 and S_2 in Fig. 8.2) at each end. For pions the time taken was 4×10^{-8} sec. as compared with 5×10^{-8} sec. for antiprotons.

The second method of discrimination used Čerenkov counters (Chapter 6, p. 161) inserted in the beam. One, referred to as G in Fig. 8.2, was operated only by particles with speed greater than $0.79\ c$. and the other, C_2 in Fig. 8.2, by particles with speed between $0.75\ c$. and $0.79\ c$. If the particle recorded by the scintillation counters were indeed an antiproton, there should be operation of C_2 but not of C_1.

Observation of the large energy release characteristic of the interaction of antiprotons with matter was successfully carried out by allowing the negative beam to pass into a suitable scintillator and measuring the energy released, per particle incident, by a pulse height analysis technique (see Chapter 6, p. 161). Nuclear emulsion methods were also used.

The bulk of the equipment required for an experiment of this kind is very great – the analysing magnets weigh many tons. It is also necessary to maintain in operation a very great amount of electronic equipment so that the whole enterprise must be on a vast scale. It illustrates what is now required in research work using the very high energy beams produced artificially from accelerators. Discrimination between antiprotons and pions was difficult enough in these experiments. It becomes very much harder still when working at energies at which all particles are moving with speeds very close to that of light.

Antineutrons

The existence of antineutrons was established very shortly after the discovery of the antiproton. The method used depended on the fact that, in passing through matter, some antiprotons are converted to antineutrons by a charge transfer process

$$\bar{p} + p \rightarrow \bar{n} + n,$$

where $\bar{n}$ is an antineutron. To verify that this occurred, antiprotons, identified as described above, were allowed to pass through an absorbing material. Beyond this material were placed two detectors. The first (A) simply recorded the passage of charged particles while the second (B) was designed to detect the large energy released by annihilation of an antinucleon. In some instances when an antiproton entered, the absorber was not activated but nevertheless a large energy release occurred in B. This could only mean that the incident antiproton had been converted in the absorber to an antineutron which did not activate A but was annihilated in B.

Antihyperons

Although there is little doubt that antihyperons exist, no direct observational evidence has so far been forthcoming except for one event which seems to involve an anti-Λ° hyperon. This is an event in a nuclear emulsion, observed by Prowse and Baldo-Ceolin which seems to involve the decay process

$$\overline{\Lambda^\circ} \to \pi^+ + \overline{p}.$$

The antiproton was identified by its annihilation and the π^+ meson by its decay first into μ^+ and then into a positive electron.

CHAPTER 9

THE STRANGEST ONE OF ALL

> *'And right and left, and round about*
> *And up and down, and in and out,*
> *He turned; but still the pigtail stout*
> *Hung steadily behind him.'*
>
> W. M. THACKERAY, 'THE PIGTAIL'

The concepts as well as the facts which we have been discussing in the last few Chapters are indeed remarkable. Common sense is a wholly inadequate and misleading guide to the world of the antiparticles and the strange particles but the phenomena which we are now going to discuss, and particularly their interpretation, are even further beyond the experiences and ideas of everyday life. As always, however, it is the experimental facts which demand the extraordinary interpretation. We are not concerned with speculative philosophy.

In the previous Chapter we were dealing primarily with the strong interactions between particles which led, for example, to the production of the strange particles by impact of very energetic primary particles on matter. It was mentioned that the relatively long mean lifetimes (between 10^{-6} and 10^{-10} sec.) of the mesons and hyperons show that a very much weaker interaction must also exist. Such interactions have actually been known since the discovery of that form of radio-activity in which electrons are produced in the course of the nuclear break-up. We shall find that this beta radioactivity, which has been referred to several times in earlier Chapters (cf. pp. 31, 181, 190), involves some very mysterious features, some of which were only unearthed in the last couple of years. Meson decay into an electron is perhaps the simplest of all beta-radio-active processes but we shall see that all the decay phenomena are in this general category. We begin by a short account of some of the relevant aspects of beta radioactivity.

Beta radioactivity and the Neutrino

Beta radioactivity

A beta-radioactive process is one in which a nucleus of charge number Z and mass number A transforms, through emission of an electron, into one of charge number $Z + 1$ and mass number A. The earliest processes of this kind observed were associated with heavy nuclei such as radium, although it was known for a long time that the nuclei of a certain potassium isotope are beta radioactive.

The simplest example of this decay is that of the neutron which is thereby converted into a proton and electron*. The half life of a free neutron is about 770 seconds. Study of this process has been made possible through the availability of intense neutron sources from a reactor (see Chapter 7, p. 183). Fig. 9.1 illustrates the plan of the experiment which first observed the decay process and measured the half life. Once again the method relied strongly upon the use of coincidence counting. A small fraction f of the neutron stream passing out

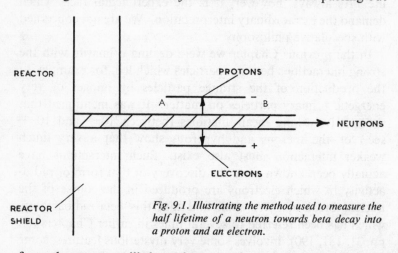

Fig. 9.1. Illustrating the method used to measure the half lifetime of a neutron towards beta decay into a proton and an electron.

from the reactor will decay between the points A and B in the diagram. This fraction is determined by the ratio between the half life time and the mean time taken for a neutron to pass

---

* The mass of a neutron is greater than the combined masses of a free proton and electron (Chapter 6 p. *144*).

between A and B. Hence if f can be measured and the mean speed of the neutrons is known the half lifetime may be deduced. Knowing the number of neutrons which pass per second between A and B, f is found by measuring the number of decays which occur in this distance. By means of an electric field applied across the stream, electrons and protons formed in these decays are swept out in opposite directions and can be speeded up to such energies as to make it possible to detect them in suitable counters. A neutron break-up is considered to occur when an electron and a proton count are recorded in coincidence.

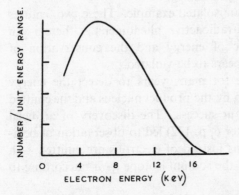

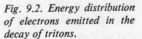

Fig. 9.2. *Energy distribution of electrons emitted in the decay of tritons.*

The next beta decay process in order of simplicity is that of the triton into a He^3 nucleus and an electron. We can use this reaction,

$$_1H^3 \rightarrow {}_2He^3 + e^-, \tag{1}$$

to illustrate many of the general peculiarities of the process. It is possible to measure without difficulty the energy of the electrons emitted in this decay. Fig. 9.2 illustrates the observed results, showing that the electron may have any energy up to 18 keV*. This is a remarkable result because the decaying nucleus is effectively at rest in all cases and it is certainly true that all have the same internal energy initially. It is equally true that the resulting He^3 nuclei all have the same energy. But if $M(H^3)$ is the mass of the triton, $M(He^3)$ of the He^3 nucleus

* 1 keV = 1,000 e.volts.

227

and m that of an electron, the kinetic energy with which the latter is emitted should be given simply by the difference*

$$[M(H^3) - M(He^3) - m]c^2$$

which is 18 kev. This is not what is observed. Some electrons are indeed emitted with this energy but many possess far less. Where has the energy gone to in these cases?

A further peculiar feature concerns the spin relations in the process. All three of the particles concerned have half-integral spins, they are all fermions. Yet it is not possible to conserve angular momentum if this is so. The resultant of two half-integral spins must always be integral.

This is by no means an isolated example. These two features are present in all beta-radioactive phenomena – there is an apparent disappearance of energy and the conservation of angular momentum appears to be violated.

Attempts were made for many years to detect the energy which was not taken up by the product nucleus and the emitted electrons, but all without success. The discovery of artificial radioactivity (see Chapter 6, p. 172) led to observation of beta-decay in which positrons instead of electrons are emitted. An example is the decay of the sodium isotope $_{11}Na^{22}$ according to the scheme

$$_{11}Na^{22} \rightarrow {_{10}Ne^{22}} + e^+.$$

It was found that the same apparent breakdown of the two conservation laws applied to these cases also.

It was natural to enquire whether, in beta-decay phenomena, the conservation of momentum also breaks down. This is difficult to investigate because of the small energy taken up by the product nucleus, most going to the much lighter electron. Nevertheless it has been established by some recent experiments that this further conservation rule does appear to fail.

Decay of Muons and of Pions

The decay of a negative muon into an electron, or of a positive muon into a positron, cannot occur in accordance with the

---

* This ignores the kinetic energy of the He^3 nucleus due to its recoil but this is so small as to be negligible in this argument.

conservation of momentum unless a further particle takes part. As the decay process is not influenced at all by the presence of matter the possibility that a nucleus in the matter takes up the momentum is excluded. The only other possibility is that a second particle is emitted. If one, and only one, such particle were indeed produced then it can easily be shown, from the requirements of the conservation of energy and momentum, that the electron resulting from decay of a muon at rest would have a definite energy, determined by the ratio of the rest mass of the hypothetical particle to that of the electron. In fact the electron emitted in this decay does not have a unique energy so that it would be necessary to suppose that at least two additional particles are emitted.

Similar arguments apply to pion decay into a muon (see Chapter 8, p. 209) but here the observations show quite definitely that the muon does have a unique energy. This would be the case if only one unobserved particle is produced in pion decay.

Pauli's Neutrino Hypothesis

The most direct way out of the difficulties we have described is to suppose, boldly, that in beta decay a second particle is emitted together with the electron (and in muon decay, two such particles). This particle must be assumed to have a very weak interaction indeed with matter as it is very difficult to observe. In order to restore the conservation of angular momentum the particle must be a fermion. From analysis of the observed energy distribution of electrons and of positrons emitted in beta decay, and from the value of the unique energy of the muon produced by decay of a pion at rest, it appears that the rest mass of the particle must be very close indeed to zero and for all intents and purposes can be taken as zero.

These particles were christened *neutrinos* or little neutrons. Pauli in 1932 suggested their existence as a way of resolving the beta-decay puzzle but the idea was not developed into a useful theoretical form until 1936, by Fermi. It was not until very recently that direct evidence of the existence of neutrinos has been forthcoming. The difficulty of carrying out suitable experiments is obvious when it is realised that, if neutrinos interact with matter only through processes of the beta-decay type, then they have very little chance of interacting at all in passing through a block of lead extending from the earth to the nearest star!

We now use the symbol v to describe a neutrino, so that we should rewrite a process such as (1) in the form

$$_1H^3 \rightarrow {}_1He^3 + e^- + v. \tag{2}$$

Similarly pion decay should be represented as

$$\pi^\pm \rightarrow \mu^\pm + v. \tag{3}$$

With muon decay the simplest representation would be

$$\mu^\pm \rightarrow e^\pm + v + v. \tag{4}$$

This is consistent with the observed result that the energy of the muon in (3) is unique but that of the electron or positron in (4) is not, both decays taking place from rest. Furthermore, if the neutrino is a fermion, an even number must be produced in a decay of the type (4) since both muons and electrons are fermions. As pions are bosons, (3) is only consistent with angular momentum conservation if an odd number of neutrinos is simultaneously produced.

The introduction of the neutrino also clarifies the difference between the effects produced when a negative pion and a negative muon are absorbed by a nucleus (see Chapter 8, p. 219). The rest mass energy of an absorbed pion is distributed among a number of nucleons, giving rise to the large stars in nuclear emulsions exposed to pion bombardment. Muon absorption will take place through some such reaction as

$$\mu^- + p \rightarrow n + v. \tag{5}$$

The neutrino, possessing no rest mass, will take away a large portion of the rest mass energy of the muon, leaving only a little to be distributed among the nucleons. As a result, only one or two nucleons are therefore emitted as a consequence of the absorption.

Detection of Neutrinos

Direct verification of the existence of neutrinos requires observation of the interaction with matter of free neutrinos in flight. Thus the reaction

$$v + p \rightarrow n + e^+ \tag{6}$$

can occur in which a neutrino is absorbed by a proton to produce a neutron and a positron. Estimation of the rate shows that a neutrino would have to pass through a thickness of 5×10^{15} miles of liquid hydrogen in order that it should have a reasonable chance of producing the reaction (6). This estimate is based on the known lifetimes of beta-radioactive nuclei.

Although this is not encouraging it is worth remembering that there must be a very great number of neutrinos emitted per second by a power reactor in operation. This is because of the powerful concentration within the pile of beta-radioactive fission products. In a volume of about 10 cubic feet of hydrogen-rich liquid exposed to a reacting pile, about one event of the type (6) will be produced every few minutes. This brings a definite experiment within the bounds of possibility and the method has been successfully exploited by Cowen, Reines, Harrison, Kruse and McGuire.

The rate at which the wanted events occur is so low that every precaution must be used to distinguish the sought-for events from unwanted background events.

The target used consisted of a tank of water containing a cadmium salt in solution. Products of the reaction were detected by allowing them to pass into large tanks of liquid scintillators in which they produced pulses of light emission. Wanted events are those in which a positron and a neutron are produced in coincidence. The positron was identified from the energy of the gamma radiation it produced when annihilated in a collision with an electron in the scintillator. The neutron, on the other hand, was captured by a cadmium nucleus in the target tank after a lapse of some tens of microseconds. Capture is accompanied by the emission of gamma rays of characteristic energy. A coincidence was only accepted if the total energies of the gamma rays involved, as well as the time delay between the signals, were within the correct limits.

Because of the low rate at which the sought-for events are

expected to occur it was necessary to eliminate spurious effects as effectively as possible. These could arise from cosmic rays or from reactor neutrons and gamma rays. The whole target and scintillation system was therefore enclosed in a thick paraffin shield to screen off the neutrons and in a lead shield to reduce the effects of cosmic and gamma radiation. In addition the whole apparatus was located underground.

The first observations were carried out at Hanford (see Chapter 7, p. 182) in 1953 and gave promising results. Conclusive data were obtained in a second more elaborate experiment in 1956. The detecting apparatus consisted of a sandwich of three scintillator and two target tanks arranged as shown in

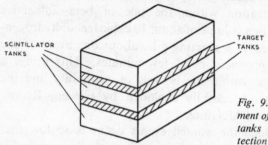

SCINTILLATOR TANKS

TARGET TANKS

Fig. 9.3. Sandwich arrangement of target and scintillator tanks in the neutrino detection experiment.

Fig. 9.3. Each scintillator tank was a chamber 2′ thick, 6′3″ long and 4′6″ wide while the target tanks were of the same length and width but 3″ thick.

Apart from the identification methods already outlined, it was verified that the rate at which apparent neutrino events occurred increased with the power level at which the reactor operated and that it was proportional to the number of protons in the target. Doubling of the cadmium content in the targets reduced the time delay between coincidences in the expected manner, without increasing the coincidence signal rate. Checks were made to provide further evidence that the apparent neutrino events were not due to neutron or gamma ray background. Thus it was shown that a large increase in the effective thickness of the shielding produced no change in the delayed coincidence counting rate.

In one set of observations the neutrino signal rate was 2.9

counts per hour while the background events were about one-third as frequent. The total running time of the whole experiment was 1371 hours. There seems little doubt at all that the neutrino hypothesis is to be taken as a practical reality. We shall see below that in fact the experiment detected antineutrinos, the particles emitted with electrons – neutrinos are emitted only with positrons. To understand this distinction and the great significance it now possesses, we must return again to some theoretical considerations. Before long, however, we shall regain contact with practical reality.

Right- and Left-Handedness in Nature – Are they Equivalent?

Right and Left-Handedness with Fundamental Particles

We now come to one of the most recent revelations of an un-expected feature of natural phenomena. It is concerned with the question as to whether there is any distinction between right- and left-handedness. Do physical phenomena follow the same course when viewed in a mirror which converts right into left or *vice versa?* One's immediate reaction is to say '*Of course*' but second thoughts would lead to more hesitation. After all there is not complete symmetry between + and − in our world. Matter is composed of positively charged protons and negatively charged electrons. We can conceive antimatter and even produce antiparticles artificially but the fact remains that our universe contains an overwhelming proportion of particles as against antiparticles, as we have defined them. Realisation of this lack of symmetry should cause us to keep an open mind about left- and right-handedness. During the last year or so it has been found that such caution is indeed justified. In weak interaction phenomena, there is discrimination between the two and our ideas about mirror images and their behaviour in relation to the phenomena reflected have undergone a drastic revision.

Before commencing the description of this quite fascinating situation it is desirable to place the concept of reflection on a slightly more formal basis. The usual method of specifying the position of a body in three-dimensional space is to set up from some chosen point O three mutually perpendicular directions

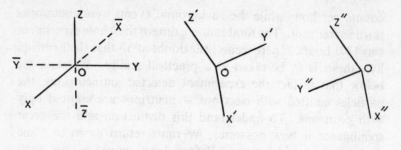

(a)   (b)   (c)

Fig. 9.4. Right- and left-handed systems of axes in three-dimensions. $OX'Y'Z'$
can be obtained from $OXYZ$ by rotation about O. $OX''Y''Z''$ cannot be obtained in
this way alone but involves reflection about O in addition. This reflection changes
$OXYZ$ to $O\bar{X}\bar{Y}\bar{Z}$ which may then be transformed to $OX''Y''Z''$ by a rotation about O.
$OX\,Y\,Z$ and $OX'\,Y'\,Z'$ are said to be right-handed and $O\bar{X}\,\bar{Y}\,\bar{Z}$, $OX''\,Y''\,Z''$
left-handed reference systems.

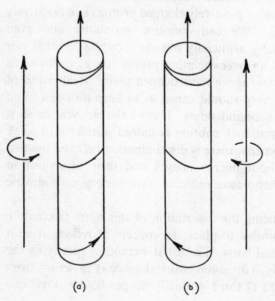

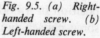

(a)   (b)

Fig. 9.5. (a) Right-
handed screw. (b)
Left-handed screw.

OX, OY, OZ (Fig. 9.4(a)). The perpendicular distances x, y, z respectively of a point from these respective axes then define its position unambiguously. OX', OY', OZ' (Fig. 9.4(b)) represent an equally suitable set of reference axes and it will be noted that this system can be reached by rotating the original system, as if it were rigid, about the point O. On the other hand, consider the system OX'' Y'' Z'' in Fig. 9.4(c). It is equally suitable as a reference system but it is not possible to convert the original system into this new system by any rotation about the point O. The only way to go from one to the other is to reflect the first system at the point O, to produce the dotted set $O\bar{X}\bar{Y}\bar{Z}$ in Fig. 9.4(a), and then rotate it to produce the set of Fig. 9.4(c). We can therefore distinguish two sets of equally satisfactory reference systems such that transformation from one system to another of the same set can be brought about simply by a rotation about O, but to go from a system in one set to one in another it is necessary to reflect at O as well as rotate about O. The set of which $OX'Y'Z'$ is typical is usually referred to as a righthanded set, while $OX''Y''Z''$ is an example of a left-handed-set. As the reflection of $OXYZ$ in O produces a set in which x, y, z are all changed to $-x$, $-y$, $-z$ respectively the test of whether right-handedness and left-handedness are equivalent is whether physical phenomena are unaltered when the positional coördinates x, y, z of all points concerned are changed to $-x$, $-y$, $-z$.

It will be noted that the operation of reflection in the point O is equivalent to successive reflections in each of the planes YOZ, ZOX, XOY. For simplicity, we shall in what follows often consider the effect of reflection in just one plane, as in a plane mirror.

We can now introduce the idea of *helicity* and how it is affected by reflection. The most homely analogy here is that of the corkscrew. We are accustomed to use right-handed corkscrews, in which the relation between the sense of rotation and the sense of forward motion is as indicated in Fig. 9.5(a). There is no reason, apart from custom, why we should not use instead left-handed corkscrews in which the relation between the sense of rotation and the sense of forward motion is reversed, being as shown in Fig. 9.5(b). The image of a right-handed screw in a mirror parallel to the length of the screw is a left-handed corkscrew (see Plate 9.1). We now enquire whether in nature there exist phenomena in which rotational and linear motions are involved in an analogous way. If so, we can test whether nature discriminates between right- and left-handedness by observing whether any phenomena depend on whether a right- or left-handed corkscrew is involved.

All particles which are fermions possess an intrinsic spin which can point in either of two opposing directions. We can have therefore a situation exactly similar to that of the cork-screw, the sense of rotation being that of the spin component along the direction of motion of the particle. There will be a right-handed and a left-handed case as illustrated in Fig. 9.5. It is convenient to introduce the term helicity to describe the relation between the spin and the linear motion. A particle for which the situation is as in Fig. 9.5(a) is said to possess right helicity as distinct from the left helicity of Fig. 9.5(b). Are there any phenomena which depend on the helicity?

Discovery of Reflection Asymmetry

Until 1956 it was believed that this question could definitely be answered in the negative. However, by that time, the study of the K-mesons had produced a curious and still unresolved difficulty. It seemed that a K-meson could decay either into two or into three pions. For reasons, which cannot here be elaborated, this seemed to point quite definitely to a breakdown of reflection symmetry. In the course of a consideration of this perplexing situation Lee and Yang pointed out that no experimental check had ever been made of the assumption of right and left hand symmetry in other weak interaction phenomena, particularly beta-decay processes. They suggested several experiments which might be carried out to test this. It was not long before Wu, Ambler, Hayward, Hoppes and Henderson performed one of these experiments and obtained conclusive evidence of a dependence on helicity. This discovery electrified the world of physical science and in the next year an astonishing number of experiments were done so that we now have quite a lot of information about Nature's tendency to favour one hand against the other. Some of the experiments were extraordinarily difficult but much of the information could have been gathered years ago if it had been thought worth while – reflection symmetry had for so long been taken for granted.

The experiment of Wu and collaborators consisted of a study of the distribution in direction of the electrons emitted in the course of the beta decay of the nuclei of the cobalt isotope Co^{60}. A reference direction was provided by partially aligning the cobalt nuclei so their spin axes were parallel to a fixed direction (see Fig. 9.6). If there is no dependence of the decay phenomenon on helicity then the distribution of emitted electrons should be symmetrical about the plane perpendicular to the direction of alignment of the nuclei. In fact the observations left no doubt about the lack of symmetry, showing that a dependence exists.

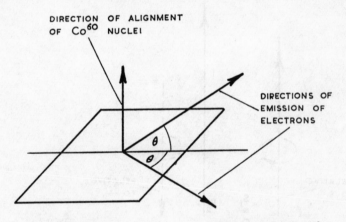

Fig. 9.6. *Illustrating the geometry of the experiment carried out by Wu and collaborators. The directions of emission of the electrons observed make equal angles above and below the plane shown.*

Many other phenomena involving neutrino emission have since been studied experimentally with the aim of detecting and measuring the asymmetry effects which exist between left and right helicity. We can best proceed now, however, by returning to a more fundamental discussion of the whole matter in relation to neutrinos.

The Neutrino as a Ghost Particle

We first raise the question – Is the helicity of a particle independent of the system of reference to which it is referred? We discuss this by reference to Fig. 9.7. To an observer S_1 fixed at a point O, the particle is moving in the sense of the arrow and the helicity is as assigned. If, however, an observer S_2 were moving relative to S_1 in the same sense as the particle but even faster, then to him the particle would appear to be moving in the opposite sense as indicated by the dotted lines and arrows. Hence, according to S_2, the helicity is reversed. As there is no absolute meaning associated with helicity, it would seem meaningless to find any dependence of natural phenomena upon it. This is true until we turn to the neutrino.

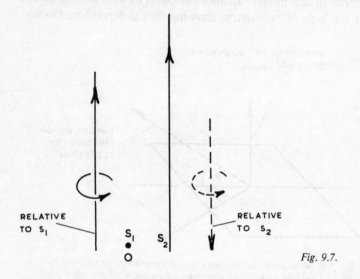

RELATIVE TO S_1 RELATIVE TO S_2

S_1 S_2

O

Fig. 9.7.

With this particle the situation is quite different. As it possesses no rest mass a neutrino is always moving with the speed of light. This follows because the energy E is given in terms of the rest mass m_0 by

$$E = \frac{m_0 c^2}{\sqrt{(1 - v^2/c^2)}}$$

where v is the speed. When m_0 tends to zero E can only remain finite if v tends to c. If now our particle in Fig. 9.7 is a neutrino no observer S_2 can possibly move faster than it does, relative to any other observer. Hence for a neutrino the helicity is absolute – once a left-handed neutrino always a left-handed neutrino! This is specially significant when we remember that most of the experimental demonstrations of right-left asymmetry have involved neutrinos.

We may carry this a little further in a way which is theoretically satisfying and for which there is increasing experimental support. So far we have not introduced the concept of an anti-particle to the neutrino although, as the latter is a fermion, it is natural to think of this possibility. One conceptual difficulty was that of distinguishing between the two without undue artificiality. It had been pointed out as long ago as 1929 by Weyl that a theory was possible in which a neutrino and its antiparticle each had definite but opposite helicities. This was not taken seriously at the time because it implied a breakdown of right-left symmetry, but now this is a real advantage. According to it a neutrino has no mirror image of its own kind. When it looks into a mirror it sees an antineutrino! In a sense it is a ghost but an even more esoteric one than usual in that it does produce an image but of its anti-self.

If we suppose now that in a particular beta-decay process the ghost particle emitted must definitely be either a neutrino or a antineutrino, then it is associated with a definite helicity, as observed. We also have a linkage with the other well known type of asymmetry, the dependence on the sign of the electric charge. If we go from the world to the antiworld in which all particles are replaced by antiparticles, we not only reverse the signs of all electric charges but go from neutrinos to antineutrinos, thereby reversing helicity. From this point of view the reflection asymmetry is part of the overall preference in our universe for particles as against antiparticles (see also 'Time-reversal Symmetry', p. 241).

The assignment of definite and opposite helicities to neutrinos and antineutrinos leads to some remarkable consequences about spin alignment in simple beta-decay processes. Consider for example the decay of a pion at rest. The neutrino emitted will have a definite helicity say, as indicated in Fig. 9.8. The muon must be emitted in the opposite direction to conserve momentum while, to conserve angular momentum, its spin must be equal and opposite to that of the neutrino. Hence the spin of the muon will be pointed along the direction of motion – in technical language it will be longitudinally polarized. This polarization will, in turn, affect the chance that, in the subsequent decay of the muon, the electron will be emitted in any particular direction. It will also lead to a correlation between this direction and that of the electron spin. The magnitude of these effects will depend on the extent to which the muon polarization is preserved up to the moment when it decays. It becomes possible, therefore, to obtain information about the interaction between slow muons and solid materials which might ultimately be of value for solid state physics, a further remarkable example of the unity of all physics.

The electrons or positrons emitted in beta decay are partially polarized even though the emitting nuclei are not aligned in any way. This polarization is nearly complete when the speed of the emitted particle is close to that of light. For positrons the spin is aligned in the sense of motion, for electrons in the opposite sense. It is surprising that this aspect of beta-decay remained undetected for so long.

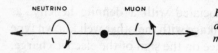

NEUTRINO   MUON

Fig. 9.8. Helicity relations in the decay of a pion into a neutrino and a muon.

A Conservation Law for Light Particles (Leptons)?

We have already explained why it is now generally accepted that a conservation law exists for heavy particles (the conservation of baryon number). It is natural to enquire whether any corresponding law holds for weak reactions involving light particles – muons, electrons, neutrinos and their antiparticles. The generic terms *leptons* and *anti-leptons* are now usually applied to these particles.

The most obvious form in which this might be expected to occur is that the number of leptons minus the number of antileptons must remain constant in any reaction (Compare with the conservation of baryons p. 216). In the muon decay (4) one of the two ghost particles would have to be a neutrino and the other an antineutrino.

The evidence at present indicates that lepton conservation does indeed apply. Moreover, it appears that the ghost particle emitted with a positron has left-handed helicity so this particle is the lepton. If the term neutrino is applied to the particle with right-handed helicity then it must be remembered that this particle is to be taken as an antilepton, the antineutrino then being a lepton, together with the negative muon and electron. It follows that the particle detected by Cowan and his collaborators (see p. 231) is the one with right-handed helicity.

Time-reversal Symmetry

We have been discussing the symmetry of physical phenomena with regard to space reflection but we must remember that we should be dealing with space-time. Symmetry with respect to time reversal implies that reversal of the sense of all motions in a system would not change its physical character. The assumption of this symmetry is basic for thermodynamics. So far we have no evidence of its failure, even in weak interaction phenomena, but no decisive experiments have yet been carried out. Even if it were found to be violated in these cases it would have no effect on the validity of thermodynamics except under conditions of extremely high density. This would be of cosmological significance but not otherwise.

It may be shown that if time-reversal symmetry exists, then complete symmetry must also exist between two systems which have opposite reflection symmetry provided that the particles in one are replaced by antiparticles in the other. In this way we could retain our conception of mirror symmetry if we suppose that an electron sees itself in a mirror as a positron and *vice versa*, and that this applies to all particles and antiparticles.

Summary of Interactions

We may classify interactions under four headings, strong, electromagnetic, weak and gravitational. The strong interactions are those between pions, *K*-mesons, nucleons and hyperons in which strangeness (see Chapter 8, p. 216) is conserved. These are on the average about 100 times stronger than the electromagnetic interactions between charged particles. Weak interactions are responsible for reactions involving neutrinos as well as those involving strange particles in which strangeness is not conserved, as in the *K*-meson or hyperon decays. These are about 10^{12} times weaker than the electromagnetic interactions but even so they are about 10^{25} times stronger than the gravitational interactions between fundamental particles.

We are still far from knowing the detailed forms of the strong interactions. Indeed, we still are by no means clear whether we have to deal with several different forms or a single universal one. Much progress has been made in our knowledge of the weak interactions since the discovery of reflection asymmetry in such cases. It seems fairly well established that, in all reactions involving neutrinos or antineutrinos, a universal form of weak interaction is alone involved. There is reason to hope that this will apply to all weak interactions and it may well be that it will assist in the interpretation of the breakdown of reflection symmetry in cases where no neutrinos or antineutrinos are involved. It will be remembered that the possibility of reflection symmetry first arose from *K*-meson decay processes which are of this type. Recent experiments have shown that the breakdown also occurs in Λ°-decay,

$$\Lambda^\circ \to \pi^- + p.$$

We cannot therefore place all the blame on the neutrino. The form of the universal weak interaction provides a possible way out.

The underlying significance of the four types of interaction still escapes us but a great deal of thought is being devoted to these basic questions, particularly in relation to the new conservation laws which seem to be valid. Conservation of energy, momentum and angular momentum can be related to the properties of the space-time of special relativity but it is difficult to see how to include baryon number, strangeness and lepton number as well. The existence of these further laws indicates a deeper underlying symmetry in Nature which we have not yet appreciated. We are at a most interesting stage – major clarification with deeper understanding may come at any time.

The Material Mansion

It is amusing to note that we may think of the various particles in terms of the building stones (electron, proton and neutron) the cements (photons, pions and *K*-mesons), the bric-à-brac (hyperons and muons) and the ghost (neutrino). This provides no place for the antiparticles but all we need do to include them is to provide mirrors within this material mansion. The bricks, the bric-à-brac and the ghost will all appear as antiparticles in these mirrors!

The Energy of the Stars

It may seem strange that we should choose to write of the energy of the stars in a Chapter devoted largely to the neutrino. Actually, however, neutrinos play a vital part in the supply of energy within our own star, the sun, as well as in most others.

We imagine that a star gradually builds up by condensation of cosmic dust under the force of gravity. As the mass gradually contracts it heats up and this was supposed, during the nineteenth century, to be the source of the energy of the stars. When considered in detail for the sun it is found that this source would have been exhausted in 20 million years whereas the span of life of the sun must already have been of the order of a thousand million. What actually happens is that, at some stage during the contraction, the temperature at the centre rises high enough for fusion of hydrogen nuclei to take place and produce helium – most of the material out of which the stars grow is hydrogen.

It appears that, for relatively small stars like the sun, the first process which occurs is the combination of two protons to form a deuteron. The reaction is

$$_1H^1 + {_1}H^1 \rightarrow {_1}D^2 + e^+ + \nu, \tag{7}$$

from which it will be seen that a positron and a neutrino (or antineutrino according as to which convention of notation is adopted) is produced. This reaction begins to be effective at a temperature of a few million degrees. As a neutrino is involved the chance that two protons will react as in (7) is very small indeed, only about 1 in 10^{23}. This is compensated for by the huge mass of the stellar core so that the net result is the supply of sufficient energy to maintain the brightness of a star such as the sun for some thousands of millions of years.

Once deuterons have been produced they combine with further protons to produce He^3 nuclei

$$_1D^2 + {}_1H^1 \rightarrow {}_2He^3 + \gamma.$$

He^4 nuclei are finally produced from the reactions

$$_2He^3 + {}_2He^3 \rightarrow {}_1H^1 + {}_1H^1 + {}_2He^4.$$

The net result is therefore the building up of a He^4 nucleus from four protons. Although the initial reaction (7) is far too weak to be observed in the laboratory we now know enough about weak interactions to be able to calculate its rate with sufficient accuracy. The other reactions have been investigated in the laboratory.

It is of interest to notice that about 2% of the energy released in the helium synthesis is carried away by neutrinos. At the earth about 10 neutrinos are received from the sun per second on a surface of one sq.cm. This might be detected through the reaction

$$_{17}Cl^{37} + \nu \rightarrow {}_{18}A^{37} + e^-,$$

provided about 10,000 gallons of, say, carbon tetrachloride (CCl_4) were available in a mine at such a depth underground as to exclude cosmic and other radiations. It is to be noted that the solar neutrinos are produced with positrons so they must be the antiparticles of those generated in a nuclear reactor which are produced with electrons.

An alternative mode of helium synthesis, known as the carbon cycle, comes into operation at a somewhat higher temperature. It requires the presence of a small amount of carbon which is not, however, used up in the process. The carbon cycle is probably the most effective one for the larger stars.

The nuclear furnace in the sun simmers away gently, converting about 800 million tons of hydrogen into helium every second. At this rate the hydrogen fuel will last for about ten thousand million years. This poses the important question – What happens to a star when the central hydrogen has all been burned up?

When this occurs, further contraction takes place under gravity until a shell, surrounding the core, which still contains hydrogen, becomes hot enough to produce helium. During this stage a major change in the structure of the star takes place. The helium core contracts whereas the outer envelope expands greatly so that the star becomes a 'red giant' – the red colour is due to the comparatively low surface temperature.

The further evolution of the star is not yet understood in detail. Under some conditions, however, the initiation of further nuclear reaction by contraction and heating after each stage of burn-out of a nuclear fuel continues until the core is composed of the most firmly bound nuclei, those of the iron elements. This stage will be reached when the central temperature approaches about $5 \times 10^9 °C$. The equilibrium is then a very delicate one for, with a comparatively small increase of temperature, it will swing over to a constitution mainly of helium. This requires an enormous amount of energy which can only come from a very rapid collapse (within a few seconds) of the core. A corresponding collapse of the envelope will also set in, leading to rapid heating to a temperature which ignites the light nuclei still present in the outer regions of the star. The sudden release of energy due to this will blow off the outer layers in a colossal explosion – virtually that of a cosmic hydrogen bomb.

Events of this type give rise to *supernovae*, which appear suddenly as extremely bright new stars from which nebulosity streams out at a high speed to vast distances. They are such stupendous cataclysms that the peak power radiated in one event is comparable with the total amount radiated by the whole galaxy (see Chapter 10, p. 266). The total energy released is of the order of 10^{35} kilowatt hours. Three supernovae have been observed within our own galaxy in historical times. The most famous, and the most interesting from many points of view (see Chapter 10, p. 266) is that observed by the Chinese in 1094. At present the expanded gas is visible as a nebulosity known as the Crab nebula. A photograph of this object is shown in Plate 9.2. It extends over a distance of about 40 billion miles and is still increasing in size at about 600 miles per second.

The two other supernovae which have been observed in our own galaxy, Tycho Brahe's star in 1572 and Kepler's star in 1604, have not produced such permanent nebulosities but the general features are the same.

Supernovae have been observed in other galaxies (Chapter 10, p. 267) and probably occur on the average at the rate of about 1 in 350 years per galaxy.

Other less drastic but severe stellar explosions occur giving rise to novae which exhibit similar effects on a rather smaller scale. About 10-20 such new bright stars occur every year among the stars in our own galaxy.

The final fate of a star after all nuclear energy has been used up is a highly condensed, steadily cooling sphere known as a white dwarf. Gravitational contraction cannot continue indefinitely because of the operation of the Pauli principle. The electrons in the condensed mass must always possess a considerable mean energy (cf. Chapter 3, p. 74 for electrons in a metal) of motion. This causes them to exert a pressure which resists further contraction. Nevertheless, in a white dwarf star the density is very high, being of the order of 100,000 times that of water or even higher.

We have proceeded in this Chapter from the very minute scale of the fundamental particles to the immensity of the stars. In the remaining Chapters we proceed to deal with large scale phenomena reaching out to the furthest extent of the whole universe.

CHAPTER 10

RADIOASTRONOMY

> '*I saw Eternity the other night,*
> *Like a great ring of pure and endless light.*'
>
HENRY VAUGHAN, 'THE WORLD'

Historical Introduction

Before the last Great War all astronomical observations were carried out using the very narrow band of optical wavelengths which penetrate through the atmosphere to the ground. It is a great tribute to the skill of observers and optical instrument makers, and the ingenuity of theoretical astronomers, that so much was nevertheless discovered about the universe around us. There is no doubt also that much will still be found out by these methods but, in recent years, a new branch of observational astronomy has developed which makes use of a quite different range of wavelengths capable of penetrating the entire thickness of the atmosphere. This is in the region of short radiowaves, extending from wavelengths of 1 centimetre to about 10 metres. Longer waves cannot penetrate the ionosphere (see Chapter 11, p. 286) while shorter waves are absorbed by atmospheric gases.

Radiowaves are radiated from the sun, the moon, some planets, our own galaxy and many intergalactic objects, with considerable intensity, sufficient to be detected and measured by suitable aerials and receivers on the ground. The first evidence that extra-terrestrial sources of radiowaves exist was obtained and interpreted by Jansky as long ago as 1932 but this was not followed up until the war years. Jansky showed that the radiation he was receiving came from a source which was fixed with respect to the stars and he correctly assumed that it came neither from the earth nor the solar system. He called it appropriately 'cosmic static' and it is now known as cosmic radio noise. Little further work proceeded until, in 1940, Reber began a survey of the noise intensity at frequencies of 160 and 480 Mc/sec.

During the war, the intensive development of radar for defence purposes provided many opportunities for studying the different sources of short wave radio noise. In the course of this work, emission from the sun was discovered by Hey and by Southworth on metre and centimetre wavelengths respectively. At about the same time Reber also observed this emission at 160 Mc/sec. (1.9 metres).

After the war, attention was directed towards a systematic study of cosmic and solar radio emission. The first major discovery of the postwar period was that there are discrete sources of cosmic noise to which the name *radio-star* was given. In many respects this has proved a misnomer. No star other than the sun has been shown to emit radiowaves. Only a small number of discrete sources have been identified with any visual object and, in all these cases, the source is immensely greater in extent than any star. Some of the most astonishing discoveries have come from the association of accurate determinations of the directions of radio-stars with the use of the huge 200 inch optical telescope at Mount Palomar to locate and identify the source. We shall describe some of this work on pp. 266-7, particularly that which led to the discovery of colliding galaxies of vast size, at an immense distance. It is possible that radio waves enable us to 'see' further into outer space than may be done with the 200 inch telescope. We are indeed dealing here with objects of stupendous magnitude. The contrast with the particles which have occupied us in the last few chapters could not be greater, a jump from the infinitesimal to the near infinite.

The second major post-war discovery was made in 1951 by Ewen and Purcell who identified, in the radio emission from the galaxy, the line at a frequency of 1420 Mc/sec. which is emitted in a transition between two of the lowest states of atomic hydrogen. This confirmed a suggestion made 6 years earlier by van de Hulst. By this discovery a means became available for the exploration of the distribution of cold atomic hydrogen throughout the galaxy. Already this has provided the first definite evidence that our own galaxy, like so many others, has a spiral structure.

We have so far been referring only to the observation of radio-emission from different sources. It is also possible to use the radar method in which the source of the waves is at a ground station and the reflection of the waves back to the earth, by the objects to be studied, is observed. During the war Hey and Stewart found that it was possible to use this technique for the study of meteors. This provided a means for extending meteor observations to daylight and has proved to be most fruitful. Meteor physics is now a highly developed subject. It is to be noted that this is possible only because artificial sources of short radio waves may be constructed which operate at a power 1000 times greater than that radiated by the sun in the radio region, a marked difference from the optical situation.

The radar method may be applied to the moon and, just possibly, to the nearer planets.

Radio-astronomical observations are now proceeding in a number of centres all over the world. Among other centres which have made big contributions are the Radiophysics Laboratory of the Commonwealth Scientific and Industrial Research Organization at Sydney, Australia, the Mullard Laboratory at Cambridge, and the University of Manchester Research Station at Jodrell Bank.

We shall now proceed to describe some of the special features of the very effective techniques, the use of which in radioastronomy has added to our appreciation of the wonder and immensity of the universe. In the course of a brief account of some of the more striking discoveries we shall seize the opportunity of describing also a little of the grand picture of the universe which had already been built up from the labours of visual astronomers.

Basic Differences between Optical and Radio Astronomy

It is worth while at this stage to compare and contrast the main features of optical and of radio astronomy.

The first difference we can expect is in the nature of the sources of emission. Light waves arise from transitions of electrons between quantum states in atoms or molecules but radio emission is usually associated with large scale motion of charged media. To some extent we can therefore expect the two methods of study to be complementary in providing information about physical conditions on quite different scales.

The same situation applies when we consider temperature in

249

relation to the emission of electromagnetic waves. A hot body at a certain temperature emits radiation with an intensity and wavelength distribution characteristic of the temperature. Thus, as a body gets hotter the wavelength of maximum intensity becomes shorter. A body such as the sun, the visible surface of which is at a temperature of about 6,000° absolute, radiates most strongly in the visible region. There is very little intensity radiated in the long radio wavelengths so that any very strong radio emission must arise from other than thermal excitation.

In two major respects radio-astronomers possess advantages which are denied to their optical colleagues. The first is the ability of radio waves to penetrate clouds either of water droplets or of fine dust. This is not only of great value in making observation possible even when the sky is overcast but it also enables obscuring clouds of cosmic dust to be penetrated.

The second advantage has already been mentioned in one connection, and that is the fact that radio observations may be made in full sunlight. This applies not only to the use of radar, as in meteor physics, but also to the study of cosmic noise.

There is one other direction, however, in which special arrangements have to be introduced to make radio observation possible. It is true that the radio-astronomer does not have to worry about sunlight but he is harassed by radio interference from terrestrial sources. There is great difficulty in preserving wavelengths free from use for broadcasting or some other earthly purpose. In addition to this there is the inherent noise in any receiver due to fluctuations in current flow etc. because of the discrete nature of the current carriers. This matter has already been discussed in connection with the promising new development of the maser (Chapter 3, p. 108). The advance of technique has already been so great that radio-astronomical signals may be observed against a background of unwanted noise one thousand times more intense.

Optical techniques have an advantage in that there is much more detail to be studied because of the great wealth of individual spectrum lines in the visible. Only one line has yet been observed in radio-astronomical emission and it is not likely that many others will ever be identified. It is true, though, that the one available line is a specially useful one (see pp. 268-270).

The biggest disadvantage which has to be faced by the radio-astronomer is the necessarily low resolution he can achieve in determining the direction and shape of the radio sources he is studying. We have already encountered this important matter of resolving power when explaining the value of the electron microscope (Chapter 3, p. 69). The longer the wavelength which has to be used the bigger the instrument required to achieve a given angular resolution. Thus, if a mirror or lens of diameter d is used with radiation of wavelength λ, it is possible to distinguish objects clearly which are at an angular separation greater than λ/d. As the radio-astronomer works with radiation of wavelength 500,000 times greater than his optical colleagues he could only achieve the same resolution by using radio 'telescopes' with lenses of radius 500,000 times greater. For the Mount Palomar telescope d is 200 inches – a radio telescope of the same resolution would need an aperture mirror of 1500 miles diameter! Much of the technical ingenuity of radio-astronomers has been concerned with this question of increasing resolving power, and we shall say something of the ways in which remarkable progress has been made.

The Search for Higher Resolution

Radio Interferometers

The quest for increased resolution occupies the major effort of those concerned with the development of receiving equipment in radioastronomy. It has been pointed out that a mirror of aperture d will resolve objects with angular separation greater than λ/d, where λ is the wavelength in which the objects are viewed. Michelson realised that it was not necessary that the whole of the mirror should be constructed, for the resolution can be attained by observing only with the edges of the mirror. This led him to develop the instrument known as the stellar interferometer for measuring the diameters of stars. Interferometers essentially similar in principle have provided the basis of most radio-astronomical receivers which are intended for the accurate location of radio sources in the sky and for the determination of their angular sizes.

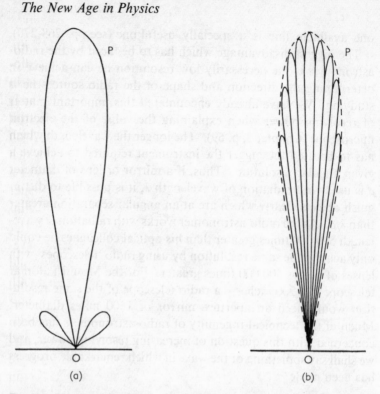

Fig. 10.1. Directional dependence of the intensity of signal of wavelength λ picked up
(a) by a single aerial,
(b) by two equivalent aerials at a distance apart much greater than λ (the side lobes are omitted for simplicity in this case).

In each case the intensity received in a particular direction such as that of OP is proportional to the length OP.

The fundamental receiver is always an aerial of some kind in which an electric current is induced by the incoming waves. All aerials are directive to some degree. This means that the current induced by a signal of particular intensity and frequency will depend on the direction from which the signal is received. It is possible to construct an aerial array which has a directional selectivity of the type shown in Fig. 10.1(a). This enables a source to be located with an accuracy depending on the width of the main lobe in this diagram or, alternatively, two sources at an angular separation greater than this width can be distinguished. It is possible to increase this resolution very greatly by using two exactly similar arrays separated by a distance d which is large compared with the wavelength of the radiowaves being studied. If the signals received by the two aerials are combined the resultant directional sensitivity diagram takes the form shown in Fig. 10.1(b). The effect of adding the two signals has been to chop the main lobe of Fig. 10.1(a) into a number of much thinner lobes. It is not difficult to understand why this is so, in terms of interference (Chapter 2, p. 49).

Referring to Fig. 10.2 we see that waves incident in a direction making an angle Θ with the line joining the aerial arrays must travel a distance greater by $d \cos \Theta$ to reach the second array than the first. If $d \cos \Theta$ is an integral number of times the wavelength λ, this means that the signals at the two arrays will be exactly in phase and will add to give a maximum net signal. On the other hand, if $d \cos \Theta$ is equal to an odd number of half wavelength, they will arrive in exactly opposite phase and the two signals, when combined, will cancel out to give no net signal. Successive maxima will occur then at angles Θ_1, Θ_2 for which

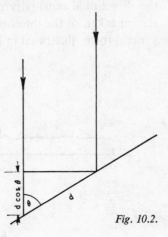

Fig. 10.2.

$$d \cos \Theta_1 = n\lambda,$$
$$d \cos \Theta_2 = (n + 1)\lambda,$$

so that

$$d (\cos \Theta_1 - \cos \Theta_2) = \lambda.$$

If d/λ is large the difference between Θ_1 and Θ_2 will be small, equal to δ, say, so that $\cos \Theta_2 = \cos (\Theta_1 + \delta)$ and $\cos \Theta_1 - \cos \Theta_2$ is nearly equal to $\delta \sin \Theta_1$. We then have approximately that

$$\delta = \frac{\lambda}{d \sin \Theta_1}.$$

This shows that, provided Θ_1 is not too nearly zero, the angular

253

width of the lobes into which the single array pattern has been divided is not far from λ/d.

If we consider now the variation with time of the signal from a source, fixed with respect to the sun or stars, we must take into account the earth's rotation. Suppose that the line joining the two aerial arrays is in the east-west direction. Consider first, for simplicity, the case in which a point source exists in the east-west plane through the aerial array. As the earth rotates the direction of arrival of the radiation from it will change gradually from 0° to 180°. The signals will therefore wax and wane according to the directional sensitivity pattern shown in Fig. 10.1(b), and a record taken of the intensity as a function of time will have the general form illustrated in Fig. 10.3(a). From such a record the

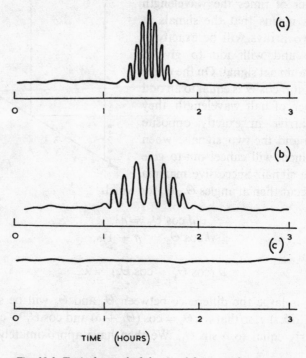

TIME (HOURS)

Fig. 10.3. Typical record of the signal from a radio source as received by a dual aerial array in the east-west direction.
(a) Source in east-west plane.
(b) Source at an elevation of 60° to the east-west plane.
(c) Source in the north-south direction.

direction of the source relative to the fixed stars can be determined from the time at which the central maximum of intensity occurs. The position of the maximum can be found to an accuracy of the order λ/d, the angular width of the central lobe. This shows how, by using the two separated aerial arrays, the resolution can be increased to the same extent as could be obtained if the receiver were a mirror of aperture d. In practice it is not possible to increase d indefinitely due to loss and distortion on the lines which carry the signals from the two arrays. Nevertheless, it is possible to work over distances at least as great as 500 metres. For 20 cm waves this gives an angular resolution of 1.5 minutes of arc.

We have so far described the way in which the bearing of a source in the east-west plane can be determined. There is no difficulty in extending this to a source which is in any position. To do this we note that the waxing and waning of the intensity received from the dual array is due to the difference in the path length of the radiation to the two separate arrays. We have already discussed the case where the direction of arrival is perpendicular to the earth's axis. If, instead, the signals were arriving in a direction parallel to the axis of rotation the path difference would remain zero and no maxima or minima would appear in the net signal. At intermediate elevations the path difference will be finite but the rate of change will be slower than for the case we have first discussed. Thus we have typical examples of time records for different elevations of the source illustrated in Fig. 10.3(b) and (c). It can be seen that, while the time at which the signal reaches a maximum gives the bearing of the source in the east-west plane, the elevation above the plane may be obtained from the duration of the signal or the time interval between successive maxima.

Multiple Aerial Arrays

The dual array interferometer has already played an important part in radio-astronomical observations but it is by no means the only type of instrument employed. A remarkable arrangement of aerials was used by Christiansen to study the distribution of 20 cm. radiation across the disc of the sun. This device

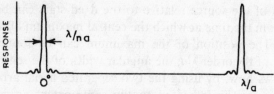

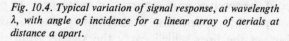

Fig. 10.4. *Typical variation of signal response, at wavelength*
λ, *with angle of incidence for a linear array of aerials at*
distance a apart.

really consisted in the use, not of two similar aerial arrays, but
a large number equally spaced in a straight line running east
and west. If there are $n + 1$ such arrays at a distance a apart,
the combined signal received varies with the angle of incidence
as shown in Fig 10.4. This consists of sharp maxima, each of
an angular width about λ/na, which occur at angular intervals
close to λ/a. With $n = 31$, $a = 7$ metres and $\lambda = 20$ cms., the
maxima are 3 minutes of arc across which is only 1/10th of the
angular diameter of the sun. On the other hand they are
separated by 1.7 degrees, nearly 3 solar diameters. Hence, by
using the earth's rotation, it is possible to scan the surface of
the sun as it passes in succession through each of the maxima.
Plate 10.1 illustrates the actual aerial system used by Christiansen. The elements are parabolic reflecting aerials 2 metres in

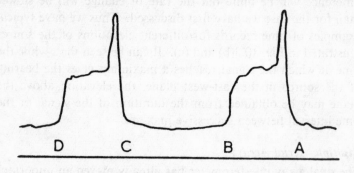

TIME

Fig. 10.5. *Record obtained with the 32 element interferometer scanning*
the sun. Between A and B and between C and D main aerial maxima have
passed across the sun's disc. The peak occurring near A and near C is due
to a patch of high intensity on the sun.

diameter. It is interesting to note that, by using the multiple array, the resolution has been increased 100 times. A typical record obtained is illustrated in Fig. 10.5.

With the Christiansen array the high resolution is achieved in the east-west direction only – it provides a line and not a point scan. By using two arrays at right angles as in the Mills Cross an approximation to a point scan can be achieved.

A considerable step forward was taken recently when it was realised that, for many purposes, it is not necessary to build the full array. All that is necessary is to take records of the intensity for 24 hours with two small aerials, and repeat this with the aerials occupying successively the positions of all the aerials in the big array. The record which would have been obtained if the full array had been used can then be built up.

Radio Telescopes

Interferometers of one type or another, using numbers of small aerials, are adequate provided the intensity of the signals is high enough. If this is not so, one is forced to employ a large aerial to increase the collecting area. In practice this means that, whereas for the observation of the lower frequencies interferometers are appropriate, it is necessary to use large single aerials for the higher frequencies. The largest such aerial at present in use is the paraboloidal aerial of the University of Manchester at Jodrell Bank. This instrument, which has a collecting area of more than an acre, is illustrated in Plate 10.2. It is 250 feet in diameter and may be rotated about a vertical and one horizontal axis so as to point to a given part of the sky with an accuracy of about 1 minute of arc.

Other large parabolic aerials are being designed. These include one of 140 feet diameter of specially high precision to be built at Green Bank in the U.S.A. and one of 200 feet diameter to be constructed at Forbes in New South Wales.

Detection of Very Weak Signals

In Chapter 3, p. 109 we have pointed out the difficulty of detecting very weak signals, not because of the high amplification required but because of the noise background. This limitation is a serious one in radioastronomy but it is remarkable that techniques have been developed which make it possible to detect cosmic noise at a power level which is only about 1/1000 of that of the receiver noise. Although it is not appropriate to explain in detail how this remarkable performance has been achieved, the principle employed is to observe over a sufficiently long interval of time so that the mean level of the total signal can be compared with the mean level of the receiver noise. Exceptionally stable and reliable comparison equipment must be used such as that designed by Ryle and Vonberg.

Radio Emission from the Sun

Some Relevant Properties of the Sun

The sunlight which reaches us on the ground is radiated from the surface of the visible disc of the sun. This is at a temperature of nearly 6,000° absolute and is known as the solar photosphere. The surface of the photosphere by no means marks the boundary of the sun. Above it there extends a region, known as the chromosphere, of lower density but higher temperature, merging into the sun's outer atmosphere or corona. This is a tenuous region which extends out to distances several times the radius of the photosphere. In the corona the temperature, as measured by the mean energy of its constituent atoms, electrons and ions, is as high as 1,000,000° absolute (see Chapter 7, p. 197).

The intensity of visible radiation from the sun is quite constant but this does not apply to other radiations which the sun emits. Most of these radiations are absorbed in the earths' atmosphere and do not reach ground level. They include, in addition to electromagnetic waves (see Chapter 11, p. 278), streams of fast charged particles which, through their interaction with the earth's atmosphere and magnetic field, produce auroral displays, magnetic storms and ionospheric disturbances which adversely affect long-distance radio transmission (see Chapter 11, p. 290). In contrast to the visible radiation, these streams of charged particles are emitted at irregular intervals, when the sun is in a disturbed condition.

While the sun is so disturbed, spots, known as sun spots, appear on its surface. These may persist for considerable periods of time and rotate with the sun, taking 27 days for a complete revolution. The sunspot number is taken as a measure of the degree of disturbance as there is a good correlation between a high sunspot number and other disturbance symptoms. These include the occurrence of solar *flares* or bright eruptions which last for periods of 20 minutes or so. A flare is visible as a bright flash and, from spectroscopic studies, it has been shown that it involves the motion of hydrogen at high speed away from the visible disc. Flares are often associated with the occurrence of characteristic phenomena on the earth. These include radio fadeouts, during which radio transmission over the daylight hemisphere becomes impossible, and, after a time delay of a day or so, the appearance of aurorae and the onset of magnetic and ionospheric disturbances.

The degree of disturbance of the sun varies in a nearly periodic fashion over an 11-year cycle. At the minimum the mean annual sunspot number may be as low as 20 whereas at a maximum it may be as high as 150. The International Geophysical Year of 1957-8 was chosen to fall during a period of maximum solar disturbance.

We are now in a position to summarize and interpret the observations of the intensity of radio emission from the sun in the wavelength region accessible from the ground.

Characteristics of Solar Radio Emission

At the shortest wavelength, about 1 cm., the intensity remains constant to within about 10%, apart from occasional small increases which last for a few minutes at a time. The level of intensity is what would be expected from a solar source at a temperature, about 15,000° absolute, considerably above that of the photosphere. This is associated with an origin in the chromosphere.

As the wavelength increases above a few cms. to about 1 metre, the occasional bursts of enhanced intensity become larger and more frequent while the general level shows a gradual rise and fall over a period of order 1 month.

Finally, at wavelengths greater than 1 metre, the general level remains fairly steady but very violent disturbances occur from time to time. These are usually classified under three headings. First there are *outbursts* during which the intensity is very greatly increased (occasionally even by as much as a million times) for a period of 10–20 minutes. *Noise storms* consist of a series of bursts lasting for hours or days, or of an enhancement of intensity over a similar period. Finally, there are *isolated bursts* which last for only a few seconds. Fig. 10.6 illustrates the general nature of the different kinds of record.

The general level of intensity in the long wavelength region corresponds to emission from a solar source at a temperature of 1,000,000° absolute, suggesting that this radiation arises in the solar corona. There is no difficulty in understanding why this should be so, whereas the short wavelengths arise in the chromosphere. The concentration of free electrons in the latter region is so high that no long wave radiation generated within or below it can penetrate it. It is not so high, however, as to prevent the passage of the short wave radiation. At coronal levels the electron concentration is low enough to permit even the long waves to pass out to interplanetary space (compare the situation in the earth's atmosphere, Chapter 11, p. 286). By following through these arguments in detail, information may be obtained about the variation of free electron concentration in the chromosphere and corona with distance from the centre of the sun.

The gradual variation of the general level of intensity in the medium wavelength region seems to be due to variation in the sunspot number. It appears also, from observations with narrow beam devices of the type described on p. 255, that noise storms originate above large sunspot groups.

Outbursts are often accompanied by solar flares and there seems to be little doubt that there is a close correlation between them. A very interesting observation made by Payne-Scott, Yabsley and Bolton on 8 March 1947 showed the occurrence of a strong outburst on three wavelengths. The records they obtained are shown in Fig. 10.7. At the shortest wavelength (1.5 metres), the outburst began almost simultaneously with a complete fadeout of radiocommunication, but its appearance was delayed on the other wavelengths, the delay increasing with the wavelength. This is consistent with the enhanced

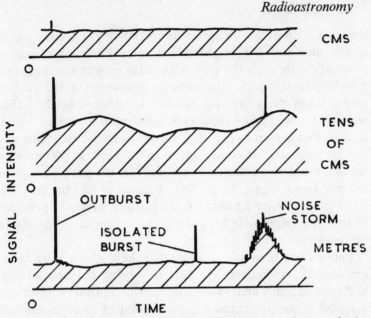

Fig. 10.6. *Typical records of solar radiation in different wavelength ranges showing outbursts, isolated bursts and noise storms as well as the steady or slowly varying radiation.*

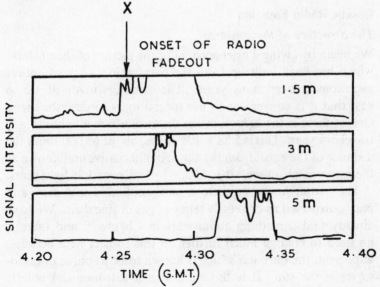

Fig. 10.7. *Records showing the occurrence of outbursts of radio noise from the sun at three different wavelengths.*

261

emission arising from an ascending column of gas. As the wavelength increases the height which must be reached before penetration through the remaining solar atmosphere becomes possible also increases. The outburst only occurs on the 5 metre record when the source has reached a sufficient height. This height is known fairly well for each wavelength so, from a record such as that shown in Fig. 10.7, the speed of the ascending gas can be obtained. It comes out to be as great as 600 miles a second, more than sufficient to escape from the sun's gravitational pull (see Chapter 12, p. 296). Because of this the emitting jet of gas may have actually left the sun as a stream of particles of the type responsible for auroral and magnetic storm effects on the earth.

Enough has been said to show that the study of solar radio emission is proving very fruitful. It is being pursued actively and systematically and, in conjunction with optical observation, will lead to greatly increased understanding of solar physics and of the influence of the sun on terrestrial phenomena (see Chapter 11, p. 272).

Cosmic Radio Emission

The Structure of the Universe

We begin by giving a brief account of the picture of the universe which has been built up from the painstaking work of optical astronomers over many years. The distances involved are so vast that it is convenient to use special units to describe them. One of these is the *light year*, the distance which a light ray will travel in a year. This is 5.88×10^{12} miles, about 63,000 times the distance of the earth from the sun. An alternative unit known as the *parsec* is also used. It is 1.92×10^{13} miles or 3.26 light years.

The matter in the universe is partly collected into stars and partly dispersed as extremely tenuous gas or fine dust. We have already said something about stars in Chapter 9 and there is no need to enlarge much further on this subject here because, at present, the only star which is known to be a source of radio-waves is the sun. It is the much bigger astronomical objects which are of interest in radioastronomy. We must therefore again draw attention to the supernovae (see Chapter 9, p. 245) which are the remains of stellar catastrophes on a grand scale.

The stars are by no means distributed at random but tend to cluster in large concentrations known as *galaxies*. Our own galaxy is fairly typical. Its general shape and size is indicated in the diagram of Fig. 10.8. It consists of a central region or nucleus which is roughly spherical with a radius of the order of 5,000 parsecs. This is surrounded by a much flattened disc-like region which includes the remaining stars. As the edges of this region are approached the density of stars falls off gradually but, at a distance of 20 to 30,000 parsecs, the star density has fallen effectively to zero. The plane of the disc is the equatorial plane of the galaxy. Our sun is located at a distance of about 10,000 parsecs from the galactic centre and is a little less than 100 parsecs above the equatorial plane.

Most of the brightest stars are concentrated in the flattened disc, as well as clouds of gas and fine dust. These clouds are effective absorbers of light so that they cut down very considerably the light which reaches us from the bright stars of our own galaxy. Nevertheless, we see in the Milky Way the strong light from these stars.

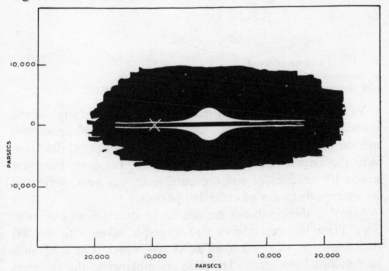

Fig. 10.8. Diagram illustrating the size and shape of one galaxy and the position of the sun (×). Note the dark obscuring cloud at the equator. Compare this sketch with the photograph in Plate 10.3 of the external spiral galaxy M 104.

In the neighbourhood of the sun the mean distance between stars of the galaxy is about 1.2 parsecs – our nearest stellar neighbour, Proxima Centauri is 1.3 parsecs, 4.3 light years, away. Towards the galactic centre the concentration of stars increases to perhaps as much as 10 times that near the sun. There are between 10^{11} and 10^{12} stars altogether in the whole galaxy.

The galaxy rotates about an axis through its centre perpendicular to the equatorial plane. It does not rotate as a rigid body, the speed of revolution varying with distance from the centre as shown in Fig. 10.9.

So far we have discussed the shape of the galaxy largely in elevation but considerable interest attaches also to the plan view. It is difficult to determine this by optical observation because of the effect of the absorbing gas clouds, and it is only in recent years that radio-astronomical studies have shown that it has a spiral structure characteristic of many other galaxies. We shall return to this great achievement on p. 268.

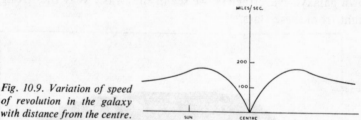

Fig. 10.9. Variation of speed of revolution in the galaxy with distance from the centre.

Vast as is the size of our galaxy it is a speck of dust in the immensity of the universe. Out to a distance of about 200 million parsecs, which is roughly the limit for optical detection with the largest telescope, that at Mount Palomar, there are about 10^8 galaxies of size comparable to our own, separated by average distances of order 10^6 parsecs.

Many of these galaxies are similar in structure to our own. Thus Plate 10.3 reproduces a photograph, taken with the 200 inch telescope, of one known as M 104, which is at a distance of 7 million light years. The close resemblance to the sketched form of our own galaxy shown in Fig. 10.8 is obvious, including the obscuring dust clouds and the nearly spherical nucleus.

Plate 10.4 reproduces a photograph, again taken with the 200 inch telescope, of a galaxy M 51 which is about 4 million light years away. In this case a plan view has been taken and the spiral structure is very clearly seen. This is a characteristic feature of many galaxies, including our own, a fact which has been established from radio-astronomical studies.

About two-thirds of known galaxies have a spiral structure. Apart from about 2 % which have irregular shapes the remainder are elliptical in equatorial section, without spiral structure. It may be that the normal sequence of evolution of a galaxy is through the elliptical to a spiral structure with gradual opening out of the spiral.

The nearest galaxies to our own are of the irregular type. They are the two clouds of Magellan, a mere 25,000 parsecs away, containing about one-tenth as many stars as our galaxy.

One of the best known external galaxies is the famous Andromeda nebula which is of the spiral type and about 200,000 parsecs away. It is roughly comparable in size and star content to our own galaxy.

Finally, we must mention the so-called red shift in the light from distant galaxies. It is found that the spectrum lines emitted from these galaxies are displaced in wavelength towards the red. If this is interpreted as a Doppler shift (see Chapter 7, p. 198) due to motion of the galaxy in the line of sight, it implies that the galaxies are receding at a rate which is proportional to their distances, increasing at a rate of 100 miles per second for every million light years. The explanation of this recession is still a matter for speculation.

Continuous Radio Emission from Cosmic Sources

The optical emission from an astonomical object consists partly of discrete spectrum lines in which the intensity is concentrated within a narrow range of wavelength, and partly of a continuous spectrum in which there is a gradual variation of intensity with wavelength. In contrast, almost all the radio emission is in a continuous spectrum. Only one line has been observed, that of atomic hydrogen at a wavelength of 21.2 cm. The importance of this one line is very great, however, and it is being actively exploited as a guide to the distribution of atomic hydrogen throughout our galaxy and beyond.

We shall begin by summarizing the results obtained from the study of the continuous radio emission from cosmic sources. The history of the development of the study of this emission has been outlined in the introduction. In general, the picture which emerges from observation of the continuous radiation does not differ very much, at first glance, from that which would be expected from the information made available from optical astronomy. There is a band of the sky along the Milky Way which emits strongly and there are small regions of high intensity, the discrete sources, or 'radio stars', which occur outside as well as within the Milky Way. In contrast to the optical situation the cosmic radio emission exceeds that from the sun by a factor of 10,000.

The centre of the galaxy does not show up visually to us as a bright region in the Milky Way because of the presence of obscuring clouds but it is clearly perceptible in the radio picture – the cosmic radio noise shows a marked peak of intensity towards the galactic centre.

Identification of Discrete Sources – Colliding Galaxies

At first the discrete sources of radio emission were thought to be stars but it was found that the emitting regions were far too large for this interpretation. Early attempts to associate the discrete sources with visual astronomical objects were very unrewarding, but with improvement in the accuracy of angular location of the sources some remarkable identifications have been made. It is still true, however, that most of the hundred or so sources which have been observed remain un-identified.

As would be expected, external galaxies have been shown to be discrete sources. In particular, the Andromeda nebula is found to resemble our own galaxy in the total intensity of its radio emission. Other intense sources are found to be associated with rapidly moving, highly ionized and very tenuous gases.

The first example of a source of this type to be identified with certainty is the Crab nebula, the gaseous remnant of the supernova (Chapter 9, p. 246). It appears that not only the radio but also the optical emission from this nebula is due to radiation from electrons moving with very high energy in a magnetic field which extends over the entire nebula. There is no doubt also that the remnants of the supernovae observed by Kepler and by Tycho Brahe are radio sources.

A further source within our own galaxy is a peculiar nebulosity in the direction of the constellation Cassiopeia. Recent optical studies have shown that the nebulosity is expanding rapidly with speeds up to 3,000 miles/sec.

The most extraordinary sources which have been identified, through co-operation between radio astronomers and the observers with the Mount Palomar telescope, are the colliding galaxies. An identification of this kind was first arrived at for the strong source in the constellation Cygnus. Close agreement was found between the position of the radio source and a peculiar external galaxy. Study of the optical spectra of the object provided evidence that it actually represents two galaxies in a collision face to face. This does not involve actual collisions between stars, as they are far too widely separated, but collisions between the gases associated with each galaxy.

A further example which is susceptible of detailed optical study is the peculiar galaxy labelled NGC1275 in the catalogue. In this case we have a collision between two spiral nebulae, one a closely wound early type and the other a late type strongly distorted due to the collision. It is estimated that the total time of collision is of the order of a million years. On the assumption that the present rate of radio emission is about average, the total energy emitted in the collision would be 3×10^{33} kilowatt hours. Great as it is, this is only about one thousandth of that available through a collision between two such gigantic objects moving with a relative velocity of 2,000 miles/sec.

These collisions between galaxies are the grandest known cosmic catastrophes. Radio methods of observation are specially suitable to detect them because the collisions produce greatly extended masses of gas with high temperature and rapid internal motions, the most effective of all cosmic radio sources. Their discovery is a testament to the usefulness of radio astronomy as a complement to the traditional optical techniques.

The Hydrogen Line and the Spiral Structure of our Galaxy

The lowest energy level of the hydrogen atom, as described in Chapter 2, p. 62, lies well below the level immediately above, but actually the situation is somewhat more complicated. Account must be taken of the fact that both the electron and proton in the atom have half integral spins. There is a very weak inter-action between these spins with the result that there is a slight difference in energy between states which differ only in that, in one the electron and proton spins are in the same sense and in the other in opposite sense. The lowest energy level of the hydrogen atom is thereby split into two very close levels. A transition from the upper to the lower levels leads to emission of radiation of frequency 1420 megacycles/sec. or wavelength 21.1 cm. Under normal labora-tory conditions such radiation would not be observed because, on the average, a hydrogen atom in the upper of the two states, if left alone, will remain in that state for 11 million years before emitting the radiation. This is not serious when we are considering the total emission

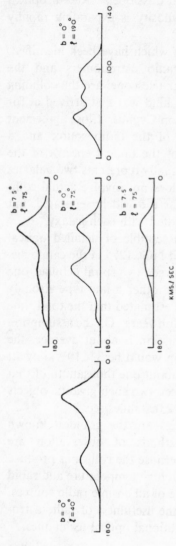

Fig. 10.10. Observed shapes of 21 cm. hydrogen line emitted from different direc-tions in the galaxy. The wavelength scale has been converted to one which gives line of sight velocities of recession directly in km./sec. l denotes the galactic longitude and b the galactic latitude (b = 0° denotes directions in the galactic plane).

from galactic hydrogen as there are enormous numbers of atoms in the line of sight.

The possibility of detecting the line in cosmic radio emission was suggested by van de Hulst in 1945 and it was observed in 1951 first by Ewen and Purcell at Harvard and shortly after by Muller and Oort in Holland and Christiansen and Hindman in Australia.

The shape of the line, which is determined by the variation of the intensity emitted, with wavelength, over the region occupied by the line, is of much importance in the interpretation of the data obtained. This is because the shape is determined by the velocity, in the line of sight, of the emitting regions. Due to the Doppler effect (Chapter 7, p. 198) the emitted wavelength depends on this velocity. It was found that the shapes of the lines emitted from our own galaxy varied markedly with the direction of observation, even in the equatorial plane. Typical shapes are shown in Fig. 10.10.

The interpretation of a shape such as shown in Fig. 10.10, in which there are two maxima, is as follows. In the direction of observation concerned there are two strong emitting regions which are moving with different velocities in the line of sight. Broadening is due partly to random motions and partly to less intense emission from other regions. It is possible to convert the line of sight velocities into distances from the sun by using the information provided from optical observations about the rotation of the galaxy (see Fig. 10.9) in relation to the known position of the sun relative to the galactic centre.

Detailed surveys of the distances of the emitting regions within the galaxy in different directions have now been carried out, particularly in Holland and in Australia. When these are plotted on a plan diagram, the spiral structure of our galaxy becomes clearly manifest as will be seen from Plate 10.5. Here we have a further major achievement of radioastronomy.

Many other applications have been made, and are being made, of observations of the intensity of the hydrogen line, both in emission and in absorption. The latter occurs when continuous radio emission is received through an intervening layer of hydrogen, which absorbs selectively the radiation with wavelength equal to that of the hydrogen line.

269

Emission of the line from several extragalactic objects has been observed, including the clouds of Magellan and the Andromeda nebula. Observation of a broad absorption line in the emission from the Cygnus A colliding galaxies has given a preliminary value of the Doppler shift associated with the recession of distant objects (p. 265) which agrees quite closely with that expected from the optical red shift. This lends support to the interpretation of the red shift as a recessional Doppler effect.

It is apparent that a great deal can be found out, not only about our own galaxy, but also more distant objects out to the confines of the visually observable universe and perhaps even beyond, from the study of the hydrogen line emission and absorption. As it provides a means of determining the distribution of neutral atomic hydrogen, perhaps the most abundant constituent of the universe, it is bound to yield results of the highest importance.

Radio Emission from the Moon and Planets

Considerable interest attaches to the observation of the thermal radio emission from the moon and planets as it gives information about the temperature of the emitting region. This may be compared with the temperatures deduced from observation of the intensity of infrared radiation using bolometric methods. Results have been obtained for the moon, Jupiter, Saturn, Venus and Mars.

For the moon, observations may be made throughout a whole lunar cycle to obtain the variation of temperature with phase. From this it is possible to obtain some idea of the nature of the moon's surface. Present indications suggest that it is covered with a heat insulating layer of dust an inch or so thick but the evidence is by no means conclusive.

The radio and infrared observations for Mars and Jupiter agree reasonably well in ascribing temperatures of between 220° and 260° absolute to the former and between 130° and 145° absolute to the latter planet.

For Venus, which is in many ways a most mysterious object, the radio temperature, about 600° absolute, is more than twice the infra-red temperature of 240° absolute. The radio results were obtained both on 9.4 and 3.15 cm. wavelengths. As the subject is still in its early stages, it is not profitable to speculate yet about the reason for the different temperatures.

In addition to the steady thermal emission from Jupiter, bursts of radio noise occur. They were first discovered at a frequency of 22 Mc/sec. in 1955 by Burke and Franklin in the United States but a search of earlier records of cosmic radio noise at 18.3 Mc/sec., taken in Australia, showed that similar bursts occurred during 1950-51. The source of the radiation during this period was found to rotate with a period of 9 hrs. 55 min. 13 sec. This made possible a provisional identification of the source with a white spot on the southern half of the planet which rotates with the same speed.

We can expect that this aspect of radioastronomy will develop to an increasing extent in the near future and provide us with much new information about the moon and planets.

As mentioned on p. 249, radar reflection methods are being used to study the moon's surface and the range can just be extended to the nearer planets – there will be a race between these methods and those in which interplanetary probes (see Chapter 12, p. 311) are employed, for the honour of first observing the electrical characteristics of the atmospheres of Mars and Venus!

Application of Radioastronomy to the Study of Meteors

In this branch of radioastronomy, use is made of radar methods to observe meteors which are producing trails of ionized atoms as they penetrate the atmosphere. Radar waves are reflected from these trails so that meteors may be detected and studied in daylight as well as at night. This has greatly enlarged our knowledge of the nature of meteors, their size and velocity distribution, and the way in which they interact with the atmosphere. There has been a corresponding increase in knowledge of atmospheric properties near the level, about 60 miles up, at which most meteors are burnt up. Lack of space prevents us from doing more than mention this important work.

CHAPTER 11

EXPLORING THE UPPER ATMOSPHERE

> '*Higher still and higher,*
> *From the earth thou springest*
> *Like a cloud of fire;*
> *The blue deep thou wingest.*'
> P. B. SHELLEY, 'ODE TO A SKYLARK'

Introduction

It will come as a surprise to many that there is much of interest to study in the atmosphere at heights of more than a few miles above the earth's surface. The importance of the atmosphere for weather and climate is well appreciated but most of this depends on the relatively dense air near the ground. Nevertheless there is much of importance, even for human activities, in the thin atmosphere at heights as great as 150 miles above sea level. In this region is located the major part of the ionosphere which makes possible the transmission of radio signals over great distances. The atmosphere exerts an invaluable filtering effect on the radiations and materials which impinge on it from outside so what eventually reaches the surface has no adverse effect on life. Ultraviolet light from the sun, which would kill all plant life, is removed by the ozone layer which is located between altitudes of 10 and 20 miles. Meteors are dealt with at much higher levels, very few penetrating nearer the surface than 50 miles. Cosmic rays, being very energetic, do penetrate to much lower levels but even they interact about 10 miles up, producing secondary particles which are less penetrating and have weaker biological effects.

The sun has a controlling influence on many of the properties of the high atmosphere. Its ultraviolet and X-rays produce the ionosphere, so that the quality of radio transmission is very dependent on the variability of the sun's radiation. As the sun is a variable star (see Chapter 10, p. 258) radio transmission is subject to its vagaries. These involve not only fluctuations in the ultraviolet and X-radiation but also emission of streams of protons and electrons which produce auroral displays and magnetic storms and cause ionospheric variations which spoil radio communication over much of the globe. It even appears, from recent studies, that the disturbed sun makes a contribution to cosmic radiation.

In recent years there has been a great intensification of study of the upper atmosphere, although much had already been done before the war.

Until 1947 all the information gained about the upper air had been derived by indirect methods based on observations with instruments on or near the ground – the greatest altitude attainable by balloons is little over 100,000 feet (20 miles). Although it is remarkable how much can be done without actually sending up instruments to make measurements *in situ*, there are some vital questions which cannot be answered in this way. Perhaps the most important of these is the nature of the radiation from the sun before it is modified by interaction with the atmosphere. Without knowing what radiation or streams of charged particles bombard the atmosphere from outside it is not possible to understand in any detail how the sun produces the various atmospheric phenomena for which it is responsible. This applies particularly to the ionosphere but it is also essential for an understanding of many other effects.

Since 1947 high power rockets have been introduced as instrument carriers. This has placed at our disposal the means for direct observation of high altitude properties. Modern rockets are capable of taking a useful load of instruments to any heights but the technique of carrying out measurements in a rocket laboratory and of receiving the observed data is a difficult one. Great progress has been made, however, in using high altitude rockets and very interesting and valuable results have been obtained. The experience gained is now being used to make observations from outside the atmosphere altogether, through the use of artificial satellites and space probes.

In the present Chapter we shall give a brief account of the properties of the upper air and of some of the methods, direct or indirect, which have been used to study them. This includes the use of vertical sounding rockets. The extension of the latter technique to include the use of artificial satellites and space probes generally will be discussed in the following Chapter. It is worth noting at this stage that the availability of artificial satellites does not remove the need for vertical sounding rockets. Satellites are very suitable for observation over long intervals of time and the whole surface of the earth but they cannot circulate for long at heights less than 120 miles. Vertical atmospheric structure up to these heights must still be studied in nearly vertical rocket ascents of a few minutes duration only.

It is convenient to describe the different indirect methods of study when considering the separate properties studied. There are many features of the use of rockets which remain the same no matter what is being explored and we shall therefore begin by describing them.

Vertical Sounding Rockets and their Applications

Rockets for High Altitude Research

All developments of high altitude rockets stem from the famous, or infamous, V2, the liquid fuel rocket which carried 1,000 lbs. of explosive from the Channel coast to bombard London during the war. If fired vertically, this rocket was capable of carrying a substantial load of instruments up to a height of 100 miles or so, well into the upper atmosphere. The first direct scientific observations at altitudes above the balloon limit (a little over 20 miles) were carried out at White Sands, New Mexico, using captured V2 rockets.

Since that time many new designs of rockets have been put into service to study the upper air. All depend on the same principle as the tiny rockets which play so large a part in firework displays. In a rocket motor a chemical reaction, usually the burning of some fuel, produces a high speed jet of vapour which is expelled through a nozzle. The expulsion of the jet produces a reaction on the main body of the rocket and so propels it in the opposite sense to the jet. It is an example of the conservation of momentum (Chapter 2, p. 43). Initially, before the motor is ignited, the whole rocket possesses no momentum. The momentum of the escaping jet must then be balanced by an equal and opposite momentum communicated to the rocket as a whole so that the net momentum remains zero. A rocket engine differs from a jet aeroplane engine in that it operates independently of the atmosphere. It carries its own oxygen, or its equivalent, as well as the fuel. The V2 rocket motor used alcohol as fuel, the oxygen being supplied in liquid form. The total weight of the propellant liquids was nearly 10 tons and that of the frame about 3 tons. When fired vertically it reached its maximum altitude in a little less than 4 minutes, the maximum speed being 4800 feet per second (3300 miles per hour).

The Viking liquid-propellant rocket was the first developed in the United States and this has been used as the basis of the launching vehicles for certain American satellites. It is capable of reaching a maximum speed of about 4000 miles per hour and can carry over 750 lbs. of instruments to an altitude of 200 miles or so. For vertical sounding experiments the Viking is far too expensive. Instead, two other liquid propellant rockets, the Aerobee and later the Aerobee Hi, were designed specially for this purpose and have been put to very good use in the United States. The Aerobee can carry 150 lbs. of instruments up to altitudes of 60 miles or so while the Aerobee Hi can reach over 190 miles with the same payload.

The Meteorological Institute in the Soviet Union employs sounding rockets similar in performance to the Aerobee but much larger vehicles, capable of attaining altitudes of 250 miles or so, carrying loads of as much as 1 ton, are used by the Geophysical Institute of the U.S.S.R. No details are at present available about these large rockets.

The vertical sounding rocket, Skylark, used in the British upper atmospheric rocket research programme, which was designed at the Royal Aircraft Establishment, Farnborough, employs solid instead of liquid fuel. It can carry a load of 150 lbs. of instruments to heights of 120 miles or so.

Because of the cost of high power rockets and the need for a great number of flights at many points over the earth's surface, considerable attention has been devoted to economic designs. One way of achieving this is by means of a rocket-balloon combination, known as a rockoon. The balloon carries the rocket up through the dense lower atmosphere so that it is fired from an altitude of 80,000 feet. As it does not encounter high air resistance, a much less powerful rocket can thus reach the same altitude as one of greater power launched from the ground.

Fig. 11.1 illustrates some of the rockets which have been or are being used for vertical sounding of the atmosphere.

Experiments with Rocket-Borne Instruments

The space available for measuring apparatus in a rocket is usually limited, as well as the weight which can be carried, but there are other difficulties which must be faced. There is the shock experienced by the rapid acceleration at launching, the vibration during the flight, and the disturbance of the atmosphere by the rocket itself. Unless special means of stabilization are fitted, a rocket will yaw, pitch and roll. This is sometimes an advantage as it enables observing equipment to scan a wide area of the earth's surface during flight. It is nevertheless a complication which has to be reckoned with. Finally there is the

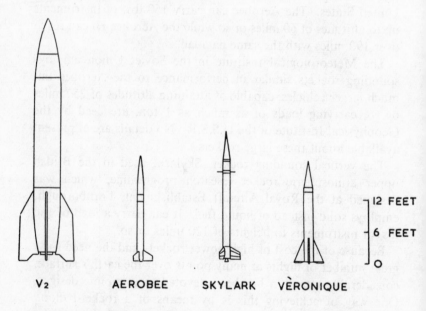

V₂   AEROBEE   SKYLARK   VÉRONIQUE

┤ 12 FEET

┤ 6 FEET

┤ 0

Fig. 11.1. Illustrating the sizes and shapes of typical vertical sounding rockets.

very short time, only a few minutes, a rocket is in flight and all the observations must be made during this time.

Because of these special features of observations from rockets, the equipment for measuring a particular atmospheric property, such as temperature, is rarely similar to that which would be used in a normal laboratory on the ground. Examples will be given below.

Recovering the Observations.

An essential for success in the use of rocket-borne equipment is that the observations which it makes can be received at the ground. Unless special arrangements are made, the rocket crashes back to the ground nose forward so that the nose section, which usually includes the instruments, is completely destroyed. Methods for braking the descent are in use and it is then relatively easy to recover photographic plates and records in a usable form. A much more usual procedure is that known as *telemetry* in which the observed data are communicated to ground, during the flight, in the form of coded radio signals.

The information obtained by the measuring instruments can be used to modify (or modulate) the form of the radio signals from a transmitter in the rocket. This may take the form of a change in frequency, or of amplitude, or of the pulse transmission rate, or the pulse spacing.

Determining the Flight Path of a Rocket

It is, of course, necessary for most experiments to have accurate information on the flight path of the rocket and the time it reached each point of its path. Under good weather conditions, precision optical methods may be used but, if the sky is overcast, radio methods remain available.

With one of these systems, known as Dovap (Doppler, velocity and position) the position can be determined to about 1 foot and the velocity to about 1 foot/second. High frequency radio signals are transmitted from the ground to the rocket which receives them and then retransmits back to three ground stations. The frequency of this reradiated signal at each station is compared with that received directly from the ground transmitter. Any difference is due to the possession, by the rocket, of a component of velocity along the line joining it to the receiving station concerned (the Doppler effect) (Chapter 7 footnote p. 198). Provided there are no effects due to the ionosphere (which only becomes important above heights of 50 miles) continuous observations at three stations give the necessary position and velocity data.

Ultraviolet and X-rays from the Sun

It was pointed out on p. 273 that it was vital, for an understanding of upper atmospheric phenomena, to know the nature and intensity of the radiation from the sun before modification by the atmosphere, and in Chapter 10, p. 247 attention was drawn to the small range of wavelength of electromagnetic rays which can penetrate to ground. One of the foremost achievements of post-war rocket sounding has been the information which it has yielded about the ultraviolet and X-rays which the sun emits but which are absorbed in the atmosphere far above the ground. We are even beginning to obtain some knowledge of the way the intensity of emission in these wavelengths varies during solar disturbances. In a sense this is the beginning of a vast new branch of astronomy for the information is important not only for the understanding of the upper atmospheric phenomena but also for the study of the sun itself. The possibility of observing these short wavelength radiations from the stars, and the galaxy generally, opens before us and, although progress in this field will necessarily be slow at first, a beginning has been made and the tools are becoming available.

Many methods have been and are being used to measure the intensity of solar ultraviolet and X-rays. These have included the use of so-called photon counters which are similar in principle to Geiger-Muller counters for the detection of fast particles (Chapter 6, p. 160). Other methods involve the exposure of photographic plates at high altitudes to the radiation which filters through selected materials so that only the wanted wavelengths reach the plates. Arrangements are made for recovery of the plates. In some cases a full scale spectrograph has been flown so that the spectrum of the radiation is photographed at different altitudes. Plate 11.1 reproduces a now classical photograph taken in an early rocket flight through the ozone layer. This shows clearly how the spectrum extends to shorter and shorter wavelengths as the altitude increases.

The intensity of light emitted by the sun in the visible is very nearly that which would be radiated if the sun were a body at a temperature of 6,000° absolute. Observations made by rocket-borne detectors at shorter wavelengths have shown that this result cannot be extended to these wavelengths. At first the intensity falls well below that from a body at 6,000° – for example, the intensity at a wavelength of 2,200 Å is nearly that which would be expected from a body at 5,000° absolute only.

There is a gap in the observations which extends down to the soft X-ray region but more data are available between 1 and 50 Å. Here the intensity is thousands of times greater than would be radiated by a black body at 6,000°. It arises from the solar corona, the outer mantle of the sun which extends far out beyond the normally visible disc. As mentioned in Chapter 7, p. 197, the kinetic temperature of the corona is as high as 1,000,000° absolute so it is not very surprising that X-rays are radiated from it.

During the International Geophysical Year, an American group under Friedman has attempted, with some success, the difficult task of determining wheter, at the time of a solar flare (Chapter 10, p. 259), there is any change in the ultraviolet and X-rays from the sun. To do this it is necessary to launch a rocket within a few minutes of the receipt of a warning that a solar flare has occurred. This is an extraordinarily difficult task. The launching of a rocket involves a complicated drill, with numerous checks at each stage, and firing to a precise schedule is hard to achieve. Nevertheless, Friedman and his colleagues have found that, shortly after a solar flare, the most intense X-radiation occurs at shorter wavelengths than usual. This may be significant for the interpretation of the atmospheric effects of a flare (see p. 288).

Special interest attaches to the observation of the intensity of a line at 1215 Å which is emitted by hydrogen atoms. It is known as the Lyman α line. This radiation can penetrate down to within 45 miles of the ground. Rocket measurements of the intensity as a function of height have been carried out using photon counters containing nitric oxide, a gas which can be ionized by the radiation. The rocket data on the absorption coefficient of oxygen for the rays agree quite well with laboratory measurements.

Pressure, Density, Temperature and Winds in the High Atmosphere

If the composition of the atmosphere remains unchanged it is possible from knowledge of the height distribution of any one of the three quantities pressure, density and temperature, to determine that of the other two. Up to heights of 60 miles there is no important change of composition (see p. 284) so it is possible to employ a careful check by measuring more than one quantity and testing whether the results are consistent.

Pressure and density may be determined up to 60 miles by using rocket-borne pressure gauges. Direct measurement of temperature is more difficult but is done by the Russians in their meteorological rockets, using resistance thermometers.

Information about the temperature variation had been obtained before the introduction of rockets, using a variety of indirect methods. The fall in temperature as one goes upward from the ground ceases at a height of 8-12 miles after which there is a slow rise. This can be verified directly up to about 20 miles, using instruments in balloons, but even in pre-rocket days the general form of the temperature variation was known up to much greater heights.

One interesting source of evidence comes from the so-called anomalous propagation of sound in the atmosphere. The sound of explosions may often be heard at great distances from the source even though there is an intervening zone of silence. This can be understood if sound waves are reflected back to ground from the atmosphere as in Fig. 11.2. The zone of silence follows if only rays which travel in directions not too close to the vertical are reflected. We can relate this reflection phenomenon to the temperature in the following way.

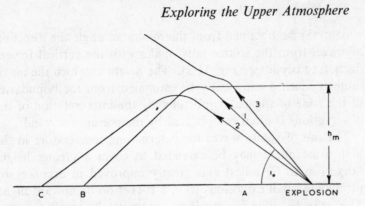

Fig. 11.2. Illustrating the path of sound waves in the atmosphere.
Ray 1 is just reflected back to ground at the height h_m of the temperature maximum.
Ray 2 is reflected back at a lower height.
Ray 3 is not reflected back – this is typical of all rays which, travel up at angles to the horizontal greater than that i_0 of ray 1.
If A is at the greatest distance from the source of sound at which it can be heard directly, then there is a skip distance AB over which no sound can be heard by reflection. At points such as C, beyond B, reflected sound will be heard.

The phenomenon is similar to that which occurs in a mirage. In this case, as the ray travels upwards, it encounters a region in which its speed increases with height. This ensures a gradual bending of the ray away from the vertical. Eventually it is incident at such a large angle on the layer above that it suffers total reflection and returns to ground along a path which is symmetrical with that traced out on the upward passage (see Fig. 11.2). Since the velocity of sound is proportional to the square root of the absolute temperature this effect will occur with a sound ray if it penetrates to a part of the atmosphere where the temperature increases with height. Such a region occurs above about 15 miles.

The reflection effect explains why the explosion is heard at very great distances (compare with the effect of the ionosphere on radio signals) but it does not explain the zone of silence. Reference to Fig. 11.2 shows that the existence of this zone implies that rays which travel up from the source at angles near the vertical are not reflected. This in turn suggests that the temperature does not rise indefinitely as we go up above 15 miles but that a maximum temperature is reached, the value of which may be obtained from the minimum angle the direction of travel from the source must make with the vertical for reflection to occur (see Fig. 11.2). The height at which the maximum is reached can clearly be estimated from the boundaries of the zone of silence. Unfortunately the interpretation of the observations is often complicated by the presence of wind.

The use of sound waves for determining temperature in the high atmosphere may be extended to cover a greater height range (up to 60 miles) and greatly improved in accuracy by producing small explosions from a rocket on its upward flight. This may be done by expelling automatically small grenades which fire close to the flight path. The position and time of each firing can be determined accurately by means of ground-based flash detectors, which record the arrival of the light from each explosion, and ballistic cameras, which photograph the flashes. If the time of arrival of the sound from each explosion is recorded at a number of microphones arranged on the ground it then becomes possible to determine, not only the mean speed of sound and hence the temperature in the atmosphere, between each grenade firing, but also the mean wind speed in the NS, EW and vertical directions. This technique has been used with considerable success at White Sands, New Mexico, at Fort Churchill, Canada (where a very considerable International Geophysical Year programme of rocket soundings has been carried out by the U.S.A.) and at Woomera, Australia (as part of the British programme). In fact it is now just becoming possible to search for variations of the temperature distribution, up to 60 miles height, with latitude, season and even time of day.

Fig. 11.3 illustrates a typical temperature and wind distribution. It will be seen that there is a second temperature minimum about 55 miles up, the existence of which had been inferred well before it was directly revealed from rocket observations. One indication of its existence is the appearance under some conditions of fine, pearly clouds which are so high that they are made visible by sunlight while it is long after dark at the ground. These noctilucent clouds (see Plate 11.2) are due to water vapour carried upwards by some vertical wind and condensing near the temperature minimum.

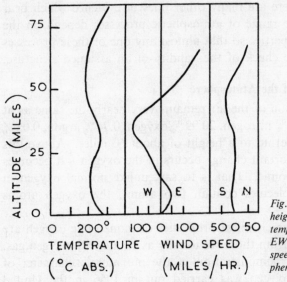

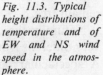

Fig. 11.3. *Typical height distributions of temperature and of EW and NS wind speed in the atmosphere.*

Even stronger evidence came from a study of atmospheric tides and particularly from the fact that, whereas lunar ocean tides are much stronger than solar, the reverse is the case in the atmosphere (see p. 289).

Above 60 miles the quantity most readily measured is the density. By means of suitably disposed pressure gauges the dynamic pressure due to the motion of the rocket, which far exceeds the pressure in the surrounding air, may be measured and, if the velocity is known from other measurements, the density may be derived. A further source of information becomes available above 120 miles from observation of the changes produced gradually in the orbits of artificial satellites due to air drag (see Chapter 12, p. 298).

Much remains to be done before we have a satisfactory picture even of the average variation of the three basic atmospheric quantities with height. It will be much longer still before the dependence on latitude, season and time of day is well established and understood.

To avoid too great detail we have referred only to some of the leading ways of gaining knowledge about atmospheric structure. There are many other lines of evidence which bear on it. A wide range of atmospheric processes depend on the structural properties so that almost any one of these processes provides some check of the validity of an assumed structure.

Composition of the Atmosphere

The composition of the air remains very nearly the same as at ground (78.03% nitrogen, 20.99% oxygen, 0.94% argon, 0.03% carbon dioxide) up to a height of about 60 miles. Above this height an important change occurs in the oxygen – it becomes mainly monatomic. That is to say, unlike normal oxygen in which the molecules contain two atoms, the oxygen atoms remain free.

Naturally the chemical properties of monatomic oxygen are very different from those we usually associate with oxygen gas. A spectacular demonstration of the monatomic character of atmospheric oxygen was carried out in 1956 in the United States. About 18 lbs. of nitric oxide gas was released into the atmosphere 65 miles up. This produced a strong pale green glow, clearly visible to the naked eye, extending over a region several times the area of the moon. At its peak this radiated as much as 45 kilowatts of power in the form of light. The glow arose from the reaction of nitric oxide with atomic oxygen to produce diatomic oxygen, a process in which the nitric oxide acts as a catalyst – it makes the recombination of atomic oxygen possible without itself being used up.

At very great altitudes, probably above 150 miles, the oxygen atoms partly float above the heavier nitrogen molecules but it is far from certain how complete is this diffusive separation and to what extent the nitrogen also becomes monatomic.

Among minor constituents, we have already referred to ozone. This is yet another form of oxygen in which the molecules are triatomic. At the level of maximum concentration of ozone there are still about a million or more oxygen molecules for every one of ozone. Nevertheless, the absorption of ultraviolet light by the ozone layer is responsible for the rise in temperature above the 15 mile altitude (see Fig. 11.3). The concentration of ozone at different heights may be determined from observations of the intensities of certain ultraviolet rays at different heights (see Plate 11.1) using balloon- or rocket-borne instruments. Standard methods have been available for determining the total ozone content, as well as the height distribution, from ground based studies, and most of the data are still obtained in this way. Fig. 11.4 shows a typical height distribution.

A much more unexpected minor constituent is sodium of which there is about 1 ton in the whole atmosphere, concentrated mainly about a height of 50 miles. The source of the sodium is very unclear but its presence is clearly shown from the spectrum of the night air glow in which the yellow lines of sodium appear quite strongly.

The existence of the night air glow may come as a surprise to many as it is very faint, about equal in intensity to the light from a candle 30 feet away. It is a regular feature of the night sky and is relatively independent of latitude. In these respects, and also in its low intensity, it is clearly distinguished from the aurora (see p. 290). The energy given out in the air glow has been absorbed in one way or another from sunlight during the day. Actually there is much stronger emission from the night sky in the invisible near infrared which comes from excited hydroxyl (OH). Most of the visible light comes from molecular and atomic oxygen, molecular nitrogen and atomic sodium.

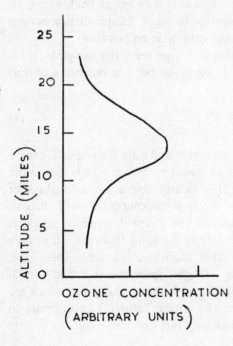

Fig. 11.4. Typical height distribution of ozone in the atmosphere.

The Ionosphere

The ultraviolet and X-rays from the sun, falling on the atmospheric atoms and molecules, can knock off electrons leaving residual positively charged ions. The electrons spend a considerable time free before recombining with ions to form normal neutral atoms or molecules once more. It follows that, at least during the day, there will be a number of free electrons in any region of the atmosphere. The number will depend on the intensity of the ionizing radiation and on the rate at which recombination occurs at the height concerned. At heights above 60 miles in the daytime the free electron concentration is great enough to affect profoundly the propagation of radio waves whose wavelength falls within the long and medium wave broadcasting bands.

The effect is very similar to that produced on sound rays by the rising temperature above the 15 mile level (Fig. 11.2). The presence of free electrons increases the speed of propagation of the radio wave so that, provided the maximum concentration is high enough, a ray sent upwards is reflected back again, so that a signal can be transmitted to much greater distances over the curved earth than would otherwise be possible.

A radio wave of wavelength λ, sent vertically upwards, is reflected when the number of electrons per c.c. reaches a critical value

$$n = \frac{\pi m c^2}{e^2 \lambda^2}, \tag{1}$$

when c is the velocity of light and m and e are the respective mass and charge of an electron, provided we ignore effects due to the earth's magnetic field. This clearly opens up a method of studying the variation of electron concentration with height. A radio signal of a definite frequency is sent vertically upwards and the time which elapses before it returns from the ionosphere is determined by a suitable electronic device. This time, multiplied by the velocity of light, gives the so-called virtual height of the reflecting region and hence the height at which the electron concentration has the critical value (1) appropriate to the frequency used. By carrying this procedure out for a wide

286

range of frequencies, the variation of electron concentration with height at a particular time can be derived. Other procedures for ionospheric sounding are also employed but vertical sounding has been put on an automatic basis. Systematic observations are desirable for commercial purposes as the quality of long range radio transmission depends on ionospheric conditions. It is important to be able, from long accumulated experience, to make predictions about these conditions.

Information about the electron concentration at any height can only be obtained by ground-based sounding methods if it is greater than that at all lower heights. This leads to unavoidable gaps in knowledge of the height distribution.

There is also the problem of relating virtual to real heights. These will be different because the speed of the radio wave while traversing the ionosphere differs from that in free space. In the lower ionosphere the difference will not be very large but it becomes more serious at greater heights.

The use of transmitters in rockets makes it possible to fill in the gaps left in ground level sounding data. Methods have also been devised for measuring the electron concentration directly along the rocket trajectory.

Fig. 11.5 illustrates a typical distribution of electron concentrations with height during the daytime. It will be seen that there are three main layers, the E around 60 miles, F_1 around 120 miles and F_2 extending upwards from 180 miles altitude, the latter being a very thick and dense layer. The critical frequencies capable of just penetrating the respective layers are also indicated in the Fig. 11.5.

At night-time the distribution is somewhat different. The rate of recombination in the E layer is so high that, when the

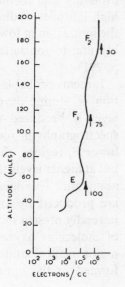

Fig. 11.5. Typical height distribution of electron concentration during daytime in the atmosphere.

Critical wavelengths for penetration of successive layers are indicated in metres.

287

ionizing sunlight is cut off, the free electron concentration falls quite rapidly, and little of the layer remains during the night. A similar situation occurs for most of the F_1 region so that the only important layer at night is located above 140 miles or so and is usually referred to simply as the F layer. Recombination is very slow at these great heights.

Actually, as is well known, the quality of long distance radio communication is better at night than in the day. This is because any ionization below the E layer has an inimical effect by causing absorption of the radio waves – the free electrons which are set in motion by the electric field of the wave lose this energy very quickly in collision with gas molecules in these comparatively dense regions, whereas at higher levels they re-radiate the energy they receive from the wave before it is lost by collision. At night, all ionization below 60 miles is almost completely absent.

There are times when the ionization below the E layer is greatly increased at all points on the sunlit side of the earth and no transmission of radio signals is possible because of strong absorption. Such *radio fadeouts* occur usually in association with solar flares. The increased ionization at low levels is probably due to the short X-rays emitted at these times. In high latitudes, radio transmission is often interrupted because the ionization at low levels is too high. Here the effect is probably due to ionization by charged particles from the sun (see p. 291).

It seems probable that the F_1 and F_2 layers arise from ionization of atomic oxygen by solar ultraviolet light, while the E layer is produced mainly by solar X-rays. By flying mass spectrographs in rockets it has been found that, in the E and lower F_1 regions, the main ions are those of nitric oxide (NO) but at higher levels the ions of atomic oxygen become the most abundant. This does not mean that in these regions the electrons are produced by ionization of neutral nitric oxide molecules normally present in the atmosphere. Instead ions such as those of molecular oxygen (O_2) and atomic oxygen (O) which are major neutral atmospheric constituents are almost certainly formed in the initial ionizing process but, on collision with nitrogen molecules, reactions take place quite readily to produce ions of nitric oxide:

$$O^+ + N_2 \rightarrow NO^+ + N,$$
$$O_2^+ + N_2 \rightarrow NO^+ + NO.$$

The variation of the electron concentrations of the different layers has been studied as a function of latitude and longitude, season, time of day and epoch in the sun-spot cycle. Both the E and F_2 layers behave in a relatively simple fashion, closely correlated with the variation of intensity of the solar radiation, but the F_2 layer is much more complex.

The interpretation of the F_2 layer variations is bound up with another very important aspect of the ionosphere. Solar and lunar tides exist in the atmosphere. As remarked earlier (p. 283) the solar atmospheric tide is of relatively much greater importance than the lunar, in contrast to the ocean tides. This is because the 12-hourly oscillations of the force due to solar gravity are in close resonance with a natural period of oscillation of the atmosphere. The lunar force has a period of half a lunar day, which is 12 hours 51 minutes, so the resonance effect is much less marked. It is possible to understand the existence of the 12 hour period of natural oscillation in terms of a temperature distribution of the shape shown in Fig. 11.3, with the second minimum at an altitude of 55 miles.

The tidal motions in the high atmosphere are much magnified as compared with those at ground. Thus, at 60 miles altitude, the wind due to the solar tide may be as great as 56 miles/hour as compared with less than $\frac{1}{2}$ mile/hour at sea level.

Because of the tidal forces, the ions in the ionosphere are set in motion in directions which will, in general, make an angle with that of the earth's magnetic field. We have then a situation similar to that in a dynamo. The ionosphere, with its free charges, is a conductor moved across the magnetic field, just as the armature of a dynamo is rotated between the poles of its magnet. In both cases an electric current is generated. These dynamo currents in the ionosphere produce magnetic effects on the ground which exhibit the same variability as the currents themselves. This is the origin of the so-called quiet magnetic variations which are observed regularly in magnetic observatories all over the world. These variations can be analysed into two sets, one of which varies with the solar period and the other with the lunar, the former being the more pronounced as is expected from the fact that it is due to the stronger solar component of the atmospheric tide. Direct evidence of the existence of the dynamo currents has been obtained by measuring the variation of magnetic field with altitude in a rocket ascent.

The dynamo currents circulate below the F_2 layer but, owing to electromagnetic effects, they produce motion in that layer, rather in the same sort of way as an electric motor is driven. It appears that these motions are responsible for much of the complicated behaviour of the layer.

Magnetic and Ionospheric Storms and the Aurora

In high latitudes the aurora is a familiar but always impressive sight, perhaps the most awe-inspiring that the sky can offer. It is most frequently seen from narrow belts of latitude (about 5° wide), about 23° from either magnetic pole, known as the auroral zones. Auroral displays can take a wide variety of forms and colours. They may be steady or show rapid fluctuations, the most spectacular being seen in the flaming aurorae in which strong pulses of light move rapidly upwards in sequence towards the magnetic zenith, the direction towards which a suspended compass needle points. Some of the forms which occur are illustrated in Plate 11.3.

Detailed analysis of auroral light shows that much of it arises from excited oxygen atoms and nitrogen molecules, both neutral and ionized, but an important constituent is apparent under certain conditions. This is light emitted from hydrogen atoms which are in quite rapid motion as judged from the Doppler width of the spectrum lines (see Chapter 7, footnote p. 198). Speeds as high as 2000 miles per second have been observed for these atoms. This is very significant for the interpretation of auroral phenomena as explained below.

Auroral displays are strong when the sun is in a disturbed condition and, in the auroral zones, occur nearly every night near the maximum of the sunspot cycle. There is a marked correlation also between auroral displays and magnetic and ionospheric disturbances. Superposed on the quiet magnetic variations due to dynamo currents in the ionosphere, there are irregular variations which are sometimes so marked as to deserve the title of magnetic storms. Intense magnetic storms are nearly always associated with great auroral displays which may be seen at much lower latitudes than is usual. At the same time, radio transmission over high latitude regions is usually disturbed and polar blackouts (see p. 288) occur.

The strong geographical concentration of these correlated effects towards the poles suggests that they arise, not from solar electromagnetic radiation, but from charged particles shot out in streams from disturbed areas of the sun. Further evidence in favour of this is afforded by the observation of a time delay of the order of a day between the occurrence of a solar disturbance and the onset of an auroral display or magnetic storm on the earth. Electromagnetic waves travelling across the space between the sun and the earth with the speed of light take only 8 minutes, so we must suppose that it is a stream of material particles, travelling much more slowly, which is effective.

The problem of determining the effects which arise when a corpuscular stream of this kind comes under the interaction of the earth's magnetism is a very difficult one and is far from solved to-day. Fresh evidence, which must ultimately be of the greatest importance, has been obtained recently from observations made with artificial satellites which are described in Chapter 12, p. 319.

The Doppler-broadened hydrogen lines observed in auroral spectra are considered to arise from atoms produced when the protons entering the atmosphere capture electrons from atoms and molecules in the air to produce neutral but excited hydrogen atoms.

Whistlers

Lightning flashes are intense sources of electromagnetic waves of long wavelength. The atmospherics which disturb radio reception arise in this way. If a suitable amplifier is connected to a tall receiving aerial, the arrival of an atmospheric is recorded as a crash in the loudspeaker. Sometimes these crashes are followed, at intervals of a few seconds, by faint whistling noises which are first heard at the limit of the audible range and then fall in pitch throughout this range in about half a second. If more than one such whistle is heard, the time for the pitch to fall throughout the audible range increases so that, if for the first whistle it takes t seconds, for the second it will be $2t$, for the next $4t$ and so on. The whistles, which get progressively fainter, occur at regular intervals. Sometimes they are not preceded by a crash and when this is so the duration of successive whistles is in the ratio 1 to 3 to 5 etc.

The explanation of these whistlers, as they are called, is quite extraordinary. Very low frequency radio waves passing through an ionized region follow a line of magnetic force. The velocity of propagation along such a path is greater the higher the frequency. When an atmospheric is produced by a lightning flash, part of the energy travels outwards along a line of magnetic force which eventually returns to the surface in the opposite hemisphere (see Fig. 11.6). Here part of the energy is reflected

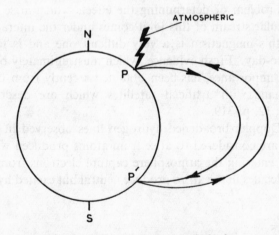

Fig. 11.6. Illustrating the production of whistlers.

An atmospheric at P produces long waves which follow the magnetic lines of force to the antipodal point P' where they are reflected to return along the same path to P when they may be again partly reflected to return to P' and so on.

to retraverse the line of force back to the original source. Because they travel faster the high frequency components arrive first, and so the returning atmospheric is heard as a falling whistle. Some of the energy may be again reflected to traverse the double path once more. The time interval between the arrival, at the source, of the highest and lowest audible frequencies will now be twice as large and so on. It is also possible to receive atmospherics produced at the antipodal point from which they have followed a line of force to arrive at the receiver (see Fig. 11.6). In this case two reflections must occur for a second whistler to be heard, and the path followed by this will be three times that for the first and so on.

This interpretation of the phenomenon enables one to estimate the electron concentrations at distances as great as 10,000 miles from the earth's surface. Unexpectedly high values, as much as 400/c.c., are found, suggesting that there is rather more of interest to be studied in interplanetary space near the earth than might be thought at first sight.

CHAPTER 12

ARTIFICIAL SATELLITES AND SPACE PROBES

'How will they find
Their way across the sky?
Some will splash in the Milky Way,
Or bump in the moon – oh dear!'
ELEANOR FARJEON,
'LIGHT THE LAMPS UP, LAMPLIGHTER'

Advantages of Satellite Observing Stations

In the preceding Chapter we described how the use of rockets as vehicles to carry instruments up to high altitudes has provided new information about conditions in the high atmosphere of the earth – difficult, if not impossible, to come by in any other way. Most atmospheric properties vary considerably with position on the earth, as well as with time of day, season and the state of the sun. As a vertical sounding rocket completes its entire path and returns to earth in a few minutes only, it is obvious that the study in this way of the variability in time of any quantity is going to be a very gradual process. A similar situation arises in relation to dependence on latitude and longitude.

It is therefore an attractive possibility to contemplate an observatory which circles indefinitely round the earth as a satellite, making observations continually which can be transmitted to receiving stations on the earth by the usual telemetry procedure (see Chapter 11, p. 277). A satellite station of this kind, transmitting data for only one month, will give as many results as could be obtained by launching 9,000 rockets to measure the same quantities. This is ample justification for the fuller investigation of the feasibility of the whole idea.

Before doing this, however, we must again notice that the use of satellite observing stations by no means eliminates the need for vertical sounding experiments with rockets. As will be shown below, satellites can only circulate for any useful time in orbits which do not approach the surface within 120 miles or so.

Vertical rocket flights therefore remain necessary for studying the vertical structure of the atmosphere up to these levels. For observations at much higher levels, satellites are very much more effective and provide a given amount of information at a much smaller total cost than would be incurred if the same amount of information were obtained from vertical rocket flights. The rate of accumulation of data is also very much higher.

Although we have been led to consider artificial satellites in order to extend the scope of direct study of the earth's outer atmosphere, it turns out, as so often happens, that once satellites are available new prospects are opened which reach out to the furthest extent of the universe. A satellite observatory offers, for the first time, the opportunity of carrying out studies of the structure of the universe in radiations other than visible light and the short range of radio wavelengths (see Chapter 10, p. 247) to which we are confined on the ground. The big discoveries made through the development of radioastronomy (Chapter 10) show what can be achieved when a new observing range of wavelengths becomes available. Artificial satellite observatories circulate outside the absorbing atmosphere and so the choice of observing wavelengths, be it in the gamma, X-, ultraviolet or infrared ray region, is unrestricted.

Another question of major importance which may be studied is that of the nature of the force of gravity. As pointed out in Chapter 9, p. 242, this is the weakest known force, as compared with the forces between fundamental particles. To investigate its nature we have to take advantage of the fact that the force of gravity which a body exerts is proportional to its mass, so that with large enough bodies the force is great enough to measure accurately. In practice this means that we have to deal with the gravitational effects of bodies of astronomical size. With artificial satellites available the scope for experiment is greatly increased. This is partly because small effects are more readily detected and measured. Many produce changes in the orbit of a revolving body which build up steadily at a constant rate per revolution. The time taken for a steady change to grow to a measurable value is therefore shorter the shorter the time of revolution. Artificial satellites make a complete revolution in an hour or so as compared with a month for the moon and much longer times for the planets – hence the advantage in using them.

There is the further advantage that, with instruments in artificial satellites or space probes (see p. 312), the size of the laboratory for gravitational studies may be extended to a substantial part of the solar system.

We shall enlarge on these matters below after first discussing some of the problems involved in launching satellites.

Orbits under Gravity

The force of gravity which a body of spherical shape and mass distribution exerts on any other body is the same as it would be if all the mass of the body were concentrated at its centre. Thus a small body of mass m moves outside the earth under a force due to the earth's gravity which is directed towards the centre of the earth and is of magnitude given very nearly by GMm/R^2 where M is the mass of the earth, G is the universal constant of gravitation and R is the distance of the body from the centre of the earth. This is not exactly correct because the earth is only approximately spherical in shape and mass distribution. However, for present purposes, the approximation is adequate.

A body moving under a central attractive force which varies inversely as the square of the distance from the centre must describe a path which is either an ellipse, parabola or hyperbola, with the centre at a focus. These three possibilities are illustrated in Fig. 12.1. If the body is launched with speed u when at a distance R from the attracting centre the orbit is elliptic, parabolic or hyperbolic according as u^2 is less than, equal to or greater than $2GM/R$ respectively. Elliptic orbits are all of the closed type in which the body never recedes from the centre beyond a certain distance (the apogee distance when referring to motion round the earth). Parabolic and hyperbolic orbits are of the open type in which the body recedes eventually to an infinite distance from the attracting centre – it escapes from its attraction. The condition that a body should just be able to escape when at a distance R from the centre is that

$$u^2 = 2GM/R = V^2, \text{ say.} \tag{1}$$

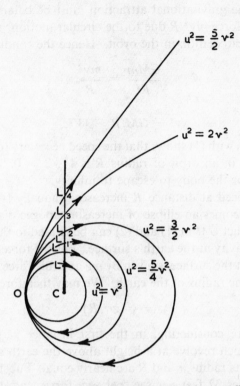

Fig. 12.1. Illustrating typical orbits of a body launched horizontally with velocity u when at a point O outside the earth whose centre is at C. v is the velocity for a circular orbit (see (2) of text). If u^2 is less than $2v^2$ the orbits are closed curves (ellipses). For u^2 greater than $2v^2$ the orbits are open curves (hyperbolas). If $u^2 = 2v^2$ it is a parabola which is also an open curve. Note also that if u^2 is greater than v^2 O is the nearest point (perigee) of the orbit to the centre but if u^2 is less than v^2 it is the furthest point (apogee) from the centre.

The shape of the orbit is specified by the eccentricity e. If the perpendicular to OC from C intersects an orbit in L say, the ratio $CL/OC = 1 + e$ for all orbits for which CL is not less than OC. For the circular orbit $CL = OC$ and $e = 0$, for the elliptic orbit CL/OC is between 1 and 2 so e is less than 1, for the parabolic $CL_2 = 2OC$ so $e = 1$, and for the hyperbolic orbit CL_4/OC is greater than 2 and e is greater than 1. For orbits for which CL is less than OC the ratio $CL^1/OC = 1 - e$.

The condition for the body to pursue a circular orbit of radius R is that the gravitational attraction must be balanced by the centrifugal force mv^2/R due to the circular motion, v being the velocity of circulation in the orbit. Hence the condition is

$$\frac{GMm}{R^2} = \frac{mv^2}{R},$$

or

$$v^2 = GM/R = \tfrac{1}{2}V^2. \qquad (2)$$

Comparison with (1) shows that the speed necessary for the body to circulate in an orbit of radius R is $1/\sqrt{2} = 0.7$ times that necessary for the body to escape to infinity.

As the speed at distance R increases gradually from v to V the orbit becomes an ellipse of increasing apogee distance.

The product GM in (1) and (2) can be related to the acceleration g of gravity at the earth's surface. For the force on a body of mass m at the surface is given by mg and this force is GMm/r^2 where r is the radius of the earth. We may therefore write

$$v = \sqrt{(gr^2/R)}.$$

Since we are considering, in the first instance at least, only satellites which revolve at a height above the earth small compared with its radius, r and R are nearly equal. Substituting the known values 32 feet per sec. per sec. for g, and 4,000 miles for R we find that the required speed is about 26,000 feet per sec. or 18,000 miles per hour. This indicates the speed which must be communicated to a body in order that it should circulate as a satellite. When it is compared with the speed reached at burnout by a Viking rocket, 4,500 miles per hour (see Chapter 11, p. 275), the problem of launching a satellite seems formidable, but in fact the attainment of the necessary speed is not the major difficulty.

A satellite will pass through some atmosphere, however tenuous, as it circulates and this will produce a drag force which will cause the orbit to spiral gradually in towards the earth at an ever increasing rate. Eventually the satellite will plunge into the dense lower atmosphere and be burnt up by the air friction. It is not difficult to estimate that, for a lifetime as great as a few months, a satellite must be launched into an orbit which at no point approaches the earth's surface much closer than 120 miles. This imposes severe limitations on the accuracy with which the sarellite must be projected initially.

To follow a circular orbit the body must be projected at the chosen height with a velocity of exactly the correct magnitude in an accurately horizontal direction. In practice this is not possible so the orbit will actually be an ellipse. It must then be ensured that the launching conditions are such that the perigee of the orbit, the point of closest approach to the earth's surface (or, strictly, to the centre of the earth), is at least 120 miles above the surface. If launched with a speed greater than the circular speed v, the launching height is at the perigee of the orbit (see Fig. 12.1) but, if the speed is less than the circular speed, it is at the apogee or furthest distance from the earth's surface (see Fig. 12.1). It is therefore highly desirable to have sufficient power in hand to impart more than the circular speed. The more that can be done in this direction the higher the error in direction of launching which can be tolerated, within limits. This is achieved at the cost of an increased apogee distance which may not be serious, and indeed may be a distinct advantage. In practice the direction of launching must be correct within a few degrees.

The problem of launching a useful satellite can be stated as follows. A useful weight of instruments in a suitable container must be carried up to a height of over 120 miles and then projected at a speed of not less than 18,000 miles an hour in a direction within a few degrees of the horizontal. Apart from the launching problem, it is necessary to track the satellite's progress so that its position at any time can be determined with very high accuracy. Finally, of course, the instruments must operate satisfactorily and transmit the data they observe to suitable receiving stations on the ground. To take full advantage of the continuous observations which may be made as the satellite revolves, the information may be stored on tape recorders and then relayed to earth as the satellite comes within radio range of a suitable receiving station. This transmission can be arranged to occur on receipt of an interrogating signal from the station.

Artificial Satellites

Use of Multistage Rockets for Launching Satellites

Although the gap between the 4,500 miles per hour which is attained by a Viking rocket and the 18,000 miles per hour required for launching a satellite seems very large, it may be bridged by using a multi-stage rocket assembly. The principle involved is quite simple.

The assembly is launched by firing the first rocket motor. When this motor has burnt out it drops off and a second motor fires. Because of the reduced weight and air drag the power of this motor may be much smaller than that of the first and yet be able to add a considerable velocity. The procedure may be repeated after second stage burnout and so on.

A sequence of this kind has been utilised by the Americans in their launching of the Explorer and Vanguard satellites and has certainly been adopted also by the Russians in launching their much heavier satellites.

The planning of the launching sequence to ensure optimum performance is quite complicated and it is necessary to decide the way in which the direction of the rocket thrust should be varied in going from a vertical take-off to a final horizontal projection into the orbit. Because of the large drag in the dense lower air it is desirable to direct the thrust initially so that the rocket rises vertically until sufficiently tenuous air is reached. The direction of the thrust is then gradually changed until the rocket is travelling parallel to the earth's surface. The thrust is maintained along this arc until a sufficiently high speed is reached at which stage the motor is shut off and the rocket coasts up to the planned launching level, arriving there in a horizontal direction. Application of a small thrust at this stage is then sufficient to launch the system into its orbit.

Actual launching sequences depart more or less from this because of various practical requirements, but are generally similar. Thus in the Vanguard sequence the first stage employs a Viking motor which burns for 146 seconds and accelerates the system to 4,000 feet/sec. By this time a height of about 33 miles is reached and the control mechanism has tilted the axis a little towards the horizontal. The first stage motor then drops off, the second stage fires and burns for 120 secs. imparting an additional speed of 8,400 feet per second, and reaching a height of 122 miles at burnout. By this time the control mechanism has turned the axis quite close to horizontal. Before the second stage motor is jettisoned the system coasts on up to the launching height of 260 miles. When it is accurately horizontal the second stage motor is jettisoned and the third stage motor fired to communicate the necessary additional 13,500 feet per second.

The control system in the Vanguard is in the second stage so, when this stage is jettisoned, there is no further control of aspect angle. Because of this the third stage is set spinning round its axis just before the separation from the second stage. It is not necessary, however, for the whole sequence to be fully automatic after launching. Thus, after the second stage, the aspect angle of the rocket could be measured by means of suitable internal equipment and the results telemetred to ground. On receipt of information showing the axis to be horizontal the final stage rocket could be fired through a command radio signal from the ground. A procedure similar to this has been used in the American Explorer satellites.

Acquisition and Tracking

It is important to locate a satellite and determine its orbit soon after launching. This is best done by using a radio beacon, a transmitter in the satellite, the signals from which may be received at ground stations. The frequency must be chosen so that the propagation of the radio waves is not seriously affected by the ionosphere. It is not desirable to go too far in this direction by choosing a very high frequency, for the following reason.

For really accurate determination of the orbit it is necessary to use optical methods, in any case, as it is not possible to make the radio observations with the necessary precision, even if there were no ionospheric distortion. If the frequency is chosen so that this distortion is not too large but is nevertheless measurable by comparison with optical observations, it is possible, not only to obtain preliminary orbit data, but also to derive information about the ionosphere from the nature and magnitude of the distortion it produces in the radio signals.

The initial American choice of 108 Mc/sec. is somewhat too high to be useful for ionospheric studies, the Russian 40 Mc/sec. being a much better compromise. The use of the two frequencies of 20 and 40 Mc/sec. is even more suitable as the propagation of the former is markedly affected by the ionosphere.

Two methods of determining position by radio methods may be used. One is essentially the same as employed in radio astronomy, the interferometer method (Chapter 10, p. 251), and the other depends on the Doppler frequency shift of the signal due to the velocity of the satellite towards or away from the receiver. By using the observations made simultaneously by either method at two different stations, the position of the satellite at the time of observation can be obtained.

Having located the satellite by radio methods it is possible to predict the path for the following day or so with sufficient accuracy to enable the much more precise optical methods to be applied. These employ instruments which cannot readily be used to find a satellite but, if the path is known approximately, they may be pointed in the right direction so as to make much more accurate observations of the satellite's passage across their field of view. Even so the problem is difficult, for a satellite is only rendered visible through its power of reflecting sunlight. During daytime it is not bright enough to be seen while at night it is eclipsed by the earth. It is only visible, therefore, at twilight or dawn. Furthermore, the high speed of the satellite poses unusual problems and completely rules out the use of large telescopes of the conventional sort. Nevertheless, optical equipment for precise tracking has been developed and already used successfully.

A further method is available for not too small or too distant satellites. This involves the use of radar reflection from the satellite (see Chapter 10, p. 248). If the radar signal is transmitted in the form of a pulse the time between the sending out of the pulse and the reception of the scattered pulse from the satellite gives the range from transmitter to satellite. Furthermore if the angular width of the radar beam which is radiated is, say, $\alpha°$, then the bearing angle can be determined to $\pm \alpha°$.

This method has the advantage that it is applicable when the satellite radio beacon has ceased transmission and also during day or night. It is not capable of as high an accuracy as the best optical methods, but provides a very valuable additional means of tracking.

Scientific Observations with Satellites

We must distinguish between two types of observation which may be made. Even for a satellite without an operating radio beacon the precise determination of the orbit and of its gradual variation with time can provide very useful data on the air density at heights near the perigee of the orbit as well as on the shape and dimensions of the earth. If a radio beacon is also in operation, radiating on two frequencies such as 20 and 40 Mc/sec. it is possible, from comparison of the apparent positions as determined from the radio observations with those determined accurately by optical methods, to obtain information, about the high ionosphere above the maximum of the F_2 layer (see Fig. 11.5, p. 287), which it is difficult to obtain in any other way. It follows that even those countries which do not undertake the launching of satellites may nevertheless carry out ground-based observations from which much of scientific interest may be gleaned.

Naturally, in addition to these considerable possibilities, a satellite normally carries equipment to make observations of the properties of the region immediately surrounding it and to transfer the observed results to ground by a telemetry system very similar in principle to the procedure involved with high altitude vertical sounding rockets (see Chapter 11, p. 277).

An important problem which must be solved is that of providing a power supply within a satellite to operate the radio beacon and telemetry systems. Conventional batteries are inadequate as the weight required for a long lifetime is prohibitive. One solution is to use solar cells which transform the energy of sunlight into electrical power.

A great number of important scientific investigations can be carried out in this way. We have already stressed the great value of being able to look at the universe around us in radiations which do not reach the ground through our absorbing atmosphere. It is not necessary to await the time, not far distant, when actual telescopes are carried in satellites. A great deal can be done with much less elaborate equipment in exploring a totally new field of observation. Already the first observations of the variation over the sky of the intensity of quite short ultraviolet radiations (near 1250 Å) have been made with simple instruments carried in vertical sounding rockets. These results show features which are by no means the same as seen in visible light and indicate what a wealth of new knowledge of the universe is opening out before us. As this becomes available our ideas about the structure and evolution of the stars and galaxies will be sharpened and expanded.

It is important to remember that the study of radiation also includes that coming from the earth itself. From this it will be possible to obtain continuous information about the cloud coverage over the earth's surface – the reflecting and scattering power of a surface depends much on its nature. With a cloudless sky over the ocean very little radiation is reflected or scattered back but a cloud layer will send back between 50 and 75% of the radiation incident on it. The value to meteorologists of this regular information about atmospheric cloud over the whole surface will certainly be very great. As development proceeds it will become possible to transmit television pictures from satellites (see p. 319), thereby recording details such as cyclonic disturbances etc. which will be of even greater value. Plate 12.1 illustrates a beautiful picture taken from a high altitude rocket showing a cyclonic disturbance, the presence of which had not been suspected from the ground. This is the type of observation which should become regularly available through satellite developments in the future.

Apart from the electromagnetic radiations, great interest is attached to observations of particles of all kinds and energies. These include extremely energetic nuclei in the cosmic rays as well as protons and electrons in solar corpuscular streams (Chapter 11, p. 291 and this Chapter, p. 323). At the other extreme there is the fine dust of micrometeorites. We must also remember that there is the important need to study the composition of the very high atmosphere and ionosphere, to follow it outwards as it merges into interplanetary space and to determine the steady state properties of this space itself. Of recent years, evidence has been accumulating that this space is by no means as empty as was at first thought (see Chapter 11, p. 293).

There are many problems associated with cosmic rays which still await solution. Any new information bearing on the origin of the rays is of value. One aspect, for example, which gives an indication of the age of the radiation, the time travelled by it from its source, is its composition. As described in Chapter 8, most of the cosmic ray particles are very energetic protons but other nuclei are also present. In the course of a very long journey through space the heavier nuclei will be partially broken up by collision with the occasional atoms they encounter. Because of this there will be a re-distribution in the relative abundances of the different nuclei, depending on the time of travel. If we make the reasonable assumption that initially the abundance ratios are the same as for the elements in the universe, it is possible from observations on the constitution of primary cosmic rays to check for consistency the assumptions made and, if the check is satisfactory, to make an estimate of the age of the rays.

Arrangements may be made, by including suitable counters in a satellite, for the primary cosmic ray intensity to be continually monitored over the path of a satellite. This can be related to the distribution of magnetic field outside the earth, for the motion of the charged particles is strongly controlled by such fields. In this way we can obtain information which is related to the presence or otherwise of solar corpuscular streams, upper atmospheric currents, etc., all of which can modify the field felt by the cosmic rays.

For the first time we have the prospect of systematic study of the softer particle radiation which is present outside the atmosphere, arising from solar corpuscular streams or otherwise. Already this has provided unexpected results and it is clear that a new field of investigation is now opening before us, the thorough exploitation of which will take years.

The solid particles which enter the earth's atmosphere vary

very greatly in size, from the large and fortunately rare meteorites which penetrate right to the ground, through the meteors which are volatilized by heating at quite high altitudes in the atmosphere (60 miles or so) to the micrometeorites, less than 10^{-4} inch in diameter, which are too small to heat up in the atmosphere. The latter are difficult to observe and a great uncertainty attaches to estimates made of the amount of this fine dust which is collected by the earth every day. An answer to this question is of interest in connection with the properties of interplanetary space. So far, rocket observations, using very sensitive impact microphones to count the fine particles impinging on a suitably exposed plate, have been inconclusive and it is clear that a long term systematic study by different methods, using instruments in satellites, is called for.

Study of the steady state composition of a satellite's surroundings involves air density measurements with suitable pressure gauges, the use of mass spectrographs to determine the composition of the neutral and of the ionized gas, and the determination of ion concentrations by collecting the current of ions which is swept up by the satellite as it moves through space with a speed much greater than that of the ions.

A whole further series of important observations is concerned with the study of the magnetic field and the strength of the earth's gravity at points on the satellite's orbit. We have already indicated how, from satellite cosmic ray observations, one could derive data about the magnetic field but direct measurement of the field would be possible using instruments already developed for, and operated successfully in, vertical sounding rockets. By comparing the magnetic variations observed at ground stations with those from a satellite it will be possible to decide whether the current system responsible for the variations circulates below or above the satellite. This would provide a valuable test of the validity of current theories of the origin of magnetic variations.

The earth's gravitational field is determined by the distribution of matter within the earth as well as on its shape. In turn, it determines the detailed form of the satellite's orbit and it is from precise observations of the orbit and its variations with time that we can hope to obtain new information about the field. No instruments are required in the satellite.

There is also the far wider subject of the nature of gravitation itself. The new opportunities which are afforded for the observational study of this subject have been emphasized in general terms on p. 295. We shall refer here to one or two specific possibilities although we cannot foresee more than the very beginning.

The only big advance in our understanding of the nature of gravitation since the time of Newton is contained in Einstein's general theory of relativity, put forward in 1915. This is a remarkable attempt to generalize the ideas of the special theory (see Chapter 4) to apply to the relations between space and time measurements made in two systems of reference which move with accelerated motion relative to each other. It will be remembered that the special theory deals with these relations only when the systems of reference move with constant relative velocity. The basic idea of the general theory is the *principle of equivalence*. Some idea of what is involved may be gained in the following way.

A particle rotating in a circular path feels an outwardly directed force, known as the centrifugal force (see p. 298). It has been suggested that the absence of gravity felt by the crew of a manned satellite station could be practically compensated for by rotating the station at a suitable rate – the centrifugal force would, to a certain extent, simulate the force of gravity. Einstein postulated that, in fact, there is no essential difference in the nature of the two forces. According to his view, the centrifugal force is due to gravitational effects introduced by the rotation of the particle relative to the vast distant masses in the universe. Once this view is accepted, it is possible to examine the relationship of space and time measurements made in two systems which are in non-uniform motion with respect to each other.

It then appears that two clocks, moving in regions in which the force of gravity is different, will not keep the same time, even when full allowance is made for any effects of the force on the material of the clock, or on the motion of its parts. This prediction can be subject to direct experimental test by comparing the time keeping of two clocks, one in a satellite and one on the ground. The sought-for effect is a very small one* but very reliable atomic clocks are now available, depending on the frequency of a particular transition between energy states in a chosen atom or molecule (Chapter 3, p. 110). As a satellite circulates any difference in timing can be built up to a measurable value. Direct checks of this kind would greatly increase confidence in the essential correctness of Einstein's general theory. Up to the present very few opportunities of observational test have been forthcoming and much more must be done before the theory could be regarded as anything like so well established as the special theory.

Further interesting possibilities also arise because of the prospect of detecting very small gravitational effects. According to the principle of equivalence we would expect that the universal constant of gravitation G (see p. 296) should be proportional to the ratio of the total mass of the universe to its mean radius. The expansion of the universe (see Chapter 10, p. 265), indicated by the high velocities of recession of distant nebulae, suggests that the mean radius is steadily increasing. Does this mean that G is slowly falling or is there a compensating effect due, say, to continuous creation of matter in the universe? The possibility of a direct observational check of the constancy of G is no longer entirely out of the question.

These are but two fascinating ways in which our understanding of gravitation, the weakest of all the known types of force (see Chapter 9, p. 242), may be deepened. Many others will doubtless be realised.

We may enquire also whether any practical applications can be made of artificial satellites. In a sense we have already mentioned one, the value for meteorological prediction – it may even open the way to long range forecasting, which would be of great economic value. The presence of two or three satellites

---

* On 30 January 1960 evidence in support of the predicted effect was reported on the basis of some remarkable laboratory experiments. This is a further indication of the speed of advance in physics today and of the extraordinary technical performances which are being achieved.

in semi-permanent orbits might well be very useful in providing navigational fixes. A further possibility is to use satellite repeater stations for long distance transmission of radio waves which are too short to be reflected from the ionosphere. This includes particularly the wavelengths used for television. As the art develops other applications will doubtless be found but, as in all pure scientific research, the stimulus is the desire to find out and understand new natural phenomena. Enough has surely been said to show how much help satellites are likely to be in this way.

The First Artificial Satellites

On 10th October, 1957, the first satellite (Sputnik I) was launched successfully from the Soviet Union. It was a sphere of about 1 foot radius containing radio beacons operating at frequencies of 20 and 40 Mc/sec. These beacons remained active for two weeks during which time a great number of Doppler and interferometer records were made in several countries. There were no other instruments within this first pioneering vehicle. It was accompanied, though at a steadily increasing separation, by the third stage rocket case which was quite a bright object in the twilight sky.

The second satellite (Sputnik II) launched on 9th November, 1957, showed how far rocket technology had advanced in the Soviet Union. The total weight of the launching rocket for Vanguard was about 11 tons and the final weight of the satellite 20 lbs. If the third stage rocket case is included the total weight to be launched is about 50 lbs. Sputnik II, in which the third stage rocket case was not separated, weighed 1500 lbs! In addition to radio transmitters similar to those in Sputnik I, it carried counters to monitor cosmic radiation as well as instruments to measure the satellite temperature and the intensity of radiation. Most of the available space was used up, however, by the chamber carrying the dog, the equipment required to maintain its oxygen, water and food supply and the instruments to measure the physiological condition of the animal.

Both of these satellites circulated in orbits the inclination of whose plane to the equator was close to 65°. Their initial perigee distances were also nearly equal (145 and 140 miles respectively) but the initial apogee distance for Sputnik II (1020 miles) was much greater than for Sputnik I (575 miles). The rocket case of Sputnik I eventually plunged into the atmosphere and was burnt up on 1st December, 1957 while Sputnik II suffered the same fate on 14th April, 1958.

The first satellite successfully launched by the U.S.A. was Explorer I on the 31st January, 1958. In this class of satellite the third stage is not separated and consists of a cylinder 80″ long and 6″ in diameter, weighing 31 lbs. A second successful launching of an Explorer satellite (Explorer III) was achieved on 26th March, 1958 and a third (Explorer IV) on 26th July, 1958. In all cases these satellites included a radio beacon transmitting at 108 Mc/sec. The first two were launched at an inclination of 33° but Explorer IV was launched into a more inclined orbit (51°). All contained counter equipment for the monitoring of cosmic radiation, as well as for the measurement of the temperature of the rocket shell and the interior, and for the observation of micrometeorites. The data obtained from the first two provided very strong evidence of the existence of a belt of very high intensity radiation extending outwards from an altitude of 500 miles or so from the earth (see Chapter 11, p. 291). It was not possible to obtain much evidence about the nature of the radiation with the simple equipment included so Explorer IV was specially fitted with apparatus of a more complex character specially adapted for this purpose. Very interesting results were obtained, some of which are discussed on p. 318. The initial perigee distances of the three Explorers were 220, 113 and 163 miles respectively and the corresponding apogee distances 1590, 1750 and 1370 miles. Explorers III and IV plunged to destruction on 28th June, 1958 and 23rd October, 1959 respectively but Explorer I is likely to circulate for 2-3 years.

In between the launching of Explorers I and III a successful test launching of Vanguard was carried out (17th March, 1958). A small sphere of $6\frac{1}{2}$″ diameter and 3 lbs. weight containing two radio transmitters at 108 Mc/sec., one powered by solar batteries, was placed successfully in an orbit with a perigee distance as high as 400 miles and an apogee distance of 2500 miles.

This object is likely to remain in orbit for 100 years or so and, although one of its transmitters has already failed, that powered by solar batteries is still in operation and may last for a long time yet. The rocket case, weighing 30 lbs., was separated and also circulates as a satellite.

By far the most sophisticated satellite to be launched up to the time of writing is Sputnik III which was placed in orbit on 15th May, 1958 with perigee and apogee distances of 140 and 1160 miles respectively. It was separated from the rocket case and weighed over 1 ton. Apart from radio transmitters operating at 20 and 40 Mc/sec., instruments were carried for the measurement of satellite temperature and voltage, gas density and composition, concentration and nature of positive ions, electric field strength, intensity of cosmic and other radiations, abundance of heavy nuclei in the cosmic rays, concentration of micrometeorites and magnetic field strength. Most of this apparatus functioned well but some information was lost through incomplete world-wide coverage of telemetry reception. The observations of radiation confirm in general terms the conclusions derived from the Explorer equipment and are discussed on p. 319. It appears that the satellite charges up to a few volts negative with respect to its surroundings.

It is clear that already we have in Sputnik III a circulating laboratory of considerable versatility. The possibility of using solar batteries to provide power indefinitely in a satellite of this type opens up the prospect of a rapid increase in our knowledge of the outer fringe of the earth's atmosphere and the neighbouring interplanetary space. It is likely that an even wider range of investigations can be carried out in future satellites in which the impressive weight and space of Sputnik III are combined with the use of miniature components for which the Americans have a special genius.

Information obtained by Analysis of the Orbits of the First Satellites

Although a worldwide observing network was not established at the time the first Russian satellites were launched, a number of valuable precision observations were made of their orbits through improvised arrangements. Taken in conjunction with the more complete data obtained from the later satellites these observations have already led to some important new results about the air density at high altitudes and about the figure of the earth.

Although it is a very good approximation for most purposes to regard the earth as a perfect sphere, it has long been known that, apart from detailed departures from this shape due to mountain ranges, etc., there is a small general flattening at the poles as compared with the equator. If a is the radius at the equator, b at the poles then the ratio $(a-b)/a$ can be taken as a measure of this flattening. The value derived for this quantity from gravity surveys over the earth's surface was $1/_{297.3}$. It is now known from analysis of the orbits of artificial satellites that this should be changed to $1/_{298.24}$. In terms of distances this means that the difference between equatorial and polar radii is now known to be 100 yards less than previously supposed. This already shows how sensitively the shape of the earth can be traced from observations of artificial satellites. In fact the analysis has proceeded to at least one stage further in determining the nature of the chief large scale deviations from the flattened spherical shape.

The Scientific Exploration of the Moon and Interplanetary Space

The successful initiation of the satellite programme and the high promise which it holds naturally leads one to enquire what are the possibilities of extending it so as to carry out direct observation of regions far out in interplanetary space. Among such investigations the direct study of the moon would naturally play a leading part. Investigations of this kind are now coming within the range of practical realisation and we shall first discuss the problems and prospects of the use of lunar probes. After this we shall say something about the possibility of any more distant excursions. It will appear in all these instances that the very wide range of scientific observations which may be made can be carried out without the use of manned vehicles. Automatic methods of control, measurement and data recovery are now so highly developed that human intervention is rarely necessary to carry out any assigned scientific tasks.

The problems in space probing are fourfold. First there is the need for sufficient rocket thrust to take the probe, containing a useful load of equipment, to the distant regions to be investigated. Next it is essential that guidance and control be adequate to ensure that the probe follows the path necessary to take it to its destination. As it is clearly of no use to obtain information from a probe without knowing where it is at the time, there must be adequate facilities for tracking it out to great distances. Finally, the transmission of data observed by the instruments within the probe must be possible over the great distances separating the observing point from receiving stations on the earth.

The first problem, the provision of the necessary rocket power, is not unduly difficult. Already, in launching earth satellites, speeds as high as 18,000 miles per hour must be reached. To send a body completely out of range of the earth's attraction altogether only requires the attainment of a speed 1.4 times larger. This does not involve very great further development of rocket motors.

On the other hand there is a great increase in the difficulty of tracking. A body in the neighbourhood of the moon is about 100 times as far away as the apogee of any of the present circulating satellites. The same problem arises in recovering data by telemetry. If it is desired to send the probe to a distant and definite location, such as for example the near neighbourhood of the moon, the requirements of control also become much more severe.

We shall illustrate these aspects by considering lunar probes in more detail.

Lunar Probes

It is important to begin by considering what kind of scientific information one is seeking by sending instruments to the moon or its near neighbourhood.

There is of course the prospect of observing that part of the lunar surface which is always invisible from the earth. Although

313

this appeals to popular imagination there is little likelihood of anything very remarkable being discovered – the hidden face is probably very similar to the visible surface. In the first instance it is of value to take quite primitive television pictures of the back of the moon from a distance of even a few tens of thousands of miles (see p. 319), although it must be realized that, for observing the visible face, this is not capable of revealing as much detail as a terrestrial telescope under good seeing conditions. If a probe could be placed, at least temporarily, as a lunar satellite accurate observations of the orbit would provide new data on the figure and mass distribution of the moon. Another lunar property of great interest to investigate is whether the moon possesses a magnetic field – the answer to this question would be of value in understanding the origin of the earth's magnetism (see p. 319). There is some indirect evidence which already suggests that the moon possesses no appreciable magnetic field, but it is very uncertain and indefinite. Further information about the nature of the moon's surface could be obtained by using the probe as an echo-sounder bouncing back radiation of various wavelengths from the moon and observing what changes had taken place in the process. All of this could be done without hitting the moon but it would be necessary to approach it fairly closely. The prospect of automatically landing equipment on the moon which would make observations actually on the surface is a much more difficult problem and represents a more advanced stage.

In the course of its passage to the neighbourhood of the moon a probe will pass 230,000 miles or more through interplanetary space so that it provides an opportunity for extending the study of the intensities of different radiations (see p. 318), the concentration of micrometeorites and of electrons, and the nature of positive ions and neutral atoms which may be present. Some of these observations, particularly those concerning the electrons, ions and atoms, will be difficult to carry out because of the low concentrations which are concerned – the density of matter in interplanetary space is about 10^{-21} times that of water.

The value of merely sending a probe out to hit the moon is relatively small as it would provide information only during its flight to the moon and would not spend time in its neighbour-hood. Nevertheless it is useful to begin by considering this particular enterprise. Insteady of launching the probe in a nearly circular orbit around the earth, the requirement now is to launch it in a highly eccentric elliptic orbit which extends out to the lunar distance. Alternatively, the orbit might be a non-periodic one of parabolic or hyperbolic type (see Fig. 12.1). The launching speed required is not very different for either case but the time taken to reach the moon differs considerably. Thus, assuming that the first launching takes place at a height of 120 miles above the earth's surface, the required launching speed varies from 24,400 miles/hour for an elliptic orbit of eccentricity* 0.97 through 24,570 miles/hour for a parabolic orbit to 24,815 miles/hour for a hyperbolic orbit of eccentricity* 1.03. On the other hand, the corresponding times of travel to the moon vary from 5 through 2.1 to 1.7 days. It follows from this that the orbit followed by the probe is very sensitive to launching speed. The problem of launching conditions is greatly complicated by the fact that the moon is a moving target. Any preset controls in the guidance system will only apply (unless extremely complicated corrections can be built in) accurately for a particular launching time. As it is notoriously difficult to launch rockets at precise times this is a special new problem.

Assuming that once launching has occurred there is no control possible by radio link from ground, then the tolerable errors in launching in order to hit the moon are as follows:

launching speed ± 150 feet/sec., direction of launching ± 0.5°, position of launching ± 30 miles, time of launch, within a few minutes.

As stated above, while the launching speed required is only 1.4 times that for launching artificial earth satellites, the accuracy necessary in launching is much higher. Nevertheless it is still well within the range attainable with modern control mechanisms.

If we turn now to consider more useful orbits, two possibilities arise. One is to choose an orbit which circulates periodically between the near neighbourhoods of earth and moon. This

* See Fig. 12.1 for the meaning of eccentricity.

would combine the advantage of long life with regular approach to the earth during which data collected and stored could be telemetred to terrestrial stations on command. It is, however, by no means easy to select such orbits.

The second possibility is to arrange for the probe to become a lunar satellite, at least temporarily. This cannot be done without provision for some correction, by rocket thrust, of the speed when the probe is close to the moon. The reason for this is as follows. We may ignore the effects of the moon on the motion of a small body such as a space probe until it comes within a sphere, centred on the moon, of radius about 40,000 miles. Inside this sphere the body will move as if acted on by the moon alone. In order that it should pursue a closed, elliptic orbit, about the moon as focus, the speed relative to the moon, at the periphery of the sphere, must be less than that for escape. Following the same reasoning as on p. 296 this is given by $\sqrt{(Gm/\rho)}$ where m is the mass of the moon and ρ the radius of the sphere of influence. Substituting numerical values it comes out to be 864 miles/hour. As the moon is moving in its orbit at a speed of 2100 miles/hour a probe approaching from the earth will always enter the sphere of influence with a speed far too high for capture.

It is necessary therefore for a rocket motor to be held in reserve to fire when near the moon so as to check the speed of the probe relative to the moon sufficiently for it to be captured as a lunar satellite. This is naturally a great additional complication. There is the problem of devising means for checking the position of the probe so that the final rocket motor can be fired when the probe is properly located. It is also necessary that the direction of the thrust applied on firing be correct. At the moment of launching from the earth, the direction of the rocket thrust could be preset by spinning the probe about an axis whose direction in space would then be maintained throughout its path. Having done this, and provided the direction of the spin axis is known, it remains to choose the position of firing which will achieve the desired result, given the thrust direction and the power of the rocket motor. This may be calculated beforehand, or after the check data have been received following the launching, because two days or more will elapse before the probe approaches the moon – ample time for electronic computation. Knowing the firing position, the actual ignition of the motor could be carried out on receipt of a command signal sent when data obtained from the terrestrial tracking stations show that the correct position has been reached. The speed communicated by the check rocket would have to be accurate to within about 1000 ft/sec. and the direction of thrust to within about 15°.

As the technique develops, methods of guidance by command signal will become possible and improve the accuracy with which a planned orbit can be followed. In the early stages, the problem of following the path of the probe is itself a very severe one.

Deep Space and Planetary Probes

The difficulties which must be overcome in launching probes to distances of millions of miles from the earth are similar in nature to those discussed above in relation to lunar probes but are very much more severe. This applies at any rate if it is desired to send instruments to the immediate neighbourhood of even the nearer planets Venus and Mars. In this case the accuracy of guidance must be much greater than for lunar probes. The magnitude of the problem is clear when it is realised that we do not even know the distance from the earth to Venus and Mars at any one time to better than 10,000 miles. Satisfactory reception of radio signals from probe beacons, over distances of the order of millions of miles, presents difficulties of comparable magnitude. In no case, however, do they seem insuperable and the exploration of the atmospheres of Venus and Mars by instrumented, but not manned, probes is likely to be practicable within a very few years.

One problem which is not much more serious for deep space probes as compared with lunar probes is that of providing the necessary rocket thrust. To reach the neighbourhood of the moon a probe has to be given a speed which is very close to the escape velocity from the earth. Once this velocity is exceeded the probe will leave the earth's gravitational field along a hyperbolic

317

path (as the upper curve in Fig. 12.1) never to return. When sufficiently far from the earth the pull of the sun will become effective, causing the probe to pursue an elliptic orbit round the sun like any planet (see below). In the course of its revolution in this orbit it will pass through regions which are many tens of millions of miles away from the earth. From this it will be apparent that the real problem in planetary probing is to effect a rendezvous with a relatively tiny object in the depths of space and to send back information to the earth even from the most distant point of the path – it is not the magnitude of the distance which the probe must be made to travel.

The First Space Probes

The first probes which were launched to distances of many earth radii into space in the general direction of the moon were Pioneer I and Pioneer III, the former on 11th October, 1958 and the latter on 6th December, 1958. In both cases the probes pursued eccentric elliptic orbits and returned to destruction in the earth's atmosphere. Pioneer I reached a distance of 75,000 miles, slightly greater than that attained by Pioneer III (67,390 miles). Fig. 12.2 illustrates to scale the projection of the orbit of Pioneer III on the meridian plane.

Instruments weighing 13 lbs. were carried and among those on Pioneer III were included two Geiger counters for the measurement of the intensity of radiation. These counters worked very satisfactorily and information was telemetred to earth almost out to apogee on the outward flight and at points between 37,000 and 6,000 miles distant on the return journey. The results obtained are discussed below (p. 319).

On the 22nd January 1959 the first probe (Lunik I) was launched, by the Russians, at a speed greater than that for escape from the earth's gravity. It was a body of more than one ton weight carrying 800 lbs. of instruments, including radio transmitters and apparatus to measure the intensity of the magnetic field and of the cosmic and other particle radiation in the space between the earth and moon. It passed the moon at a distance of a few thousand miles only, to become the first artificial planet. Two months later (March 3, 1959) the Americans also launched a probe, Pioneer IV which went into orbit round the sun. It contained, apart from radio transmitters, counter equipment to study particle radiation.

The next spectacular event, achieved on September 14, 1959, was the first impact on the moon of an object launched from the earth. This was a body similar to Lunik II again launched by the Russians. In addition to attaining actual contact with the moon, measurements made close to the moon's surface indicated that the moon's magnetic field is at any rate very much weaker than that of the earth.

To crown a remarkable year of extraordinary success the Russians launched a further cosmic vehicle on 4th October, 1959 with equipment which succeeded, not only in taking low resolution photographs of the back of the moon, but also in transmitting the pictures back to earth by a television scanning procedure – a technical feat of the first magnitude even for these days. Unlike the earlier Luniks and Pioneer IV the orbit of this vehicle was chosen to be in the form of an eccentric ellipse so as to pass, in its first circulation, round the moon and thence to behave as an earth satellite with high apogee distance. The data taken in the neighbourhood of the moon were stored for transmission, on command, at the next point of lowest approach to the earth. Apart from the photographic equipment the vehicle included scientific instruments similar to those carried in the earlier Luniks.

At the beginning of 1960, the time of writing, we are clearly at the threshold of very large scale enterprises with space vehicles. Much of this effort will undoubtedly be devoted to the development of manned space travel but the possibilities of scientific research with automatic equipment are also very great. It is appropriate to conclude by describing the biggest scientific discovery which has been made in this field – this has involved an accomplishment as spectacular in many ways as those which we have just described.

The Discovery and Origin of the Great Radiation Belts
We have already mentioned on p. 310 that the counters included in the first Explorer satellites provided unexpected information

about the intensity of particle radiation at points along the tracks of the satellites which were more than 500 miles above the earth's surface. This proved to be the beginning of a fascinating story which involves the most remarkable discovery yet made with satellites and space probes and set the stage for the largest scale scientific experiment yet carried out successfully. We shall now give some account of the sequence of events.

Returning to the counters in Explorer I and III, it soon became clear that they were behaving in an extraordinary fashion. As long as the satellites were passing within 500 miles of the earth's surface everything was normal, the counting rate being closely that expected from cosmic rays. At greater altitudes, however, no counts were recorded. Nevertheless, on returning within the 500 mile distance the equipment functioned normally again. This happened regularly and was interpreted by van Allen as probably due, not to absence of radiation at the greater altitudes – this was inconceivable because the cosmic rays at least would still be there – but to the presence of an intensity of radiation so great as to 'choke' the counters. An experimental test in the laboratory with similar counters showed that they did indeed cease to record when the counting rate rose to 10,000 times the normal rate due to cosmic rays. van Allen checked his interpretation by including in Explorer IV modified counters capable of handling such high counting rates. The records obtained showed clearly that, at points more than 500 miles above the earth, the true rates were indeed very high.

The orbits of the Explorer satellites did not pass over points on the earth at latitudes above 50° on either side of the Equator. Van Allen's observations showed that, within this range of latitudes, a belt of high intensity of particle radiation extended outwards at distances greater than 500 miles from the surface. Although there was only a little information available from the observations about the nature and energies of the particles concerned, it seemed clear that they must be much less energetic than the cosmic rays.

Meanwhile Sputnik III was launched into orbit and began sending back information about the concentration and energies of the charged particles encountered. In this case the orbit passed over points at latitudes as high as 65°. Evidence in support of van Allen's observations was soon obtained and it suggested that there may be two distinct belts of intense radiation, one concentrated around the equatorial plane, as observed by van Allen, and a second concentrated near the auroral zones (see Chapter 11, p. 290) which penetrated closer to the earth's surface. The results obtained about the energy distribution of the particles confirmed that in all cases they were much less energetic than the cosmic rays. In both regions, electrons with energies of a few tens of keV were major constituents, but in the equatorial region evidence of the presence of rather more energetic protons (up to 10 MeV or higher) was forthcoming. All of these results have proved to be very significant.

The next phase began with the launching of the first deep space probes. Counters carried in Pioneer I and Pioneer III showed that there are indeed two distinct radiation belts somewhat as illustrated in Fig. 12.3 and Plate 12.1. The inner one is that first discovered from instruments in the Explorers, while the outer one is a great extension of that which was first observed with instruments in Sputnik III. This outer region reaches in very close to the surface at the auroral zones but actually is most intense at a distance of 15,000 miles or so from the surface.

Although there has not yet been time to confirm the picture of the radiation belts shown in Plate 12.1 in detail, all evidence at present available confirms its general validity. The question immediately arises as to why these belts arise and are maintained.

The shapes of the belts are closely related to the earth's magnetic field. Thus in Plate 12.1 the smooth full lines are lines of force of the field and it will be seen that the belts are confined within regions bounded by these lines. As long ago as 1913 the Norwegian mathematician Störmer showed that electrically charged particles could under certain circumstances be "trapped" within the earth's magnetic field. Typical tracks of such particles are shown in Plate 12.1 as lines which oscillate between two extreme positions symmetrically placed on each side of the magnetic equator. It will be noted that, at the extremes, the particle is moving at right angles to the line of force about

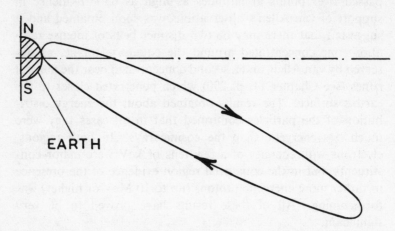

Fig. 12.2. Projection to scale of the orbit of Pioneer III in the meridian plane of the earth.

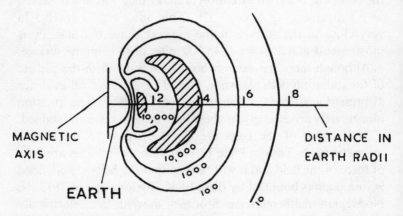

MAGNETIC AXIS

DISTANCE IN EARTH RADII

EARTH

Fig. 12.3. Distribution of intensity of radiation up to distances of 8 earth radii from the earth suggested from observations made by counters in the Explorer satellites and the Pioneer III space probe.

The curves pass through points of equal radiation intensity indicated on each curve by the number which represents the counting rate per sec. Within the shaded areas the counting rate is greater than 10,000 per sec.

which it has been oscillating as it progressed. Because of this trapping we would expect the concentration of charged particles to be built up, providing there is an adequate supply, until the rate of loss due to collision with other particles or to magnetic field fluctuations, equals the rate at which fresh particles are trapped. It is important to notice that the trapped orbits gradually revolve round the earth so that the radiation belts become annular regions as shown in Plate 12.2.

If it is accepted that the radiation belts arise in this way we must identify the sources of charged particles which maintain the concentration despite loss from various causes. It seems likely that the outer belt is maintained by ejection of streams of charged particles from the sun. This is in agreement with the fact that observations made by the Russians with energy discriminating counters in their deep space probes have shown that there are no appreciable numbers of particles with energies exceeding 100,000 e.volts or so in this region. Furthermore, counters in Pioneer IV which became an artificial planet showed that, during the flight of this probe, the intensity in the outer belt was many times greater than when observed in the earlier Pioneer flights. It is significant that the sun was in a disturbed state during the Pioneer IV flight but not in the earlier ones.

The inner zone seems to be relatively stable and does include quite energetic particles. It was therefore suggested that it is maintained from a quite different source – secondary cosmic ray particles. Primary rays collide with the nuclei of atmospheric atoms. In these violent collisions nuclear break-up occurs. Among other fragment particles there will be energetic neutrons which are moving outwards away from the earth. They will pursue a straight path unaffected by the earth's magnetism, until they decay into protons and electrons (see Chapter 9, p. 226). These are considered to be the particles which build up and maintain the inner belt, a view consistent with the observed presence of relatively energetic particles in the belt and its independence of solar activity. Further support has been provided from the remarkable observations of Friden and White in the U.S.A. They sent up nuclear-sensitive emulsions (see Chapter 6, p. 167), to a height of 600 miles into the inner zone, in a vertical sounding rocket. The exposed emulsions were then recovered and processed. Tracks of protons of the type expected were observed on the plates.

Much remains to be done before these interpretations can be fully accepted but they are at least suggestive. Further progress has, however, been made in one direction – it has been demonstrated experimentally that charged particles may be trapped in the earth's magnetic field.

The 'Argus' Experiments

The three experiments which established this are on a cosmic scale – by far the greatest ever carried out successfully by man. In saying this we must make clear the distinction between observation, in which we seek to study what is present in a certain environment with as little as possible disturbance from natural conditions, and experiment in which we deliberately change the conditions in some controlled way and observe the consequences. The importance of experiment in physical science should have been amply demonstrated in earlier chapters. Until recently, geophysical and astronomical science has had to proceed through observation alone. The availability of rockets and satellites has now made it possible to carry out large scale experiments which are capable of providing much insight into the mechanism of various phenomena.

It would clearly be desirable to demonstrate that charged particles may actually be trapped in the earth's field by creating an artificial and observable belt. A way of doing this was suggested by Christofilos. This consisted in conveying an atom bomb of conventional type (not a hydrogen bomb) to an altitude of a few hundred miles above a suitably selected part of the earth's surface and exploding it automatically. The explosion produces a great number of charged particles including electrons from the beta decay of fission products (Chapter 7, p. 190). According to Störmer's theory some of these should be trapped in the earth's field to build up a radiation belt. This would be observed with suitable counters on board an artificial satellite circulating through the region.

Three experiments of this type were successfully carried out over a point in the South Atlantic. In each case an artificial belt about 60-100 miles thick was set up around the whole earth, located largely between the natural inner and outer belts. This was intense enough to be observed for 5 days after the explosion, by counters on the satellite Explorer IV.

On all these occasions an artificial auroral glow was produced close to the point of detonation and, in one case, an auroral glow was observed above the Azores Islands in the North Atlantic. This was doubtless due to particles which travelled along the line of force through the point of detonation in a northerly direction in which case they would indeed enter the atmosphere over the Azores. Here we have then an experiment which modified the properties of a region of cosmic dimensions for several days and incidentally produced artificial auroral displays of considerable intensity. What could be a more impressive demonstration of the technical power now wielded by man?

RETROSPECT AND PROSPECT

After having considered, albeit rather briefly, several of the directions in which major progress in physics is taking place, it is worthwhile using a few remaining words to glance backwards and forwards to try to get some impression of where it is all leading us.

Prophecy in science is at least as ill-fated, probably more so than in other directions. It is hard to see, however, why the present very fast tempo of research in physics should slow down in the foreseeable future.

The application of the new insight obtained in the understanding of the solid state of matter, and particularly of the effects which can be produced by introduction of a controllable proportion of impurities, is gaining momentum in introducing new devices of all kinds. In Chapter 3, which only touched very lightly on the subject, mention was made of transistors and masers, but there are very many other developments of great technical importance. The impact of these developments on other branches of physics is profound – we need only think of the solar battery as a power source in space research. Perhaps of even greater influence is the effect of the new devices on the technique of automatic computation and control. Here the possibilities are virtually unlimited. One can expect profound improvements in the design of electronic computers. Even in the one direction of storage capacity advance is likely to be so rapid as to transform the scope of numerical computation. At the time of writing the full possibilities of automatic calculation have only just been touched. Once a big expansion in this direction sets in the implications for all branches of science cannot easily be overestimated.

In Chapter 3 we gave a brief account of those twin mysteries, superconductivity and superfluidity. It is likely that before very long these will be properly understood in terms of the micro-structure of the substances concerned. How long it will take before this is achieved is hard to say – both phenomena have already defied interpretation for so long. It is of interest to notice in this connection that suggestions are now being made that, under certain circumstances, nuclear matter, the matter within atomic nuclei, also exhibits properties similar in some ways to super-conductivity. If this should prove to be the case we would see one more striking illustration of the essential unity of all physics.

The situation in nuclear and high energy physics is particularly interesting. We await a big theoretical advance which will clarify our understanding of the many puzzling features which have been revealed in recent years, such as the role of the strange particles, including the neutrino. The nature of the interaction which holds nucleons so firmly together in atomic nuclei is still very incompletely understood. In the absence of any unifying theory we must go on to obtain more and more experimental data designed to assist in the search for understanding. Already, however, this has meant the construction of large, very costly machines for accelerating charged particles to very high energies. The need is continually for information about what effects occur at higher and higher energies. We have now reached a stage at which virtually more and more has to be done to gain less and less. This is because of an effect of the special theory of relativity. Consider for example an impact between two protons, one of which has been accelerated to a energy E in a laboratory machine and the other is effectively at rest say in a liquid hydrogen target. The whole of the energy E is not available to produce transformations, materialisation of new particles, etc., but only a certain fraction which, according to relativistic requirements, is

$$\frac{2\lambda}{\lambda+1} \text{ where } \lambda = \sqrt{(1-v^2/c^2)},$$

v being the speed of the incident proton and c that of light. Once the energy E becomes so high that the accelerated protons have velocities close to that of light the fraction available to produce reactions decreases rapidly. Thus the available energy of protons provided by the CERN 25 GeV proton synchrotron is 7 GeV. Increase of the beam energy to 100 GeV would only increase that available to 14 GeV and so on. Since the size and cost of the machine is determined by the beam energy and not that available to produce reactions it is quite clear that we are now facing a very difficult situation. To make a significant extension of the energy range beyond that planned in existing machines, or machines under construction, will require an increase in cost of an order of magnitude. This is not far from prohibitive as the capital cost of present large machines is several million dollars.

One possibility which is being considered very seriously is to use the 'beam crash' principle. In the case we have just considered of the impact of the two protons the situation could be restored if the protons were both moving in opposite sense with high energy. The suggestion is then to accelerate two beams of protons in orbits which intersect at some points so that collis ons between particles from each beam can be observed. This is by no means as simple as it sounds. Among other requirements, it is necessary to increase the intensity of the beams far beyond that usually attainable in present machines. When all these factors are taken into account a useful beam-crash machine will be very expensive indeed. Nevertheless this does represent a promising line of future development in high energy physics.

In another direction also relativisitic limitations are becoming serious. This concerns the identification of the particles which are produced in reactions at high energies. As the speeds of particles approach that of light it becomes very much more difficult to distinguish one particle from another – methods of discrimination by velocity measurement become very insensitive unless very big equipment is employed. Will the great increase in effort required to continue to explore higher and higher energy phenomena eventually slow down progress drastically or will greater and greater resources, financial and otherwise, be deployed as required? In other words, at what stage does a high energy accelerator and its attendant experimental equipment become prohibitively expensive? Before rushing to conclusions about this it is well to remember that the study of the strange particles and high energy phenomena generally is the most fundamental of all subjects in physics and is surely worth much effort.

The situation reached about the strange particles is itself a very intriguing one. In 1946 we had no idea that any of this remarkable family existed at all. Once their discovery began all became confused – there seemed no end to them. In the last few years things have settled down and indeed the size of the family now seems to be established as slightly smaller than seemed likely, say, in 1954. Some order has been disclosed and there is a general feeling, which may prove ill-founded, that no further particles remain to be detected. If this is so then it may not be long before the slight lightening of the haze of mystery about the place of the particles in the scheme of things becomes a general and widespread clearing, providing us with a much deeper insight into the underlying symmetries of Nature. Meanwhile there is great scope for the exercise of that combination of ingenuity, intuition and insight which leads, through that form of enlightened guesswork known as inductive reasoning, to the big forward steps such as the theory of relativity, quantum mechanics and the concept of anti-matter.

Space research is a subject of a quite different kind, involving the exploration of nature on the grand scale. In the coming years, space probes will certainly reach out to great distances, even as far as to Venus and Mars. The whole development will be mixed up with manned space travel but in fact there is, from the scientific point of view, no need for this. The greatest advantages can be secured from satellite observatories fitted with automatically operating instruments, circulating outside the earth's atmosphere. Full use of these possibilities can only be secured if the instruments are capable of operation without maintenance for long periods. There is little doubt that this will be achieved as the development proceeds.

We have said little or nothing about many other major branches of physics which are also expanding rapidly. The study of the structure of materials is leading to the artificial production of substances with all sorts of special properties. An intensive effort is being directed towards the study of high temperature plasmas, with large scale release of energy from nuclear fusion as the goal. New developments in the physics of clouds open up the prospect of artificial rainmaking on a significant scale. The properties of matter at very high pressures, of the order of tens of thousands of atmospheres, are being studied to an increasing extent as well as the problems of high speed flow and so on.

Despite all these major developments it is still possible, and indeed probable, that the most remarkable progress in the near future will be in a rather different direction, in biophysics, the application of physical methods to the study of processes characteristic of living organisms. Already a major break-through in this direction has occurred, concerned with the understanding of the physical basis of inheritance. This has resulted from a combination of remarkably involved experimental studies of the structure of the genes, which are the bodies within the nuclei of living cells through which inherited characteristics are transmitted, and ingenious theoretical interpretation. It is as if the code employed to represent different characteristics in the huge molecules within the genes has been deciphered. In a few years time the advance in our understanding of these vital living processes may outweigh even the astonishing progress in the directions we have discussed in the Chapters of this book. Whatever the main lines of progress in physics may be, there is no doubt that the next few years will continue to be at least as exciting as the last few. Technical skill and invention is now so great that nothing possible in principle would seem to be impossible to achieve in practice.

INDEX

Absorption, of mesons 230; of neutrons 172, by deuterons 179, by protons 179, by uranium 177, 179; of radio waves 288.

Accelerators, linear 156-7; particle, 18, 149-159, 35.

Aether, luminiferous 112, drag of 115; the new 127, 138.

Allen, 100.

van Allen, 320-1.

Alnico V, 87.

Aluminium, 87, 172.

Ambler, 236.

Ammonia, 109.

Amplifiers, 79, design of 108, junction transistors as 83, noise in 109.

Anderson, 129, 203, 206.

Andronikashvili, 97.

Anode, 26-8.

Antigravity, 137.

Antihyperons, 223.

Antileptons, 240.

Antimatter, 20, 112, 137, 150, 233.

Antineutrinos, 138, 233, 239, 242.

Antineutrons, 136, 211; discovery of 223; magnetic moment of 137.

Antiprotons, 136, 150, 168, 211; discovery of 221.

Apogee, 296.

Argon, 66, 284.

Arsenic, 82.

Aston, 39, 143.

Asymmetry, reflection 276.

Atmosphere, of earth, atomic oxygen in 284, structure of 280, composition of 214, 305; of Mars and Venus 271, 317.

Atmospherics, 291.

Atoms, 22, mesic 219, nuclear 32, of hydrogen and wave mechanics 60, 'plum pudding' 32, stability of 32, strange 142, 218.

Aurora, 258-9, 261, 272, 290.

Avogadro, 23, hypothesis 24, number 24, 27, 30.

Babbage, 102.

Baldo-ceolin, 224.

Balloons, 273, 275, 280.

Balmer, 26.

Band-width, of amplifiers, 111.

Barium, 175.

Baryon, 216, number, conservation of 216.

Becquerel, 30.

Belts, radiation 310, 319-323; artificial 323.

Beryllium, 41, as moderator 179, production of neutrons from 170.

Beta-radioactivity, 181, 225, 323; of C^{14} 190; of Co^{64} 237; of neutron 206; spin-alignment in 239.

Bevatron, 154, 166, 212, 214, 218.

Corona, solar, 197, 258, 260, 279.

Cosmotron, 155, 211, 214.

Counters, 20; Cerenkov, 161, 223; Geiger-Möller 160, 260, 318, 320-1, 324; and radiocarbon dating 191, 193; scintillation 69, 160, 219, 223, 231, 278.

Cowan, 231, 241.

Curie, 172.

Cycle, carbon 244; sunspot, 259, 289-90.

Cyclotron, 50; frequency-modulated 153, 156.

Cygnus, 267.

Dating, by C^{14}, 190.

Davison, 55, 56.

Deuterium, 40, 42, 179, 200; liquid 220.

Deuterons, 42, 140, 200; absorptive power of, for neutrons 172; binding energy of 143; reactions between 171, 194; reactions of, with tritons, 194.

Demagnetization, adiabatic, 94.

Diamagnetism, 85, 89; of superconductors, 96.

Diffraction, of electrons 55, 56, 58, 68; of light 50, 51; of neutrons 67, 68, 183; of particles, 19; applications of 67; of sound 50; of X-rays, 51, 55-6, 67.

Discharge, carbon arc, 200; electric 27; high temperature, 195.

Dirac, 57, 126, 128.

Dispersion, 29.

Disturbances, cyclonic, 304; magnetic 259, 291; of ionosphere 258-9, 291; solar 202, 258, 291, 323.

Domains, in a ferromagnet, 90.

Dovap, 275.

Drum, magnetic, 107.

Dust, cosmic 250; see micrometeorites.

Dysprosium, 88.

Earth, the figure of, 312.

Edlèn, 197.

Effect, Compton 54; Doppler 198, 265, 270, 277-8, 290-1, 302; fountain 99; Hall 77, 79; photoelectric 53, 161; pinch 195; Wigner 181; Zeeman 29.

Einstein, 19, 33, 36, 53, 116, 122, 124, 143, 307.

Electrolysis, 26.

Electrons, 18, 26, 29, 49, 51, 58; energies of, in crystals 72, in semi conductors 76; in atoms 30, 32, 34, orbits of, 34, 55; in nuclei 40, 42; in solids 71; magnetic moment of 89, 133, 135; mass of 30, 124; positive 128; spin of 62.

Electron-volt, 43.

Elements 22, periodic table of 24.

Ellipse, 296.

Emission, of radio waves, by sun 248, 259, 262, cosmic, 248, 262, 265, from moon and planets 270, in hydrogen line 265, 268.

Emulsion, nuclear photographic 167, 207, 209, 212, 223, 278, 323; stacks of 167, 202.

Energy, allowed values of, for free electrons in relativity 126; for hydrogen atom 35, 61, 62; effect of vacuum poarization and field fluctuations on, 133; for lithium atom 62; binding, of deuteron 144, of helium 6, 144, of normal helium nucleus 144, of nuclei 142, of triton 144, per nucleon 144, 174; conservation of, 44, 49, and space-time 242, in beta decay 228, in electron-positron annihilation

130, in muon decay 229, in pair production 129, in pion decay 229, in strange particle reactions 215; in atomic explosions 124; in relativity theory 123; kinetic 43; nuclear 20; of activation 140; of rest mass 124; of stars 193, 243; zero-point 60, of helium atoms 96.

Entropy, 93.

Establishment, Atomic Energy Research 154; Royal Aircraft, 275.

Euratom, 184.

Ewen 248, 269.

Experiment, Argus 324; direct current 199; Lamb-Retherford 133; Michelson-Morley 113, 115, 116.

Factor, noise, of amplifier 109, of ammonia maser, 110.

Fadeouts, radio, 259-0, 288.

Faraday, 26, 148; the 27, 30.

Fermi, 175, 179, 229.

Fermions 64, 209, 211, 228, 230, 236.

Ferrites, 87, 214.

Ferromagnets 19, 85, 90; and neutron diffraction 68; and storage systems 106.

Field, electric 28, 30; electromagnetic fluctuations of 60, 131, 134, 204, 219; magnetic 60, deflection of alpha rays by 31, effect on frequencies of light 29, electron motion in 124, of earth 258, 289, 291, 305, 321-23.

Fission, as source of energy 174; discovery of, 175; of heavy nuclei 174, of protoactinium 176, of thorium 176, of uranium 20, 174.

Fitzgerald, 115.

Flares, solar, 259-60.

Focussing, strong, 155.

Forces, between small magnets 89; centrifugal 29, 34, 298, 307; nuclear 139, 327.

Fowler, 212.

Franklin, 271.

Freedom, degree of, 92.

Frequency, critical, 286.

Friden, 322.

Friedman, 279.

Frisch, 149.

Fusion, of nuclei, and energy of stars 243, as source of energy 174, 190.

Gadolinium, 88.

Galaxies, collision of 21, 248, 263; peculiar 267; recession of, 265, 270; spiral structure of 264-5.

Galaxy, the 21, 245, 247-8, 263-4, 278; spiral structure of, 269.

Galileo, 15, 37.

Gamow, 58

Gay-Lussac, 23.

Geiger, 32.

Gell-Mann, 216.

Genes, 35-.

Geometry, of Euclid 121, hyperbolic 121.

Germanium, 77, 82, 83.

Germer, 55, 56.

Glow, air 285.

Gockel, 201.

Gold, 95.
Graphite, as moderator 179, Wigner effect in, 181.
Grid, of triode 81, 84.
Group, of waves, 48, velocity 48.

Halban, 176.
Hahn, 175.
Harrison, 231.
Hayward, 236.
Heisenberg, 57, 59, 91.
Heitler, 66.
Helicity, 235, of neutrino 238.
Helium, 31; as coolant 180; atom, structure of 64; liquefaction of 94; liquid 91, and superfluidity 96, creeping film of 100, two-fluid theory of 97; nucleus, 144, in stars 245; solidification of, 96.
Henderson, 240.
Hess, 201.
Herz, 249.
Hindman, 269.
Holes, positive, conduction by 77, in transistors 83, 84.
Hopper, 236.
van de Hulst, 269.
Hydrogen, 22; atom, allowed orbits in, 35, mass of 30; atomic, in galaxy 248; conversion into helium in stars 250; liquefaction of, 94; liquid, 220.
Hydroxyl, 285.
Hyperbola, 296.
Hyperdeuteron, 220.
Hyperons 208; artificial production of 214; discovery of 212; in strange nuclei, 220, 225; lambda-nought 212, 221; properties of 214, 217; sigma 213; xi-minus 213; xi-nought 213.
Hypertriton, 220.

Icebreaker, nuclear propelled, 186.
Information, amount of, 104.
Institute, Geophysical, of USSR 275, Meteorological, of USSR 275.
Insulators, 66.
Interactions, gravitational 242, 295, 308; strong 215, 242; universal 237; weak 215, 225, 242.
Interference, radio 250; of waves 49, 114, 253; of X-rays, scattered by crystals 68.
Interferometer, dual array 255; Mills cross 257; radio 251-2, 302; stellar, 248.
Interval, 121.
Ions, 154, 164-5, 194, 286; nature of, in ionosphere, 288.
Ionosphere, 247, 272, 278, 281, 286, 301-303, 305, 309; currents in 289, 305; disturbances of, 273.
Iron, 84, 87-8; solar corona 197; nucleus of 144.
Isotopes, 38, 39; and superconductivity 95; of carbon; of cobalt 237; of helium 91, 171; of hydrogen 40, 171; of sodium 228; of potassium 226; of uranium 176, 180; separation of 177.

Jansky, 247.
Johnson, 202.

Joliot, 41, 172, 176.
Jones, 100.
Jordan, 57.
Jupiter, 270.

K-mesons, 211, 236; artificial production of, 214; discovery of, 212; neutral 212; properties of 214-5.
Kowarski, 176.
Kruse, 231.
Krypton, 66.

Laboratory, Brookhaven National 155-6, Cavendish 176, Mullard 249, Oakridge, National 200, Radiation, Berkeley, 166, Radiophysics 249, Rutherford 155, 159.
Lamb, 133.
Lambda-point, 97.
Landau, 98.
Lattes, 207.
von Laue, 51.
Lavoisier, 22.
Law, Lenz's, 88.
Lawrence, 150.
Lead, 95.
Lee, 236.
Left-handedness, 233, 236.
Lennard, 53.
Length, and relativity 117.
Leptons, 240, conservation of, 241.
Lewis, 208.
Light, electromagnetic theory of, 113; velocity of 51, 116, 117.
Lithium, structure of atom of 64; transformation of nucleus of, 170.
London, 66, 101.
Lorentz, 116, 117.

McGuire, 231.
Magnetite, 84, 87, 90.
Magnetization, spontaneous, 91.
Manganese, 87, 88.
Mars, 270, 317, 329.
Marsden, 32.
Maser, 108, ammonia, 110.
Mass, conservation of in chemical reactions, 22; effective, 78; initial 123; in relativity theory, 123; negative, 78, 127; of electron 30; of hydrogen atom 30; of neutrino 238; of neutron 143; of nuclei, 142; of proton 143.
Massachusetts Institute of Technology (MIT), 157.
Matter, creation and annihilation of 19, 112, 124, 128.
Maxwell, 51, 113.
Mechanics, classical 37, 56, 112, 116; quantum 15, 37, 42, 44, 56, and Bohr orbits 61, and bulk flow 91, 96, and chemical properties of elements 66, and electron spin 63, foundation of, 55, probability interpretation of 59; Newtonian 19; relativistic 112, quantum 112, 126; wave, see quantum.

336

Mendelèef, 24.

Mercury, electrical resistance of, 94; as coolant 186.

Mesons 206, 225, see also mu-mesons, pi-mesons, K-mesons; artificial production of, 209; decay of, 207; negative, mean life time of, 207, slowing-down of, 219; neutral, 208; properties of, 209; radiation of, by protons, 208.

Meteorites, 306.

Meteors, 249, 271, 272.

Methods, microchemical, 142.

Michelson, 113, 115-6, 251.

Micrometeorites, 304, 306, 310-11, 314.

Microscope, electron 19, 69; optical, 69.

Microphones, 282, 306.

Millikan, 30.

Mirrors, magnetic, 199.

Moderator, 179.

Molecules, 23; in a gas 92; mu-mesic, 220; of hydrogen 23, of oxygen 23, of water 23.

Moment, magnetic, from electron spin, 89; of a magnet, 89; of deuterons 144, of electrons, 89, of mu-mesons 219, of neutrons 89, 144, 148, of nuclei, 144, of pi-mesons 219, of protons 144, 149.

Molybdenum, 87.

Momentum, angular 33, 145; and uncertainty principle, 59; conservation of 44, 49, in beta decay 228, 230, in pi-meson decay 240, in space-time 242, in strange particle reactions 215; of electron orbital motion 63, of electron spin 63, 89.

Momentum, linear 43, conservation of, in collisions 44, in Compton effect 54, in electron-positron annihilation 130, in pair production 129, in rocket propulsion 274; in relativity theory 123, 124.

Moon, figure of, 314; magnetic field of, 214, 319; surface of, 270, 314; temperature of, 314.

Morley, 113, 115, 116.

Moseley, 38.

Muirhead, 212.

Mu-mesons, 138, 165, 201, 209, 211, 230; in liquid hydrogen, 220; properties of 217.

Muons, see mu-mesons.

Müller, 269.

Murphy, 40.

National Institute for Research in Nuclear Science (NIRNS), 155.

Nautilus, 186.

Nebula, Andromeda, 265-6, 270; Crab, 246, 266.

Neon, isotopes of, 39; structure of atom of, 65.

Neptunium, 177.

Neutrino, 16, 20, 211, 219, 229, 242, and energy of stars, 243-4; as ghost particle 238; detection of 231; helicity of 238; rest mass of 238.

Neutrons, absorption of, 172; as bombarding missiles 141; and fission 175; charge of, 42; decay of, 206, 226, 323; diffraction of 67, 68; discovery of 41, 170; magnetic moment of, 137, 144, 168, 212; mass of 143; production of, 180, 183; reactions of, with boron nuclei, 171.

Newton, 15, 37, 56, 112, 116, 307.

Nickel, 84, 87, 88, 144.

338

Polarization, longitudinal, of electron, muon and positron 238; of a vacuum 15, 134, 218.

Positrons, 129, 165, 172, 201, 211, 228, 231, 243; and soft showers, 203; annihilation of, in electron impact 130, in positronium 218; discovery of, 203.

Positronium, 136, 218.

Potassium, 66, 72, isotope of, 226.

Powell, 207, 212.

Power, resolving, 69, 251.

Precession, 145.

Principle, exclusion (of Pauli) 64, 65, 73, 75, 102, 128, 221, 246; of equivalence, 307, 308; of uncertainty 59, 96, 205.

Probes, lunar 21, 312; Lunik, 318-9, 322; Pioneer 318-9, 321, 323; space 17, 271, 273, 313, 317, 329.

Products, fission, utilisation of, 188.

Protoactinium, fission of, 176.

Protons, 42, 49, 136; in cosmic rays 202, 208; mass of 143; magnetic moment of, 144, 149, 210; radius of, 42; spin of, 64.

Protonium, 220.

Prout, 24, 26, 38, 40.

Prowse, 224.

Pumping, magnetic, 199.

Purcell, 248, 268.

Quantum, of action, 33, 34, 37, 53, 205.

Radar, 17, 247-50, 271, 302.

Radiation, absorption of, 33; emission of, 33, electromagnetic, from hot body, 53, 245, 279, from earth 304, ultra-violet, from sun 272, 278, 288, from sky 304, visible, from sun, 258, X-, from sun 278-9, 288.

Radioactivity, 30, artificial, 172.

Radioisotopes, 183; uses of 189-90.

Radiotherapy, 188.

Radium, 41, 188.

Ratio, breeding, 187.

Rayleigh, 175.

Rays, alpha 30, 41, 168; anode, 39; beta 30, 41, 42; cathode 27, 28, 31, 39; cosmic 17, 190, 201, 232, 272, 304, 310-1, 318, 320, 321-22, age of, 305, anomalous absorption of, 115, constitution of, 305; primary 202; gamma, 30, 51, 232, materialisation of, 128, 203; X-, 38, 49, 272.

Reactions, chemical 139; nuclear 140; fission chain 176, critical size for, 177; of alpha particles with nuclei 169, 202; of nuclei in stars, 243-4; of protons with deuterons, 220, with nuclei 170.

Reactors, and He^3 production 101; as neutrino sources 231; as neutron sources 225; at Hanford 182; at Windscale 182; breeder 183, 187; boiling water 188; fast 186; fission 180; for marine propulsion 185; graphite-moderated natural uranium 184; homogeneous 188; large scale primary 183; materials testing 181; nuclear 17, 124.

Reber, 247.

Recombination, of electrons and ions, 287.

Rectifier, 79, p-n junction as, 82.

Reines, 231.